PRENTICE-HALL GEOGRAPHY

Exploring Physical Patterns

Paul Aves
Resource Teacher
Metropolitan Separate School Board

Dennis DesRivieres
Resource Teacher
Metropolitan Separate School Board

Frank Fohr
Teacher
Welland County Separate School Board

Prentice-Hall Canada Ltd., Scarborough, Ontario

Canadian Cataloguing in Publication Data

DesRivieres, Dennis,
  Exploring physical patterns

"Prentice-Hall geography."
Includes index.
ISBN 0-13-297466-5

1. Physical geography – Juvenile literature.
2. Natural resources – Juvenile literature.
I. Aves, Paul,   . II. Fohr, Frank,
III. Title.

GB55.D48 1988   910′.02   C88-093871-4

Prentice-Hall, Inc., Englewood Cliffs, New Jersey
Prentice-Hall International, Inc., London
Prentice-Hall of Australia, Pty., Ltd., Sydney
Prentice-Hall of India Pvt., Ltd., New Delhi
Prentice-Hall of Japan, Inc., Tokyo
Prentice-Hall of Southeast Asia (PTE) Ltd., Singapore
Editoria Prentice-Hall do Brasil Ltda., Rio de Janeiro
Prentice-Hall Hispanoamericana, S.A., Mexico

ISBN 0-13-297466-5

Project Editor: Judy Dawson
Production Editor: Jane A. Clark
Production: Pamela Russell, Lois Enns
Design: John Zehethofer
Map art and illustrations: Julian Cleva
Illustrations: Colin Gillies
Composition: Q Composition
Cover image: courtesy of the Atmospheric Environment Service

Printed and bound in Canada by Bryant Press Limited

   4 5 BP 93 92

Policy Statement

Prentice-Hall Canada Inc., Secondary School Division, and the authors of *Exploring Physical Patterns* are committed to the publication of instructional materials that are as bias-free as possible. The student text was evaluated for bias prior to publication.

The authors and publishers also recognize the importance of appropriate reading levels and have therefore made every effort to ensure the highest degree of readability in the student text. The content has been selected, organized, and written at a level suitable to the intended audience. Standard readability tests have been applied at several stages in the text's preparation to ensure an appropriate reading level.

Research indicates, however, that readability is affected by much more than word or sentence length; factors such as presentation, format and design, none of which are considered in the usual readability tests, also greatly influence the ease with which students read a book. These and many additional features, such as a glossary, have been carefully prepared to ensure maximum student comprehension.

The cover illustration is a satellite photograph showing a section of the East Coast of North America. The photograph is partly infrared, which means the colours indicate certain patterns. The dark blue area in the ocean is the warm Gulf Stream. Clouds appear pinkish-white. Red areas on land indicate the locations of dense populations, and bright green areas show marshlands or cultivated valleys. The photograph also shows a pattern of ridges that is the Appalachian Mountains.

Contents

To the Student

The world is an exciting place, waiting to be explored. Every day the news brings us more information about the earth. From an earthquake in Central America to a heatwave in the central United States, we continually learn about world environments. These events are not isolated things. They are part of patterns that can be understood. This book will help you find the patterns of our physical world by making you the explorer. That is why it is called **Exploring Physical Patterns**.

The chapters in this book are designed to help you learn about the many different physical patterns in the world. Each chapter is organized in the following way:

What you will learn outlines the main ideas in the chapter.

Key words list the geographic terms used in the chapter. Use the definitions in the margins and in the glossary at the end of the book to build a personal dictionary in your notebook.

What you have learned summarizes the main ideas of the chapter.

Looking back contains review activities based on the information in the chapter.

Expanding your learning contains suggestions for further investigation.

The body of the chapter makes you the explorer. Short reading sections with maps, photographs, diagrams and charts invite you to find patterns in our world. Activity sections at the end of each section help you use the information you have been given to discover new ideas and concepts.

You will also practice many skills in this book. Some of these are geographic skills. Special round symbols in each of the Activity sections following a lesson identify the geographic skills you are using. These symbols are:

🌐   maps and globes

📊   charts and graphs

📷   photographs and diagrams

🧭   field studies

You will also learn and practice many skills shared by other subjects. These skills are identified in the Activity sections by the following square symbols:

inquiry

communication

group co-operation

research

In addition, special sections called "How geographers work" show you how to do many geographic skills. At the end of the book you will also find a section called "Additional skill boxes" that explains how to do a number of the shared skills.

Acknowledgements

It takes a lot of time and patience to prepare a textbook! We owe a great deal to our families and editors for being so generous with both.

The editorial staff at Prentice-Hall have been patient in their efforts to steer the project to completion. MaryLynne Meschino was a continual source of energy and encouragement. Judy Dawson and Jane Clark worked painstakingly to meld the work of three different authors. Though their input has been vital, we remain responsible for the accuracy of the information which is presented.

We owe thanks to our families for the time we took from them to complete this work. Linda Aves, Shirley DesRivieres and Marina Fohr patiently typed and helped with changes in manuscript. A special thanks to all those who provided their skill, suggestions and support throughout. We only hope that our children will have the opportunity to study Geography from the book that they already know so much about!

Paul Aves, Dennis DesRivieres, Frank Fohr

UNIT I
Introduction

Let's Go Camping

2

WHAT YOU WILL LEARN

Location is one of the basic ideas in geography. Everyone and everything occupies a place on earth, and this place can be described. Phrases like "at the North Pole" or "under your foot!" tell you where the person or thing is. But geographers do more than describe where something is located. They also try to understand why it is located there.

In this chapter you will learn about location and how geographers study location. You will use charts, maps and aerial photographs to answer the questions "Where?" and "Why there?" Finally, you will use what you have learned to plan a new park.

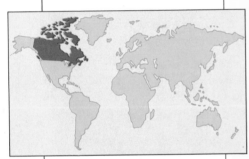

Fig. 1-1 The location you will learn about in this chapter.

KEY WORDS

location	topographic map	legend
geography	aerial photograph	
environment	block diagram	

What is geography?

Some people's names have a meaning. For example, Johnson once was "the son of John," while Larivière means "the river." Many first names come from the Bible or from people who are famous or historically important. What is the origin of your name?

"Geography" is one of those words with meaning. It comes from the Greek language. The *geo* part of geography is from the Greek word meaning "the earth." The *graphy* portion of the word tells us that the subject is described by writing or by drawing maps, diagrams, graphs or charts. Geography presents a picture of the earth. A fuller definition tells us more about the subject.

geography (jē og′ rə fē) n., the study of the earth, its landforms, its climate, the living things on its surface and the interactions among all of these. Geography describes the earth's countries and peoples, its mountains and waters, and its resources and industries.

To understand what geography is, let us begin with a familiar example. Although you may never have thought of it in this way, decisions about camping trips involve geography. For example, you can use maps, pictures and charts for information about where to go. These will tell you about the mountains, waters, climate and outdoor resources of the camping area you choose. Using this kind of graphic information about the earth is geography.

Each year more Canadians go on camping trips than on any other kind of holiday. However, types of campsite accommodation range from pup tents to motor homes complete with refrigerators, microwave ovens and video equipment. "Getting back to nature" means different things to different people!

Fig. 1-2 Some Canadians go on camping trips with pup tents and sleeping bags.

Fig. 1-3   Some campers stay in camper-trailers with their own electricity and running water.

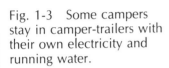

It is easy to understand why camping is the most popular Canadian vacation. About three out of every four Canadian families live in towns or cities. These urban areas offer some green spaces for rest and play, but city parks cannot compare to the wide-open spaces that can be found beyond Canadian cities.

Canada is the second largest country on earth. It offers a huge variety of scenery and outdoor activity for different tastes. There are many different camping **locations** to choose from. Some are small, privately-owned campgrounds. Others are large national or provincial parks, such as Banff National Park

A **location** is the position, place or site where something can be found.

Fig. 1-4   A guide to park facilities.

NAME OF PARK	picnic tables	barbecue grills	campsites	washrooms	hook-ups for trailers	swimming	sandy beach	change rooms	boat launch	boat/canoe rentals	fishing	hiking trails	cross-country skiing	ski chalet	OTHER FEATURES
Mountain Fort	●	●	●	●	●	●	●	●		●	●	●	●	●	museum, store ice fishing huts
Prairie Dunes	●	●		●		●	●	●	●	●	●				park closed Nov.-April golf course nearby
Holiday Valley	●	●	●	●	●	●		●			●	●		●	pool
Maple Sands	●	●	●	●		●	●	●		●					park closed Nov.-April sugar bush
Highland Hills	●		●								●	●	●	●	rope tow, tobogganing

in Alberta or Parc des Laurentides in Québec. Every park is different. Let us look at the kind of activities people enjoy in our parks by using Fig. 1-4 and Fig. 1-5.

Fig. 1-5   The number of park visitors in one year.

PARK	NUMBER OF VISITORS	
	May-October	November-April
Mountain Fort	75 000	41 500
Prairie Dunes	66 500	closed
Holiday Valley	72 000	26 500
Maple Sands	42 500	closed
Highland Hills	13 500	61 000

ACTIVITY ONE

1. Use Fig. 1-4 to make a list of the activities available at these parks.

2. At which of these park locations could you
   a) enjoy day use only?
   b) hook up water and electricity to a camper trailer or recreational vehicle?
   c) get fresh maple syrup in the spring?
   d) enjoy downhill sports?

3. a) Which of these park locations would you most like to visit during summer vacation? Why? Compare your choice to the information on park visitors in Fig. 1-5.
   b) Which of these park locations would you most like to visit for a day in winter? Why? Do the park visitors listed in Fig. 1-5 agree with your choice?

4. a) Use Fig. 1-5 to add up the total number of visitors who used each of the five parks.
   b) Draw and label a bar graph showing the total number of visitors to each park.

5. Use Fig. 1-4 to explain why
   a) Mountain Fort Park is so popular year-round.
   b) Highland Hills is the most popular winter park.

Refer to Chapter 12 for more information about the new park on south Moresby Island.

Refer to Chapter 2 for more information about the new park on the Bruce Peninsula.

6

The **environment** is the surroundings and conditions that affect each person, animal and plant.

Planning a camping park

In 1987 two new national parks were created in Canada. One is South Moresby National Park Reserve on Moresby Island, located off the British Columbia coast. The other is found on the tip of Ontario's Bruce Peninsula along Lake Huron. You will learn more about both of them later in this book.

The selection and design of a new park shows how geographers work. Geographers study pictures of the earth when they choose park locations. They use detailed maps which show the height of the land and many other natural landmarks, as well as roads and buildings. These are called **topographic maps**. They also use **aerial photographs,** which are pictures taken above the earth from an airplane. After studying the maps and photographs, geographers visit the area, looking for interesting routes for hiking and skiing. They need information about climate, too. They need to know if it is warm enough for swimming or if there will be enough snow for Christmas skiing. Such information is important when choosing a park location.

Geographers design parks, as well. When they are familiar with the **environment** of the chosen area they begin to plan

Fig. 1-6 An aerial photograph.

Fig. 1-7 A topographic map.

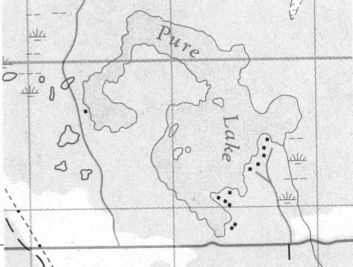

the park. Campsites are located in scenic areas, not too far from the water. Fishing and boating areas are kept away from swimming areas for safety reasons. Roads are planned which are not too steep or winding for trailers and recreational vehicles. Winter sports areas are planned in open spaces, away from dangerous obstacles such as barbecues or fences which could be hidden by snow. Campsites are not located near marshy areas because there are often many insects in these areas. Then a map is drawn to show the final plan. Use the information provided on pages 7 and 8 to design your own park in Activity Two.

Fig. 1-8   An editorial in *The Weekly Word*.

7

We need a new park

ANYTOWN, CANADA—

Parks Canada officials have decided that this area needs another year-round park. The Mountain Fort, Holiday Valley and Maple Sands facilities are very heavily used. Almost every summer weekend campers must line up for hours to get a campsite. Often trailers and recreational vehicles are turned away. The swimming pool at Holiday Valley is so busy that lifeguards are concerned about safety.

In winter the problem is just as severe. The cross-country ski trails at Mountain Fort, Holiday Valley and Highland Hills were often too crowded on the weekends last winter. Skilled skiers complained about a lack of challenging trails and good facilities. Parks Canada must open a new year-round park soon.

We draw their attention to the land which has become available at Bonham Bay just north of us. The land seems suited for skiing,

hiking and camping, and the area receives plenty of snow. This is the average amount which falls each year:

AVERAGE SNOWFALL IN CENTIMETRES

MONTH	CENTIMETRES OF SNOW
November	25 cm
December	64 cm
January	65 cm
February	50 cm
March	32 cm
April	14 cm

The site at Bonham Bay also offers good swimming and fishing. A new year-round park at Bonham Bay should be planned now.

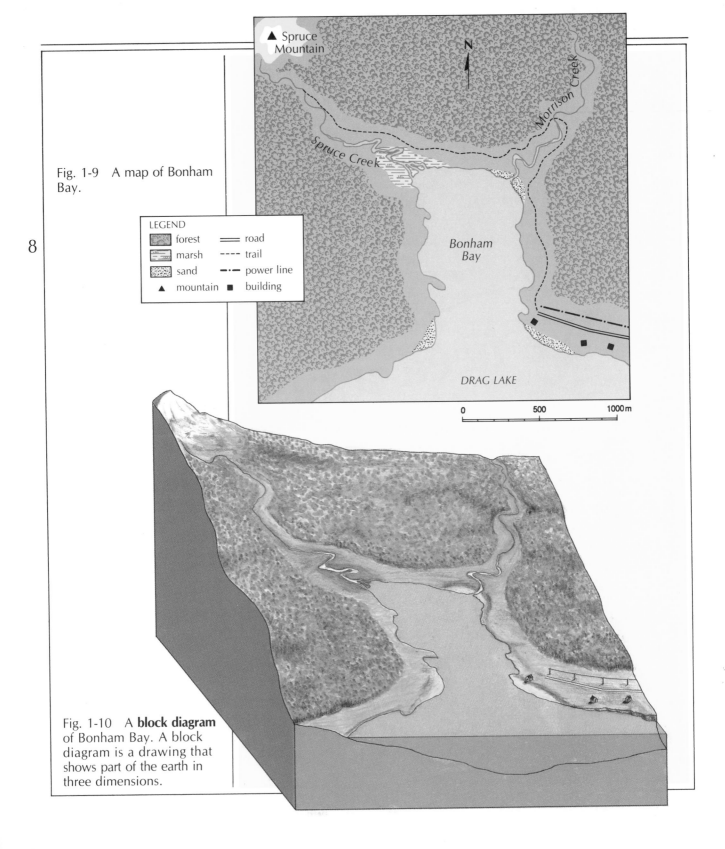

8

Fig. 1-9   A map of Bonham Bay.

LEGEND

forest		road	
marsh		trail	
sand		power line	
▲ mountain		■ building	

▲ Spruce Mountain

N

Spruce Creek

Morrison Creek

Bonham Bay

DRAG LAKE

0   500   1000 m

Fig. 1-10   A **block diagram** of Bonham Bay. A block diagram is a drawing that shows part of the earth in three dimensions.

ACTIVITY TWO 📝 🌐

1. Read the newspaper editorial in Fig. 1-8.
   a) What is the main point of the editorial?
   b) What reasons does the editor give?

2. How much snow falls at Bonham Bay
   a) in centimetres?
   b) in metres?

   (Measure this distance up your classroom wall to see how much snow this is.)

The map **legend** is the part of a map that explains the symbols and markings used on the map.

3. Look at the map **legend** in Fig. 1-9. Find the location of each of the following features on both Fig. 1-9 and Fig. 1-10:
   a) Bonham Bay, Spruce Creek, Spruce Mountain
   b) the trail up to Spruce Mountain
   c) the marsh, the Morrison Creek beach

4. Draw up a report in which you suggest that Parks Canada open a park at Bonham Bay. Include
   a) a list of the main activities to be available at the park.
   b) a map of the main activities available in your plan for the new park, based on Fig. 1-10.
   c) a paragraph to explain why your plan is a good one.

WHAT YOU HAVE LEARNED

This chapter introduced you to location, an idea that is very important in geography. Geographers frequently ask the location questions, ''Where?'' and ''Why there?''

You have also seen some of the tools that geographers use. Charts, statistics, graphs, diagrams, maps and photographs are all important information sources.

In the next chapter you will learn more about the methods of geography and the exciting careers it can offer.

9

LOOKING BACK 📝 🌐

1. a) Write a simple definition of geography.
   b) List at least three examples of the kind of topics it includes.

2. In which Canadian province is each of these parks located?
   a) Laurentides   c) Bruce
   b) Banff   d) South Moresby

3. Use an atlas or road maps to locate examples of provincial or national parks in
   a) the Atlantic provinces.
   b) the Northwest Territories and Yukon Territory.

EXPANDING YOUR LEARNING 📖 📝 🎭

4. Obtain brochures that give information about parks found in your area of Canada.
   a) What kind of facilities and activities are available?
   b) Find out how many students in your class have been to these parks.

5. Design a travel brochure for the new park at Bonham Bay. Include maps, charts or diagrams to present your information in an interesting way.

6. Write two or three paragraphs describing your trip to a camping park. The trip could be one you took with your family or friends, or an imaginary one. What activities were available? Did you stay overnight in a tent or motor home?

Geography: People and Their Earth

Fig. 2-1 The location you will learn about in this chapter.

WHAT YOU WILL LEARN

A major theme in this book is the link between people and their natural surroundings. Each affects the other. People change the earth as they use it. For example, the wilderness is changed when a campground is created. At the same time, the environment influences humans. Park planners will not usually put campsites in marshy areas or on steep, rocky ground.

This chapter gives several examples of how people and their environments are linked together. It outlines the method that geographers use to learn more about this link. It also tells you about the interesting careers offered by geography.

KEY WORDS

natural resources	**cartographer**	**geologist**
escarpment	**meteorologist**	**peninsula**

Geography in the news

Have you ever seen or heard news items like the ones in Fig. 2-2? If so, you have been learning about geography. Even if you only listen to sports and weather information you are learning about geography. Downhill racing in Europe, the Montreal Canadiens' road trip to the west coast, or a miserable heat wave are all topics related to geography in some way.

FAMINE IN AFRICA

Storm shuts down city

Canadian woman conquers Mount Everest

New park for Bonham Bay

Regional shopping mall proposed

Fig. 2-2   Geography in the news.

Geography looks at people and the earth, and at the ways they affect one another. Geographers try to find patterns between the two and to give reasons for the patterns they find. Some of the headlines in Fig. 2-2 deal with how people use the earth. For example, "New park for Bonham Bay" is about the plans you made for a new park in Chapter 1. The headline "Regional shopping mall proposed" is also about location—in this case, the place chosen for a new shopping mall.

Other news stories are about how the earth affects people. "Storm shuts down city" shows the impact of weather on people. The headline "Famine in Africa" is another story of the earth affecting people. Many people in north-central Africa have suffered hunger and death because rainfall in this location dropped to less than half its normal level between 1972 and 1983. Explain how the headline "Canadian woman conquers Mount Everest" shows that geography deals with the relationship between people and the earth.

Fig. 2-3   How the earth can affect people.

New Bruce park becomes reality today

By David Israelson Toronto Star

Canada's newest national park to be created today on the rugged Bruce Peninsula, could become as big a tourist attraction as Banff, the federal environment minister says.

"The Bruce Peninsula has the potential to become as world famous as our national parks at Banff, Jasper and Prince Edward Island," Tom McMillan said in a statement marking the setting up of the new park.

McMillan and Ontario Natural Resources Minister Vince Kerrio were to attend a ceremony today marking the federal-provincial agreement signed earlier this month.

The park, Canada's 34th national park, is the fifth in this province — and southern Ontario's largest.

The new park covers 270 square kilometres (104 square miles) of the narrow, craggy **peninsula** that divides Lake Huron from Georgian Bay, is less than half the size of Metro Toronto and is about four hours' drive from the city.

It takes in the northern end of the Bruce Trail, a popular hiking trail that runs along the Niagara Escarpment from its southern end at Niagara Falls.

Under a new policy announced by McMillan last year, the park is also to include Canada's first national marine park — protecting the shoreline, lake bottom,

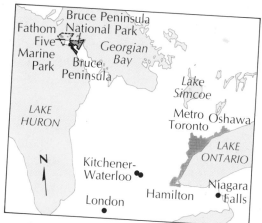

nearby islands and more than 40 shipwrecks. [It will be called Fathom Five National Marine park, and will provide opportunities for scuba diving on the many shipwrecks.]

Setting up the park became possible only last year, after Kerrio agreed to give Ottawa $8.5 million worth of facilities and land — about half the park area — including two existing provincial parks that will now be within the national park's boundaries.

Most of the other half of the park must still be bought from private owners. Ottawa intends to buy that land when the owners are willing to sell.

13

Fig. 2-4   A new national park is announced.

A **peninsula** is a piece of land that is almost surrounded by water.

ACTIVITY ONE

1. Which of the following topics are about people affecting the earth? Which are about the earth affecting people? Which could be both?
   a) students cleaning up a local stream
   b) a volcano in Central America
   c) a new gold mine opens in Ontario
   d) a forest fire in New Brunswick
   e) the Holland Marsh is drained
   f) downhill skiing in Europe

An **escarpment** is a long cliff where the land drops away sharply on one side.

Natural resources are the products of the earth, including minerals, trees, animals, water, air and soil.

2. Write a dramatic headline for each event in question 1.

3. Read the newspaper article in Fig. 2-4.
   a) Identify the following: Tom McMillan, the Bruce Peninsula, the Bruce Trail, the Niagara **Escarpment**.
   b) What will be a special attraction at the new park?
   c) List two activities that will be available at the park.

4. a) Use an atlas and the map in Fig. 2-4 to locate the new park on a map of Ontario.
   b) Use an atlas to locate the other three popular national parks mentioned in the news article.

5. Find news articles that show how the following topics made news in your area:
   a) the weather   c) the earth's **natural resources**
   b) pollution

How geographers work: Inquiry skills

Geographers have an organized way to look at the links between people and the earth. They begin with a question or problem, then work through a series of steps to solve the problem or to answer the question. You did the same thing in the first chapter of the book when you planned your park.

Inquiry skills: the eight steps

1. **Focus** Geographers begin research by asking questions such as what, where, when, why and how? For example, the focus questions of the Bonham Bay planning activity in Chapter 1 were ''What facilities should the park have, and where should they be located?''

2. **Organize** Geographers prepare to answer the research focus questions by organizing. They decide what information they will need and what the best way might be to organize this information. In this stage they plan out the method they will follow to get answers. A chart outlining the ''plan of action'' is a commonly used organizer.

3. **Locate**   Next, geographers find the information they need to answer the focus question. As you began planning the Bonham Bay park, you located information in the newspaper article, the map and the block diagram in Chapter 1.

4. **Record**   The information that is located is then summarized and recorded. Often, geographers draw simple maps, sketches, graphs and charts. Both written and visual information is selected to answer the focus question.

5. **Evaluate**   Geographers think about the information they have recorded. They decide which information is most useful and will help them to answer the focus question. For example, as you planned Bonham Bay park, you probably made changes to your design as you decided on the activities to include and where they might be located.

6. **Conclude**   Next, geographers combine all the useful information to reach conclusions. For example, at this point in the planning activity, you made your final decisions on what to put in your plan for the park.

7. **Apply**   Geographers use their conclusions to make suggestions or predictions. They may apply their conclusions to other situations. To do so they should be able to discuss what they have learned, the practical uses of their findings and how they could be applied to other questions. When you reached your conclusions on which activities would be the best choices for the Bonham Bay location, you designed a park plan based on those conclusions.

8. **Communicate**   Finally, geographers outline their conclusions to others. They might write a report or give an oral presentation. They might show their findings in maps, graphs and diagrams. You completed the park planning activity by listing activities, by drawing a map and by writing a paragraph to describe your plan.

Fig. 2-5   Using this eight-step method can help you to investigate many subjects.

15

Fig. 2-6 How students at
Allenby School researched
the need for a new
crosswalk.

ACTIVITY TWO

1. The principal of Allenby School used a local newspaper headline to get her students started on some geographic research. The pictures in Fig. 2-6 show the steps the students used, but the pictures are mixed up.
   a) Which picture shows the first step? Explain your choice.
   b) Organize the other pictures in the correct order.
   c) Name the steps of inquiry which are shown in these pictures.

2. Which of the following questions would be good focus questions for a geographic study? Explain why.
   a) Is the level of the Great Lakes changing?
   b) Who will be the next Prime Minister?
   c) Why is there hunger in north-central Africa?

3. Glance through this book. List five different forms of information used by geographers.

4. Give three ways in which the findings of a report can be presented. Which do you find most interesting?

17

Geography: A career for you

Have you thought about what you might be doing for a living ten years from now? Some of the subjects you enjoy now may lead to a satisfying career in the future. You could, for example, be working in one of the many interesting careers that the study of geography prepares you for. Do you enjoy using maps and photographs? Do you like learning about the earth, its resources and people? If so, then you would like a career in geography.

Every day there are different careers advertised in the newspaper that require knowledge of the earth and its people. Fig. 2-7 gives examples of jobs which geography prepares you for. Of course, there are many more. In each unit of this book you will find information about a different geographic career.

METRO SCHOOL BOARD
Qualified Grade 7 and 8 Social Studies teacher required immediately. Recognized university degree with geography or history specialty and teaching certificate required.

Northern Resources
Crew leader needed for reforestation area to organize and supervise replanting. A college diploma or experience in Forest Management an asset.

City of Hastings
University degree in Urban Planning required of person to review plans for housing subdivisions presented to city planning department.

Gallagher's Tours
Person wanted to make travel arrangements. A high school diploma and good knowledge of the world important. Will train right person.

MARKET PROBE
Ready for the challenge of Market Research? If so, we will train the right person with a knowledge of surveying and report-writing. High school grads with geography or math skills.

Citymaps Company
Work available in our cartography department for people with map-making skills. College diploma in drafting or surveying required.

GOV'T OF MANITOBA
Person to tag animal species and study their migratory routes required to work in north part of province. University degree in Biology and/or Environmental Science necessary.

PARKS CANADA
Junior planner to assist in plans and surveys for future park areas. College diploma necessary, university grad preferred.

Goldstar Exploration
Geologist required for mineral exploration surveys. Special interest in people with fieldwork abilities. University degree in Geology necessary.

T.V. Station C.O.L.D.-T.V.
Scriptwriter wanted to prepare weather report. Strong writing skills and a proven knowledge of meteorology required. University graduate, or person with college diploma plus experience sought.

Ontario Ministry of Environment
Lab technician to test water samples for pollution and to prepare reports. Environmental Science degree, or college diploma plus experience required.

United Co-op Ltd.
Salesperson wanted. Will train friendly person to sell farm and hobby-farm supplies at new store. High school grad with farm interest/experience suitable.

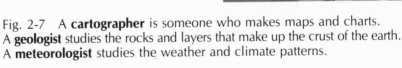

Fig. 2-7 A **cartographer** is someone who makes maps and charts.
A **geologist** studies the rocks and layers that make up the crust of the earth.
A **meteorologist** studies the weather and climate patterns.

ACTIVITY THREE

1. Choose the classified ads in Fig. 2-7 which describe careers that interest you. What would you enjoy about the careers you chose? Would you need a degree or diploma for these careers?

2. Match each of the photographs in Fig. 2-7 to one of the ads.

3. Make a simple chart to show which of these twelve careers require
   a) a high school education
   b) a community college diploma
   c) a university degree

4. Choose any four careers from Fig. 2-7. Explain how learning geography would help prepare you for each of them.

5. If any of the careers interest you, ask your teacher/counsellor to help you get more information about them.

WHAT YOU HAVE LEARNED

This chapter outlined the important geographic theme of how people and the earth affect one another. Evidence of the link between the two is all around us. People affect the earth when they build a new park or shopping mall. The earth affects people when there is not enough rainfall or when the location is chosen for park campsites.

You learned that geographers study the relationship between people and their earth by using a series of steps to organize their questions and to answer them. You saw that geography offers a wide range of interesting careers. All geographers use maps, photographs, graphs and charts to learn about some part of the earth. You will do the same as you study geography with this book.

LOOKING BACK

1. What does each of the following people study?
   a) a meteorologist   c) a geologist
   b) a cartographer

2. Think of a focus question about your community that would interest a geographer. List the steps you would follow to answer that focus question. Then mix up the order of your steps. See if another student can arrange your inquiry as a geographer would.

EXPANDING YOUR LEARNING

3. Use the newspaper to collect articles that show how the earth and people are linked. Divide the articles into these three categories:
   a) people are changing some part of the earth
   b) the earth is affecting people
   c) people and the earth are affecting one another
   Present your articles to your classmates.

4. Look at the ''Careers'' section of your local newspaper. Collect ads for careers that would require the knowledge or skills of geography.

UNIT II
Our Community Is Unique

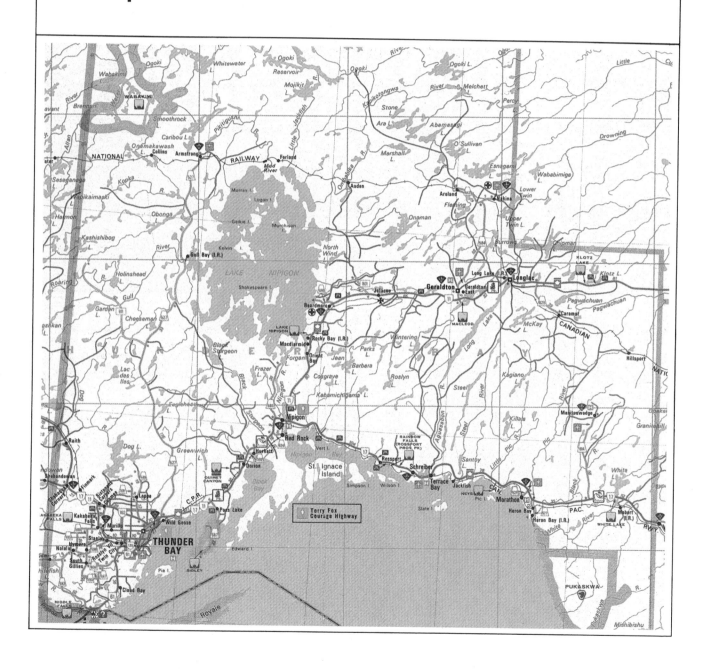

What Is a Community?

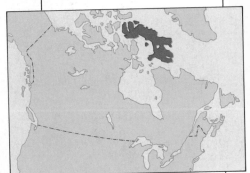

Fig. 3-1 The location you will learn about in this chapter.

WHAT YOU WILL LEARN

A community is a place that has an identity. There are many unique cultural and physical features which give a place a sense of identity. Sometimes these features are obvious, making it easy to define the community. At other times, there are no obvious features and communities can be quite difficult to define.

In this chapter, you will learn how physical and cultural features create a sense of identity. You will examine places of different sizes and decide whether these places can be called "communities."

KEY WORDS

community	neighbourhood	municipality
physical feature	urban	regional municipality
cultural feature	rural	

The meaning of community

Community is a word that can mean different things. The photographs in Fig. 3-2 show various types of communities. In each photograph, community means something a little different. What are the differences? What are the similarities? How would you define the word community, based on these photographs?

Fig. 3-2 What kind of communities are shown in these photographs?

Though community may mean different things, when geographers use this word, one of the following two ideas is present:

1. A community is a group of people who share a common *identity*.
2. A community is a *place* where a group of people live.

To a geographer, these two meanings of community can be combined in the following definition: a **community** is a place that has a sense of identity.

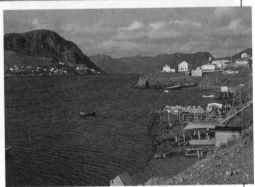

Fig. 3-3 What are the physical features in these photographs of Niagara Falls, U.S.A.; Newfoundland, Canada; Venice, Italy and Mürren, Switzerland?

What gives a place a sense of identity? Most communities have a focal point, a feature that dominates the community in some way. This focal point is usually a source of pride, reminding the people who live there that their community is unique. In many cases, the focal point of a community is an obvious **physical feature** such as a valley, a waterfall, a large hill or a mountain. Examine the photographs in Fig. 3-3. What physical features dominate these communities?

In other cases, the focal point of a community is a **cultural feature**, such as an unusual building, a bridge, or a factory. Examine the photographs in Fig. 3-4. What cultural features dominate these communities?

Cultural and physical features are often closely linked. For example, a farming village in Saskatchewan is built around a group of grain elevators, tall wooden structures used for storing grain. These grain elevators are a cultural feature that act as the focal point of this community. The grain elevators are there because of a physical feature, the rich prairie soil, which is ideal for growing grain. A castle in Inverness, Scotland is a cultural feature of the community. The hill on which the castle is built is an important physical feature linked to the castle. It is the hill that gives the castle its commanding position over the town.

A community's sense of identity comes from its physical and cultural features. These physical and cultural features are often closely related to one another.

ACTIVITY ONE

1. Design a questionnaire to find out how people define your community.

2. Decide who you want to fill out your questionnaire (your parents, your neighbours, students in your school).

3. Decide how you will record and summarize the results of your questionnaire.

4. Write four sentences using the word ''community'' in four different ways.

Fig. 3-4 What are the cultural features in these photographs of the Great Wall, China; Segovia, Spain; southern Saskatchewan and Inverness, Scotland?

How geographers work: Drawing maps

Maps are pictures that provide people with a great deal of information. They are drawn from a ''bird's-eye'' view. Imagine that you are an eagle soaring high above a community. What would you see? How would it be different from what you see when on the ground? To draw a map, you have to imagine that you are an eagle looking down at the community from above. If you have ever been in a plane or looked down from a tall building, you have had a ''bird's-eye'' view of the ground.

Maps are used to show a particular kind of information. You cannot put everything on your map. If you try to show too many things, your map will be crowded and messy. Choose only the most important things to show on your map. For example, you might want to show a parking lot. Show the parking lot on your map but not the cars in it. The cars can move and might not be in the same place the next time you use your map. Consider the purpose of your map when you decide what things you will show on the map.

Fig. 3-5 Two views of the same house—one is a ground-level view, the other is a ''bird's-eye'' view.

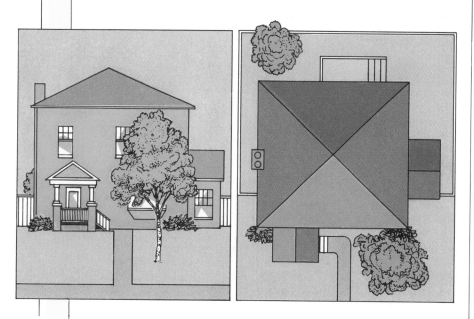

Draw a rough sketch map first, making corrections and additions until you are satisfied that the map is accurate. As you draw the good copy of your map, keep the following points in mind.

- Your map should have a title that tells the place shown and the purpose of the map. For example, your title might be ''Road Map of Homedale.''

- Your map should indicate where the direction ''north'' is. This allows a person using the map to turn it so that streets or other features on the map run in the same direction as the real features.

- Your map should have a legend to explain any symbols that you used which might be confusing to the person using the map.

- Your map should tell the person using it the size of the area that has been shown. This is called the map scale and is explained in more detail in Chapter 4.

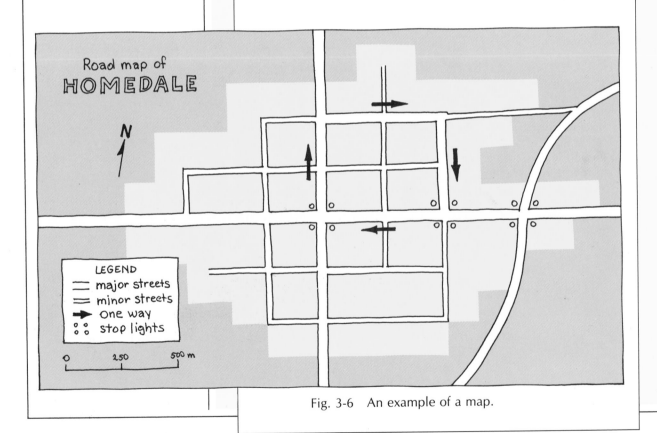

Fig. 3-6   An example of a map.

What is your community?

Neighbourhoods, cities, regions and countries are all places, although they vary greatly in size. Each of these places may have a sense of identity, but are they all communities?

A **neighbourhood** may have a name that distinguishes it from other neighbourhoods. It may be separated from other neighbourhoods by a road, a river, a railway line or some other feature. There may be a park, a school, a church or a shopping plaza that acts as a focal point for the neighbourhood. Do you think of your neighbourhood as a community?

A **municipality** is an area that has its own local government. Municipalities can be **urban** or **rural**. In urban areas, people live close together and most of the land is used to build houses, stores, factories and other buildings. In rural areas, people do not live as close to each other. Most houses and other buildings are further apart, and much of the land is not built on.

Fig. 3-7 Budapest, Hungary is an urban community. The farm on the Chaudière River in Québec is in a rural area.

Municipalities can be **cities**, **towns**, or **townships**. Cities are municipalities with many neighbourhoods and large populations. Towns have fewer neighbourhoods and smaller populations than cities. Both cities and towns are urban municipalities. A township is a rural municipality where people do not live in neighbourhoods, but are spread out over a larger area. Do you think of your municipality as a community?

Most people think of their community as their neighbourhood or municipality. Sometimes, though, the neighbourhood or municipality may lack the focal points that help to create a community identity. People may live in one municipality, but work and shop in a nearby municipality. They may feel closer ties to this municipality than to their own.

A **regional municipality** is a group of neighbouring cities, towns and townships. An example is the Regional Municipality of Waterloo, in Southern Ontario. This region includes the cities of Kitchener, Waterloo, Cambridge and the surrounding rural areas. Kitchener and Waterloo have grown together until they now appear to be one city. The city of Cambridge was created in 1973 when the towns of Galt, Preston and Hespeler had also grown into one community. Many people in the surrounding areas shop or work in one of the cities. Do you think a regional municipality is a community?

Fig. 3-8 Map of the Regional Municipality of Waterloo.

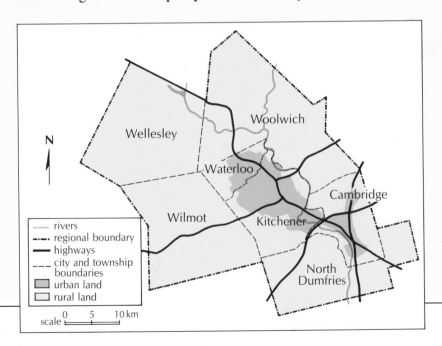

ACTIVITY TWO

1. How can you tell when you have left your neighbourhood? What forms the boundaries of your neighbourhood? /4

2. Draw a map of your neighbourhood. (See "How geographers work: Drawing maps.") Include any features that act as focal points for the neighbourhood. /25

3. Use the photographs in Fig. 3-7 to explain the difference between an urban and a rural area. /4

4. a) What is the name of your municipality?
   b) In what type of municipality do you live? Is it a city, town, or township? /3
   c) Is it an urban or rural area?

5. Find examples of other types of municipalities near you. /4

6. Examine Fig. 3-8. Name the cities and townships that are part of the Regional Municipality of Waterloo. /3

7. Which municipalities within the region are
   a) mainly urban?   b) mainly rural? /6

Case study of a community: Iqaluit, Baffin Island

Baffin Island, in Canada's Arctic, is Canada's largest island and the fifth largest island in the world. The largest settlement on Baffin Island is Iqaluit. In 1981, Iqaluit had a population of 2333.

Iqaluit is probably very different from your area. It is isolated from the other settlements on Baffin Island by the mountainous terrain and the absence of roads. Water transportation is limited to the short summer season when the ocean is not frozen. Iqaluit depends on its airport to provide a link with the outside world and with other island communities.

Other settlements on Baffin Island are smaller and more isolated than Iqaluit. You might expect that each of these

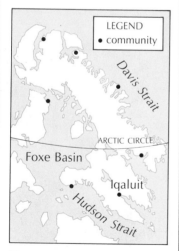

Fig. 3-9 Communities of Baffin Island.

Fig. 3-10   Iqaluit, on Baffin Island.

settlements would have its own community identity, but would lack a sense of regional identity because they are isolated. In fact, Baffin Island has a strong regional identity.

The inhabitants are the Baffin Island Inuit, who have a strong sense of identity because of their shared culture. Iqaluit was once called Frobisher Bay, but changed its name in 1987 to reflect its Inuit culture.

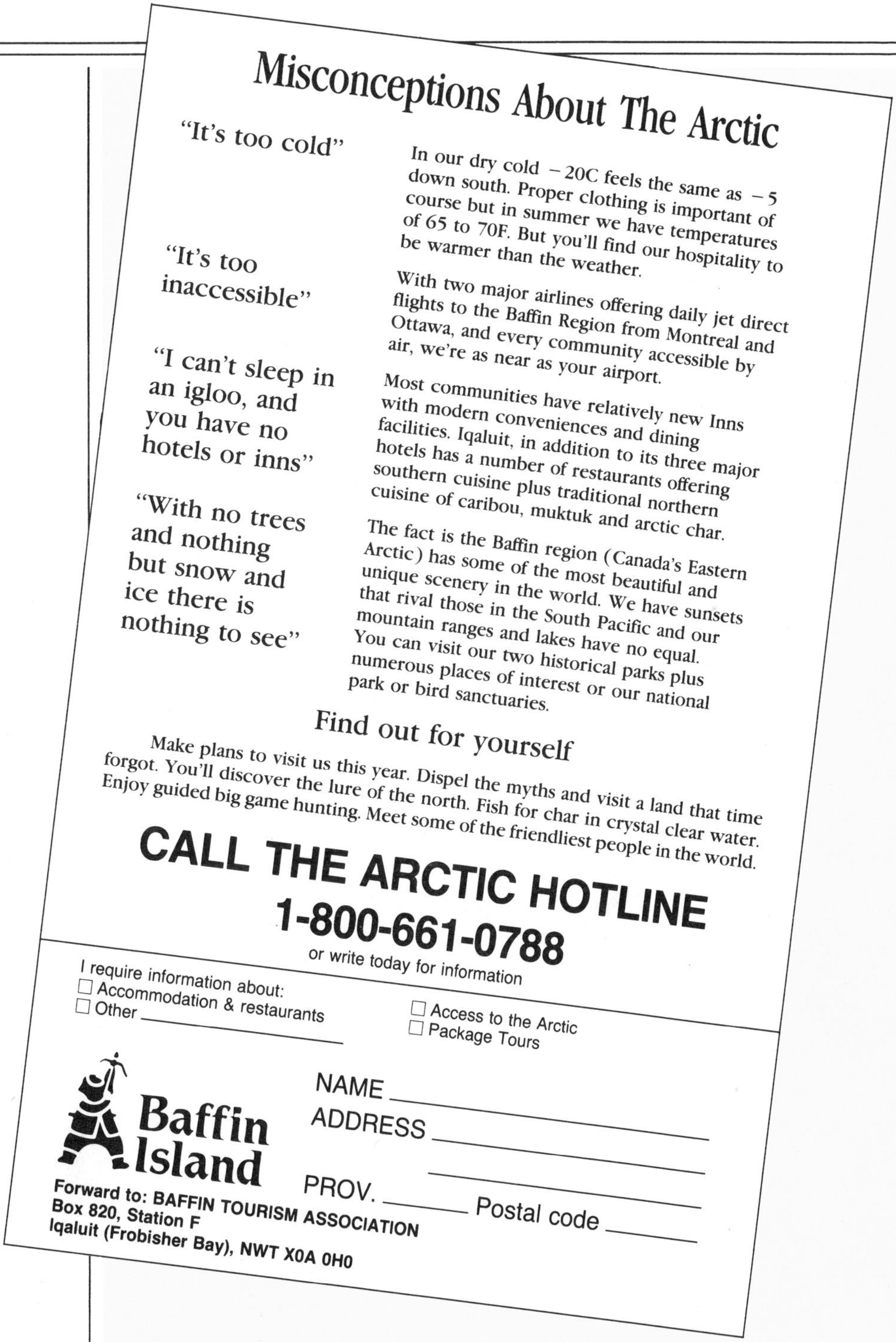

Fig. 3-11 A tourism advertisement from the Arctic.

Misconceptions About The Arctic

"It's too cold"

In our dry cold −20C feels the same as −5 down south. Proper clothing is important of course but in summer we have temperatures of 65 to 70F. But you'll find our hospitality to be warmer than the weather.

"It's too inaccessible"

With two major airlines offering daily jet direct flights to the Baffin Region from Montreal and Ottawa, and every community accessible by air, we're as near as your airport.

"I can't sleep in an igloo, and you have no hotels or inns"

Most communities have relatively new Inns with modern conveniences and dining facilities. Iqaluit, in addition to its three major hotels has a number of restaurants offering southern cuisine plus traditional northern cuisine of caribou, muktuk and arctic char.

"With no trees and nothing but snow and ice there is nothing to see"

The fact is the Baffin region (Canada's Eastern Arctic) has some of the most beautiful and unique scenery in the world. We have sunsets that rival those in the South Pacific and our mountain ranges and lakes have no equal. You can visit our two historical parks plus numerous places of interest or our national park or bird sanctuaries.

Find out for yourself

Make plans to visit us this year. Dispel the myths and visit a land that time forgot. You'll discover the lure of the north. Fish for char in crystal clear water. Enjoy guided big game hunting. Meet some of the friendliest people in the world.

CALL THE ARCTIC HOTLINE
1-800-661-0788
or write today for information

I require information about:
☐ Accommodation & restaurants
☐ Other _____

☐ Access to the Arctic
☐ Package Tours

Baffin Island

NAME _____
ADDRESS _____
_____
PROV. _____ Postal code _____

Forward to: BAFFIN TOURISM ASSOCIATION
Box 820, Station F
Iqaluit (Frobisher Bay), NWT X0A 0H0

ACTIVITY THREE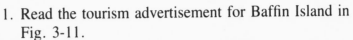

1. Read the tourism advertisement for Baffin Island in Fig. 3-11.

   a) What are the average summer temperatures on Baffin Island in Fahrenheit degrees?

   b) What would these temperatures be in Celsius degrees? (To convert from Fahrenheit to Celsius degrees, use the following equation: $°F - 32 \times 5/9 = °C$)

   c) Compare these temperatures to the average summer temperatures in your community.

   d) How long would it take to travel from Montréal, Québec to Iqaluit by air? (Jet airplanes travel at 800 kilometres per hour.)

   e) Give three reasons why a tourist might want to visit Baffin Island.

   f) Why might people think that there are no hotels on Baffin Island?

   g) What symbol is used to represent Baffin Island? Do you think it is an appropriate symbol? Why or why not?

2. a) In what ways is Iqaluit different from your community?

   b) In what ways is Iqaluit a typical community?

3. What clues are there in the advertisement that the people of Baffin Island share a common identity?

4. a) In what part of Canada do you live?

   b) Are there any characteristics that give your region an identity similar to Baffin Island's regional identity?

WHAT YOU HAVE LEARNED

In this chapter, you have learned that a community is a place that has a sense of identity. This sense of identity is influenced by physical and cultural features within the community. You examined your neighbourhood, your municipality and your region to identify the features that create a community identity.

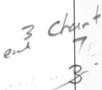

Careers in geography: Planner

Planning is important to the orderly growth of communities and to the comfort of people who live and work within them. Urban and regional planners are university graduates in geography, urban planning, architecture or engineering. Map-reading skills are very important. Planners often require the help of planning technicians, who prepare maps and other information for use by the planners. These technicians are usually graduates of a community college program.

Bruce Fischer is a senior planner for the Regional Municipality of York in Ontario. He has been working for the municipality for twelve years.

Fig. 3-12   Bruce Fischer helps to plan the Regional Municipality of York.

"One of my jobs is to review plans for the development of new sub-divisions in the region. There has been very rapid growth in this area. We want to create surroundings that are satisfactory to both residents and businesses. Planners work with land developers, governments and citizens to achieve this goal. It is a necessary and challenging career."

LOOKING BACK

1. How is a map different from a photograph?

2. a) What is a municipality?
   b) What is a regional municipality?

3. Explain the similarities and the differences between an urban and a rural community.

4. Find out more about the municipality in which you live. Your public library, your municipal government and local organizations such as the Chamber of Commerce or local historical society can help you with your research.
   a) How did your municipality get its name?
   b) Does your municipality have a coat of arms or a motto?
   c) Does your municipality celebrate any important festivals during the year?
   d) What are the physical and cultural features that act as focal points within the municipality?

EXPANDING YOUR LEARNING

5. Obtain a map of your municipality from the planning or engineering department of your municipal government office. Locate important features on the map, including your neighbourhood.

6. In this chapter, you were asked if neighbourhoods, municipalities and regions were communities. To what extent can the word community be used for even larger areas, such as whole continents or the whole world?

7. One of the meanings of community is co-operation. How do people in your neighbourhood, municipality and region co-operate with one another?

Where in the World Are We?

Fig. 4-1 The location you will learn about in this chapter.

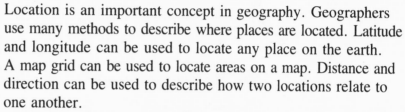

WHAT YOU WILL LEARN

Location is an important concept in geography. Geographers use many methods to describe where places are located. Latitude and longitude can be used to locate any place on the earth. A map grid can be used to locate areas on a map. Distance and direction can be used to describe how two locations relate to one another.

In this chapter, you will learn in more detail how geographers describe locations. You will use these methods to describe locations on the earth and within your own community.

KEY WORDS

latitude	Prime Meridian	International Date Line
longitude	gazeteer	
Equator	map grid	
hemisphere	map scale	

Making sense of location

Have you ever noticed people in large parking lots, wandering around as if they are lost? Often they are loaded down with bags of purchases, but they do not know where they left their car. There were probably not as many cars when they parked earlier in the day. They may approach

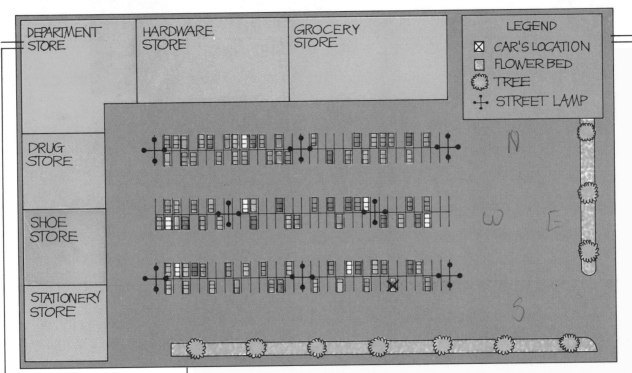

Fig. 4-2 How would you describe the location of the car in this parking lot?

several cars which look like their own, but have different licence plates. Finally they find their car hiding behind a large van.

Other people are able to survey the sea of cars, then walk straight to their own car. The second group of people probably used a system to remember where they left their car. They remembered that they parked in Row 5 of Section B, or perhaps they used a landmark such as the streetlamp south of the drugstore.

When geographers study the earth, they face a problem similar to the problem faced by the lost shoppers in the parking lot. There seem to be a countless number of communities on our planet. Many of them are very similar to one another and difficult to tell apart. How can we find Iqaluit, Amsterdam, Toronto or New York on such a big earth? It is helpful to have a system to locate places on the earth.

ACTIVITY ONE

1. Examine Fig. 4-2. Describe the location of the car using three different methods.

2. Describe the location of your desk in the classroom in relation to the teacher's desk.

3. Describe the location of your home in relation to the school.

4. Describe the location of your community in relation to the rest of the province.

Latitude and longitude

Geographers use a system that divides the earth into sections to help them locate places. The earth is divided into **hemispheres**, or halves. These halves are called the Northern and Southern Hemispheres, and the Eastern and Western Hemispheres. Geographers can begin to identify the location of a place by noting which hemisphere it is in. In which hemispheres is Canada located?

Latitude and **longitude** are a much more precise way to identify location. Latitude and longitude are imaginary lines that run around the earth, allowing geographers to identify location very accurately. Likely you have heard about the **Equator**. It is the line of latitude halfway between the **North Pole** and the **South Pole**. All lines of latitude run parallel to the Equator.

Fig. 4-3 The hemispheres. There are four hemispheres—can you explain why?

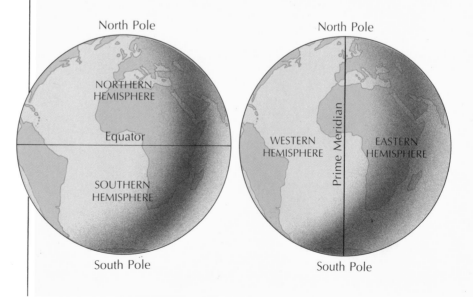

The symbol ° is usually used to represent degrees. The four directions are represented by the capital letters N, S, W, and E.

Lines of latitude run east-west, parallel to the Equator. Lines of longitude meet at the North and South Poles. To remember these definitions, just look at the second letter of each word—the **a** in latitude means **across**, and the **o** in longitude means **over** the poles.

40

Each line of latitude has a numerical value. The Equator is 0°, the North Pole is 90°N and the South Pole is 90°S. A community halfway between the Equator and the South Pole is 45°S. It is the Equator that divides the Northern and Southern Hemispheres.

Lines of longitude are imaginary lines that run from the North Pole to the South Pole. They also have numerical values. There are two important lines of longitude. The **Prime Meridian** runs through Greenwich, England, and has a value of 0°. On the opposite side of the earth, another line of longitude known as the **International Date Line** runs through the Pacific Ocean. Its value is 180°. These two lines of longitude are the dividing lines between the Eastern and Western Hemispheres. A community in the Western Hemisphere, halfway between the Prime Meridian and the International Date Line, would have a longitude of 90°W.

An atlas is a book that contains maps of locations all over the world. These maps have latitude and longitude marked on

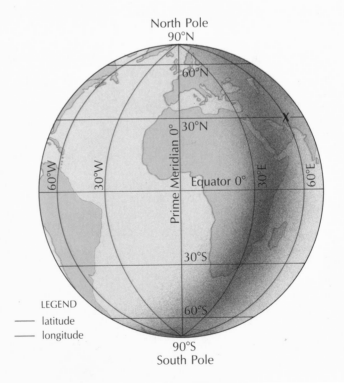

Fig. 4-4 Latitude and longitude can be used to locate any place on earth. What is the latitude and longitude of the place marked **X**?

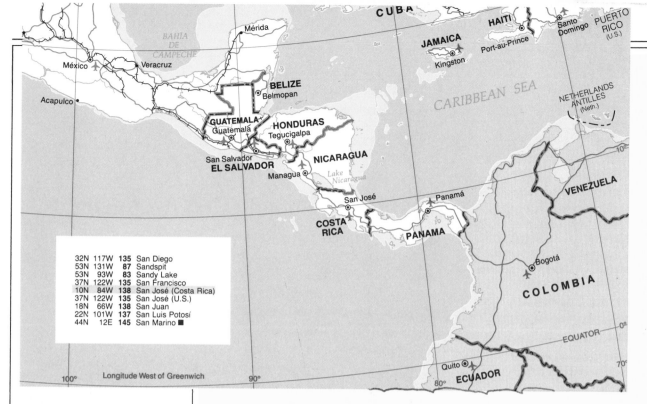

32N 117W **135** San Diego
53N 131W **87** Sandspit
53N 93W **83** Sandy Lake
37N 122W **135** San Francisco
10N 84W **138** San José (Costa Rica)
37N 122W **135** San José (U.S.)
18N 66W **138** San Juan
22N 101W **137** San Luis Potosí
44N 12E **145** San Marino ■

Longitude West of Greenwich

Fig. 4-5 Using an atlas to find locations.

Remember that latitude describes how far north or south a community is.

them, so that you can locate many places on the earth. How do you know where to look in the atlas to find a particular place? Most atlases have **gazeteers**. A gazeteer is an index that lists the places found in the atlas, the page each place can be found, and its latitude and longitude.

ACTIVITY TWO

Hand in

1. Find your community or a nearby community in an atlas. Record its latitude and longitude.

2. Find the following communities in an atlas. Record the latitude and longitude of each and which hemispheres each is in.
   a) Moscow, U.S.S.R.
   b) San Francisco, California
   c) Paris, France
   d) Manila, Philippines
   e) Lima, Peru
   f) Tokyo, Japan
   g) Sydney, Australia
   h) Oslo, Norway
   i) Edmonton, Alberta
   j) Halifax, Nova Scotia

3. Which of the communities in question 2 are north of your community?

4. Which one of the communities in question 2 is closest to your community's longitude?

Locating communities on road maps

Geographers have other ways of locating places in addition to the system of latitude and longitude. The latitude and longitude system describes one specific point on the map, but it is not always the best way to locate features which cover an area of the map.

Another way of locating places on maps is by using a system called **map grid**. The map grid system describes an area of the map instead of one specific point. Map grid is a good system to use on a road map, because many of the features that you want to locate cover an area of the map, rather than one specific point.

If you look at the map in Fig. 4-6, you can see that the map has letters along one margin and numbers along another margin. This produces a grid, or system of squares within which every feature on the map can be located. Killarney Provincial Park, for example, is located in the P36 square. Highway 566 can be located by looking in the M36 square.

Road maps usually have a map index that lists all of the towns or roads on the map, as well as their location on the map grid. For example, to help you find the town of Englehart on the map, the index lists the grid reference M37.

People who use road maps want to know how far away places are, as well as where they are. On the road map of Ontario, North Bay is located in the O38 square. New Liskeard is located in the N37 square and can be reached by following Highway 11. This highway travels north, climbing over hills and winding around lakes. The distance a car would have to travel between these two places is quite a bit more than the straight-line distance would suggest.

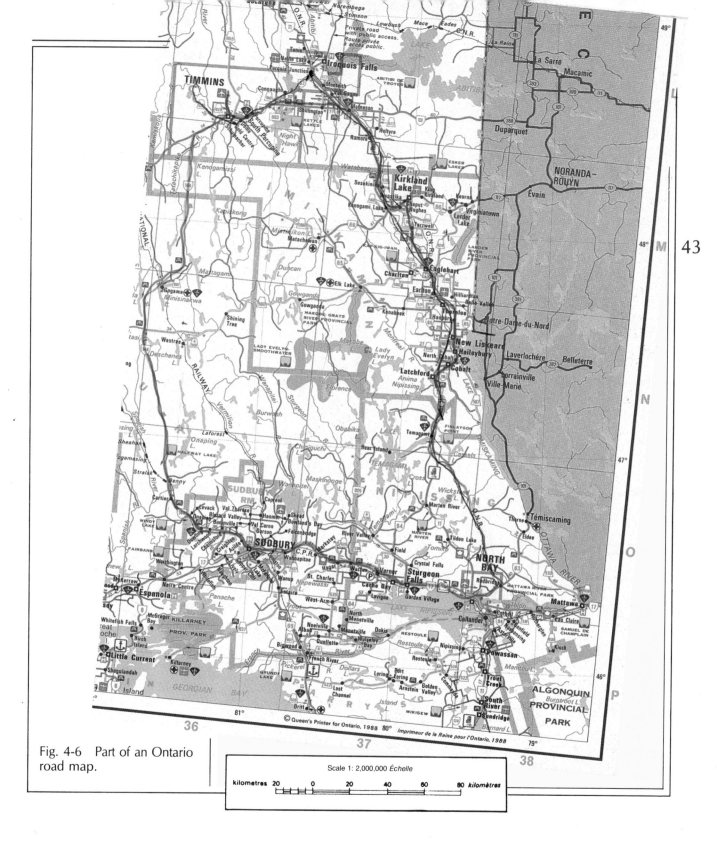

Fig. 4-6 Part of an Ontario road map.

Scale 1: 2,000,000 Échelle

kilometres 20   0   20   40   60   80 *kilomètres*

Most road maps provide distance charts which tell the number of kilometres from one point to another. The chart in Fig. 4-7 indicates that the distance by road from New Liskeard to Timmins is 206 km. If you want to know the distance to a place that is not in the distance chart, the road map provides other useful information. Small numbers printed beside the roads on the map tell the distances between various points. For example, at the junction of Highway 11 and Highway 17 in North Bay, there is a small red star. There is another red star north on Highway 11 at Marten River. The distance between these two points along this stretch of highway is given as 58 km. What is the distance from Marten River to the next star at Latchford?

Fig. 4-7 Many road maps include a distance chart. This example shows the distance in kilometres.

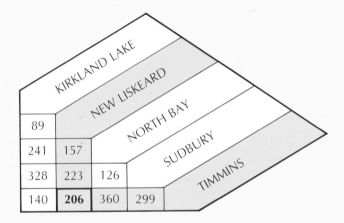

89				
241	157			
328	223	126		
140	**206**	360	299	

ACTIVITY THREE

1. Plan a round trip from North Bay to New Liskeard, Kirkland Lake, Timmins, Sudbury, then back to North Bay.
   a) What highways will you follow along the way?
   b) What direction will you travel along each section of your trip?
   c) How far will you have travelled when you return to North Bay?
   d) Between Kirkland Lake and Timmins, you decide to make a side trip to Cochrane. How many kilometres will this side trip add to your total distance?

2. a) Obtain a road map of your province. Plan a trip from your community in a large circle so that the total distance you would travel is about 1000 km.

   b) Gather information about the communities along your route. How are these communities different from your community? What physical or cultural features give the communities a sense of identity? What points of interest are there that you might like to visit?

How geographers work: Map scale

The distances shown on a map are much smaller than the real distances. The **map scale** compares the distances on a map to the real distances measured on the earth's surface. For example, on the road map of Ontario in Fig. 4-6, each centimetre on the map represents 20 km on the earth's surface. This information can be used to calculate the straight-line distance between places on the map. To find the straight-line distance, measure the distance between two points on the map with a ruler. If the distance on the map is 3 cm, you can find the distance on the earth's surface like this:

   1 cm on the map represents 20 km on the earth's surface, therefore 3 cm represents $(3 \times 20) = 60$ km

1. If you measure the distance between North Bay and New Liskeard on the map, you should get 7 cm. What would be the straight-line distance between these two points? Why is the straight-line distance less than the road distance?

2. Calculate the distance you would fly to complete a round trip from North Bay to New Liskeard, Kirkland Lake, Timmins, Sudbury, then back to North Bay.

Mental maps

Most of us do not walk around with road maps in our pockets. However we do carry ''maps'' of familiar places in our heads. These mental maps do not have lines of latitude and longitude or a map grid, but they do have important features which we use to find our way around.

If visitors to your community stop you and ask where Mountain Road is, you use your mental map to give directions. To follow your directions, the visitors need to create mental maps as you describe the route. Since visitors are not familiar with the local geography, their mental maps cannot be as detailed as yours. If your description contains too much information, they will not be able to picture the route they must follow. Read the following directions to Mountain Road:

''Keep driving along this street until you get to a stoplight. You will be in the downtown area. Turn left onto Main Street and go about five blocks until you come to Cedar Road. You will know you are getting close to Cedar Road when there aren't any more stores along Main Street. You will be in a residential neighbourhood like this one. Turn right and drive down into a river valley and across a bridge. There are a lot of open fields and trees on that side of the river. Keep going on Cedar Road until you see an old stone house with a barn on the right side. Mountain Road turns off to the left a short distance afterwards.''

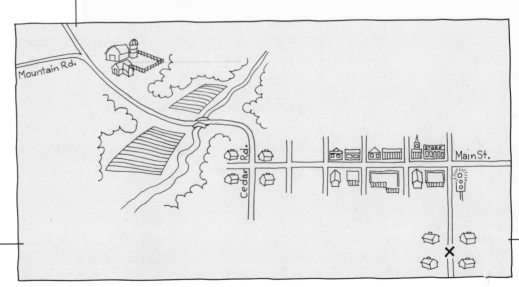

Fig. 4-8   The route to Mountain Road.

ACTIVITY FOUR 🌐 📝 📖

1. Compare the directions given to Mountain Road to the sketch map in Fig. 4-8.
   a) Would you have been able to draw this map by following the directions?
   b) Simplify the set of directions to make it easier to form a mental map of this route.

2. The following game can be an entertaining way to practise giving directions and using your mental map of your community.

    One person is chosen to be the game director. The director thinks of a local landmark that can be reached from the school and writes it on a piece of paper. The director then gives oral directions to the landmark from the school. The other players use their mental maps of the community to follow the route described. They guess what the landmark is and write down their answers. Since the object of the game is to give directions which are as clear as possible, the director gets one point for each correct answer. The other players receive one point if they have the right answer. Each player takes turns being game director.

WHAT YOU HAVE LEARNED

In this chapter you learned how geographers describe location. You used latitude and longitude, map grid, distance charts, map scale and oral directions to describe the locations of places. In the next chapter, you will learn why communities are located where they are.

LOOKING BACK 🌐 📝

1. What are two ways that you can use a road map to find the distances between places?

2. When you give directions to a visitor to your community, why is it important to keep the directions simple?

3. Use an atlas to find the following places:
   a) a country in Europe that borders the Mediterranean Sea and has Yugoslavia and Greece as neighbours.
   b) a city located at 30°N latitude by 90°W longitude.
   c) the most southerly point in England.
   d) the continent you would reach if you travelled straight south from California.
   e) an island nation located between 15°N and 20°N, 75°W and 80°W.

EXPANDING YOUR LEARNING

4. Lines of latitude and longitude are sometimes used as political boundary lines. Examine atlas maps to find five examples.

5. Use encyclopedias and other reference books to find out why the 180° line of longitude is called the International Date Line. Why does the Date Line bend occasionally even though the 180° line of longitude is straight?

6. If you examine the road map in Fig. 4-6 carefully, you will notice that transportation routes other than roads are shown. Describe the route you would follow from North Bay to New Liskeard
   a) by railway   b) by river

5

This Spot Is Special

Fig. 5-1 The locations you will learn about in this chapter.

WHAT YOU WILL LEARN

The location of a community does not occur by accident. When people decide to establish a community, they look for certain physical features which will provide their community with the most advantages. The exact spot that is chosen for the community is known as the site.

In this chapter, you will study many examples of sites. You will learn that sites for these communities were chosen for many different reasons when the communities were planned.

KEY WORDS

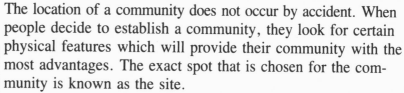

site	ghost town	portage
harbour	tourist industry	

Communities have unique sites

Winter in Canada usually brings snow. It is a time when many children build snow forts. To be successful, you need to find the right place for your snow fort. You need a place that provides a good supply of snow and perhaps protection from the wind. If you might have to defend yourself against ''attack,'' you must build your fort where it will be easy to see the ''enemy.'' What else would

Fig. 5-2 Have you ever built a snow fort?

Fig. 5-3 The site of Québec City provides protection for its harbour.

be important when you choose the spot for the fort?

The spot you select for your snow fort is called the **site**. Site refers to the exact location of a community and its physical characteristics. Each community has a site which is in some way unique. However, sites can be put in groups according to the reasons that the sites were chosen. Some of these reasons are:

- They are protected from weather.
- They are easy to defend.
- They are located on a transportation route.
- They have a useful resource such as a mineral deposit or a source of power.

Which of these site choices would be important when building a snow fort?

Protected sites

Some sites are chosen because the surrounding landforms protect them from bad weather. As an example, communities along the shores of oceans are seldom located on an unprotected coast.

A **harbour** is a protected area of water where ships can anchor in safety.

Waves could blow in during storms and cause a lot of damage to the community. Most coastal communities are located on an inlet or where off-shore islands help to reduce the damage caused by storms. A sheltered **harbour** is chosen, where ships can dock safely in bad weather. Coastal sites which are exposed to rough weather are seldom chosen for anything except lighthouses.

Defensive sites

Historically, defence was an important consideration when choosing a site for a community. During the seventeenth century, Britain and France were struggling for control of North America. There were a number of wars between the two nations, and every community had to be prepared to defend itself against attack by its enemies. Sites were chosen that allowed a clear view of an attacking enemy. Many communities began as forts that were built to protect an important transportation route or resource.

Fig. 5-4 Why was this a good site for the fort at Québec City?

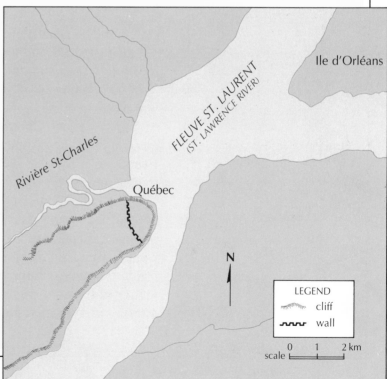

ACTIVITY ONE 🌐 📝 📖

1. Examine Fig. 5-3 and Fig. 5-4 to see the advantages of the site of Québec City.
   a) What physical characteristics did this site have that made it a good harbour?
   b) What physical characteristics did this site have that made it easy to defend?

2. Examine Fig. 5-4. How would you attack the fort at Québec City if you wanted to control it?

3. Look in history books to find out how the British overcame the French defences at Québec City in 1759.

4. Examine a map of Canada and explain why the British capture of Québec City allowed Britain to extend its control over all of Canada.

5. Examine a map of Canada. Find other locations that seem to be good sites for forts or harbours. Explain your choices.

Sites on transportation routes

Communities usually want to trade with other communities to sell their products and to buy the things they need. Transportation routes link communities and help them to trade their goods.

In the eighteenth and early nineteenth centuries, there were few roads in Canada. Rivers were used as the major means of transportation. Communities were built along rivers to take advantage of these transportation routes. The junction of two rivers was a popular site for a community because it allowed transportation in several directions.

Some communities benefitted from a location at the junction of land and water routes. Many early roads were built as portages. A **portage** is a land route that connects two water routes. The ends of portage routes were another favourite site for communities, since products had to be unloaded from boats and reloaded onto wagons. Hotels were often located at these sites to provide food and overnight accommodation.

A junction is the spot where two things join together.

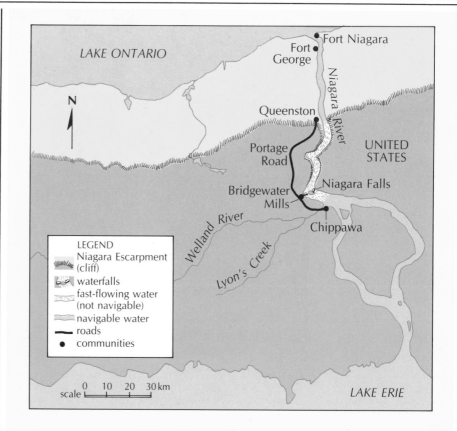

Mill sites

Every community needs energy. Today, important sources of energy are electricity and natural gas. These energy sources can be carried long distances by wires and pipelines. Therefore, a community today does not have to be located close to a source of energy.

In the nineteenth century, however, these fuels were not available to people who were building communities. One of the most important sources of energy was water power. Fast-moving water was used to turn water wheels, the power source for saw mills and flour mills. Sites were chosen at waterfalls or places where a small dam could be built to create a mill pond. The need for water power as well as the need for water transportation explains why so many early communities were built on rivers.

Fig. 5-6 Fast-flowing water provided many early communities with a source of energy.

54

ACTIVITY TWO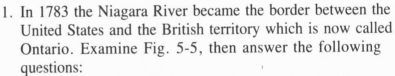

1. In 1783 the Niagara River became the border between the United States and the British territory which is now called Ontario. Examine Fig. 5-5, then answer the following questions:
   a) Why are there two forts at the mouth of the Niagara River? (The mouth of the Niagara is where it enters Lake Ontario.)
   b) Which fort is on a better site to guard the entrance to the Niagara River?

2. Explain the advantages of the following sites:
   a) Queenston
   b) Bridgewater Mills
   c) Chippawa

3. Describe the route that would be used in 1800 to transport products from Lake Ontario to Lake Erie.

4. Why do communities need a source of energy?

Mining sites

At first glance, some communities seem to lack site advantages. For example, Flin Flon, Manitoba is not located on a river. It is an isolated northern community on the Saskatchewan-Manitoba border. Why is it located there? The advantage of the site at Flin Flon is hidden in the rocks under the community. These rocks are rich in metals. The mines at Flin Flon have been an important source of zinc and copper for over fifty years.

Communities such as Flin Flon can face a problem. What happens to the community if the mines close down? Canada has many **ghost towns**, towns that died because the resources on which they were based ran out or were no longer in demand. These areas have lost their advantage as sites for communities. Will this happen to Flin Flon some day?

Once a community has grown, it develops additional advantages that help it to survive. Flin Flon is now linked to other communities by roads and railways. It has become the centre of a **tourist industry**. If its mines shut down some day, these other advantages may help this community to continue.

55

Tourist industry is a term that refers to all the businesses that develop to serve visitors to an area.

Fig. 5-7 Flin Flon, Manitoba in 1928. This community was located near a rich source of metal ore.

ACTIVITY THREE 📝 🗺️

1. Why is a mining community so dependent on its mines?

2. Do all mining communities become ghost towns? Explain your answer.

3. Use atlases and encyclopedias to find out about one of the following mining communities which has faced the problem of its mines closing down:

> Barkerville, British Columbia
> Fort Steele, British Columbia
> Dawson, Yukon
> Schefferville, Québec
> Atikokan, Ontario
> Kirkland Lake, Ontario

a) Describe the location of the community.
b) What mineral was mined in this community?
c) When was the community most prosperous?
d) What transportation routes or other advantages does the community have?
e) What has happened to the community since the mines closed down?

Changing advantages of a site

Mining communities are communities that can be greatly affected by change. Many mining sites have declined in importance since the demand for metals is not as great as it once was. Sites can lose their advantages due to changes in technology. For example, today plastics have replaced metals in many products.

Other types of sites can also face losing their advantages as the result of developments in technology. In the mid-nineteenth century, river sites declined in importance. Water power was replaced by other sources of energy. Also, boats were larger and could not navigate many of the smaller rivers. Canals were dug to allow water transportation to compete with the growing number of roads and railways.

Technology refers to advances in science that result in new and easier ways of doing things.

For example, the first Welland Canal was built in 1829 to allow boats to get from Lake Ontario to Lake Erie without having to portage around Niagara Falls. In 1853, the Great Western Railway was completed from Windsor to the Niagara River. Fig. 5-8 shows how these changes affected the communities in the Niagara Peninsula.

Today, there are still developments occurring that are changing the advantages of many sites. Railways have now become less important as transportation routes, while large highways have become more important. Four-lane divided highways are especially important because they allow large trucks to travel more quickly and safely.

Fig. 5-8 Communities in the Niagara Peninsula in 1860. What changes have occurred in the years since 1800?

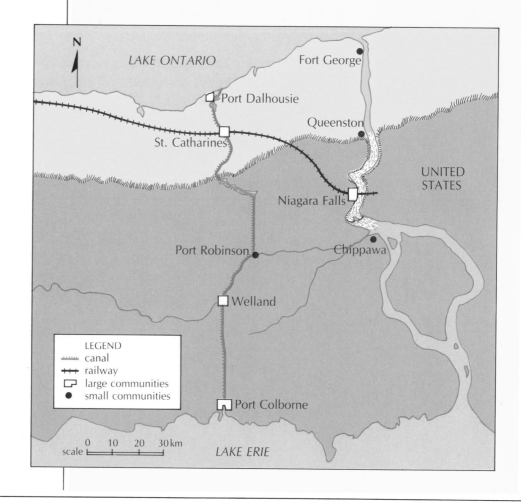

ACTIVITY FOUR

1. Examine Fig. 5-8 and compare it to Fig. 5-5. Use both figures to answer the following questions:
   a) Along which transportation route were most of the larger communities in the mid-nineteenth century?
   b) Sites along the Niagara River such as Queenston and Chippawa declined in importance in the mid-nineteenth century. Why?
   c) What was the advantage of the new community of Niagara Falls?
   d) St. Catharines had become the largest community in the Niagara Peninsula. What were its site advantages?

2. Think of three products that were made from metal in the past, but are now made from plastic.

3. Examine a road map of Ontario to see where the four-lane divided highways are located. Which communities have the advantage of the best transportation routes today?

WHAT YOU HAVE LEARNED

In this chapter, you have learned the reasons why communities are located where they are. Certain characteristics of the site give a community advantages. These site advantages allow a community to grow. Communities sometimes decline because changes in technology change a site's advantages.

LOOKING BACK

1. a) Compare the energy sources of the early nineteenth century with those of today.
   b) Compare the transportation methods used in the early nineteenth century with those used today.

2. How have these changes affected communities?

3. Prepare a chart to compare the site factors of communities founded near
   a) a harbour
   b) a fort
   c) a transportation route
   d) a mill
   e) a mine

EXPANDING YOUR LEARNING

4. Examine the site of your community.
   a) Describe or sketch the site.
   b) What were its advantages in the past?
   c) What are its advantages today?

5. Modern technology allows us to change the physical environment in order to improve a site. For example, an island might be built to create an artificial harbour. Look for examples in your community where an attempt has been made to change the site.

6. By changing the natural environment, we sometimes create problems. For example, removing trees along a river might cause the river bank to wear away faster. Look for examples in your community where human actions have damaged the environment.

59

What Is Our Situation?

WHAT YOU WILL LEARN

A community exists as part of its surroundings. The human and physical factors in the surrounding area affect what people in the community do and the way a community develops.

In this chapter, you will study the impact of four physical features on communities: landforms, climate, vegetation, and soils.

KEY WORDS

situation	**natural vegetation**	**humus**
landforms	**growing season**	**sedimentary**
climate	**rock outcrops**	**soil**

Fig. 6-1   The locations you will learn about in this chapter.

Site and situation

Geographers look at a community's location in two ways. One way is by describing a community's site, as you did in Chapter 5. Site refers to the features of the local area where the community has been built. It describes these features within or very close to the community itself.

Situation is another way that geographers look at a community's location. When geographers examine situation, they look at the community in relation to its surroundings. Situation describes a community's location on a larger scale than site. It describes the features in the area surrounding the community, rather than features in the community itself. For example, Montréal, Vancouver and Toronto are each situated near excellent farmland.

There are many things in the surrounding region that affect a community. Transportation routes link communities within a region. These routes allow communities to sell products to one another. If the surrounding region contains many people, there will be more customers to buy each community's products. This will help the community to grow. Transportation routes and the population of the surrounding region are examples of the human factors that can affect a community's situation.

A community's situation also contains physical factors that affect the community. These physical factors include landforms, climate, vegetation and soils.

Fig. 6-2 What are the differences between site and situation?

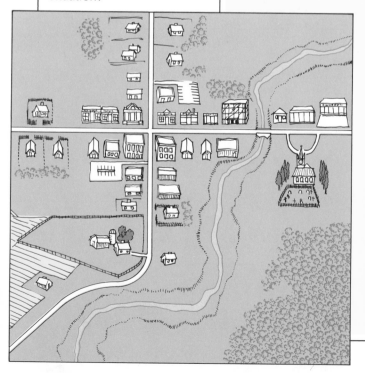

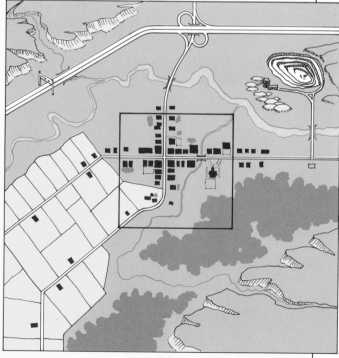

ACTIVITY ONE

1. Examine Fig. 6-2.
   a) What does the site diagram show that the situation diagram does not show?
   b) What does the situation diagram show that the site diagram does not show?
   c) What is the difference between site and situation?

2. Suggest ways that each of the four physical factors might influence a community.

3. Which do you think has more influence on a community, its site or its situation? Explain the reasons for your answer.

How situation affects a community

Landforms

Landforms have an important influence on a community's situation. **Landforms** are the unique shapes of the land caused by the underlying rock. One example of the influence of a landform occurs when the rock forms steep slopes. In this type of area, soils are usually very thin, and rocks appear on the surface. This means that the area is not well suited

Fig. 6-3 Communities are affected by the landforms of the region.

Rock outcrops are places where solid rock is visible on the surface of the earth because there is little soil covering the rock.

to farming, for example. Steep slopes cause problems in transportation and the construction of buildings, as well. However, **rock outcrops** make it easy to find mineral deposits, so mining is common.

On the other hand, when rocks lie flat, they are often covered by thick layers of soil. Since the rocks are not visible on the surface, it is more difficult to locate mineral deposits. There is usually less mining but more farming in these areas. Transportation and construction are easier on flat land.

Climate

Climate refers to the weather conditions that we expect to find in a specific area. For example, in most of Canada we expect it to be cold and snowy in January. In July we expect temperatures to be warm.

Climate is another situation factor that has a very important effect on a region. The way houses are built, the clothes people wear and the types of recreational activities available are all affected by the climate of that region.

The **growing season** is the time of the year in which a particular crop will grow in a certain location.

Crops require certain climate conditions in order to grow. Some of the climate conditions that affect crops are the length of the **growing season**, the amount of rainfall, and the season

Fig. 6-4 A house in Bermuda. How does climate influence the way houses are built?

in which the rain falls. If a region has the right climate conditions for a certain crop, the local community may develop an industry that uses that crop. For example, if a region has the right climate for growing grapes, a community within that region may develop a wine industry as a result.

ACTIVITY TWO 🔘 🎐 📷

1. Examine the photographs in Fig. 6-3.
   a) Describe the landscapes. How are the landforms different?
   b) Why is there very little soil covering the rocks on the hills?
   c) For what purposes could humans use the land in these photographs?

2. What are the landforms and climatic conditions of your community?

3. List four ways that climate can affect a community.

4. You have a million dollars to spend. You have decided to spend it on a tourist resort. You have a choice between a ski resort and a beach resort. Before you decide which resort to buy, what information do you want to know about the landforms and climate conditions of the regions in which the resorts are located?

5. You are a farmer in your local region. A new tree called the loconut has been developed. It produces a large crop of loconuts, which have many different uses, on very little land. The farmers who grow loconut trees become prosperous. However, the loconut needs special climate conditions to grow. These include:

   - a winter temperature that never drops below minus 20°C;
   - no frost after April 20;
   - at least 4 months with temperatures of 15°C;
   - at least 700 mm of precipitation per year;
   - no more than 20 mm of precipitation during the month of harvest. (The month of harvest for the loconut is normally September.)

Find out how these climate conditions compare to the conditions in your region. Can you grow the loconut in your community? If not, which climate conditions prevent you from growing it? Make a chart similar to the one in Fig. 6-5 to compare the crop-growing conditions in your community to the conditions needed to grow loconuts.

Fig. 6-5 Could the loconut thrive in your community?

	LOCONUT REQUIREMENTS	LOCAL CONDITIONS
lowest winter temperature		
last frost date		
growing season– length/temperature		
lowest annual precipitation		
highest precipitation in September		

Natural vegetation

Natural vegetation refers to the plants in an area that grow naturally, without the influence of people. The trees that grow along a city street, for example, are not part of the natural vegetation because they have been planted there by people. They may be trees that have been brought in from another area, and are therefore not part of the vegetation normally found in that area.

In many communities the natural vegetation has been removed to make room for buildings, parking lots and for other purposes. In the region surrounding a community, the natural vegetation may or may not still exist. Natural vegetation is important to each community. It provides homes for wild animals so that people in the community can enjoy nature. It provides materials that the community can use to make products. A community that includes a furniture industry will likely be in a region that has

Fig. 6-6 How would natural vegetation such as the hardwood forest, softwood forest and tundra shown in these photographs affect communities?

a supply of hardwood such as maple or oak. A community that has a paper mill needs a large supply of softwood such as spruce or poplar.

Soil

Soil is the surface layer of the earth. It is made up mainly of small particles of broken rock. Clay is a type of soil with very fine particles. When the particles are slightly bigger, we call the soil sand. Larger rock particles are called gravel. Soil also contains humus. **Humus** is partly decayed vegetation which makes the soil better for farming. The type of vegetation in each location affects the amount of humus in the soil. For example, evergreen trees such as pine and spruce do not produce as much humus as trees that lose their leaves each autumn, such as the maple.

Soil type affects a region in many ways. Some crops need certain types of soil to grow well. For example, sandy soil is needed to grow peanuts. Soil is sometimes used as a raw material for certain industries. Sand and gravel are used to

Fig. 6-7 How do soil types such as the soil found in Holland Marsh farmland, in marshland or in Northern Africa influence communities in these regions?

make concrete and cement blocks for construction. The pottery industry depends on special types of clay. Soil also affects the drainage of water in a region. For example, clay does not absorb water as quickly as sand does. Flat land with clay soils is often marshy because the water has difficulty draining away.

ACTIVITY THREE

1. Examine the photographs in Fig. 6-6. Which photograph looks most like the natural vegetation in your community?

2. List two ways in which natural vegetation can affect a community.

3. Look at the photographs in Fig. 6-7. What soil and drainage conditions are shown?

4. a) Which soil types are found in your community?
   b) How do these soils affect your community?

Sedimentary rock is formed from small particles of eroded material that is deposited in layers and hardens over a long period of time.

How physical characteristics define regions

Let us look at how physical situation factors have combined in the southern part of the Prairie provinces. The landform here is a flat to rolling plain of **sedimentary** rock, covered by a thick layer of soil. The climate is too dry for trees but wet enough for the grass which forms the natural vegetation of the region. Grasslands produce large amounts of humus. This has made the soils of this region especially rich as well as very thick. The climate conditions are ideal for the growth of spring wheat, which grows well in the grassland soil. This region is one of the most important wheat-producing areas in the world.

The sedimentary rock underlying the soil contains important deposits of oil and natural gas. It is common to see gas and oil pumps working in the middle of the wheat fields. The landform, climate, natural vegetation and soil have created a unique region.

Fig. 6-8 The Prairies are a unique region of Canada.

ACTIVITY FOUR

1. a) Describe the landform in Fig. 6-8.
   b) What colour is the soil? Suggest why.
   c) How is the land being used in the photograph? Give reasons for your answer.

2. What products are produced in the southern part of the Prairie provinces? Explain why.

3. Use an atlas to research the physical situation of your own region, and compare it to the Prairie provinces. Copy the chart shown in Fig. 6-9 in your notebook. What are the similarities and the differences between these regions? Explain why they have occurred.

Fig. 6-9 Compare the situations of two regions.

	SOUTHERN PRAIRIE	MY REGION
landform		
climate conditions		
natural vegetation		
soils		
how humans use the physical environment		

How geographers work: Field trips

Since geography studies the earth, one of the best ways to learn about it is to go outside and investigate the earth. Field trips are fun and can make your study of geography much more interesting. However, remember that the purpose of a field trip is to learn. You might go on a field trip with your teacher, or you might go on your own field trip. With both types of field trips, there are certain guidelines that you should follow.

1. Understand the purpose of your trip. What information do you want to gather?

2. Understand your tasks. If you are working with others, divide tasks between you.

3. List the supplies you will need. Check your list before you leave to make sure you did not forget anything. When preparing your list of supplies, keep these points in mind:
   a) Have you made preparations in case someone gets hurt?
   b) Are you prepared for a possible change of weather?
   c) Pencils are more useful than pens for recording data in the field. Pens sometimes freeze up in cold weather and will not write. A pencil with an eraser allows data to be changed neatly.

4. Gather and record your data carefully. The success of your field trip depends on the accuracy of the data you collect. Photographs, sketches, written descriptions and samples will help you to analyse your data back in the classroom.

5. The material that you gather needs to be summarized in some form. Will you show your information on a map, in a graph, a table of statistics or a chart?

6. Behave courteously while you are on your trip.

7. Remember the environment. Carry your garbage until you find an appropriate place to dispose of it. Stay on sidewalks and paths whenever possible to avoid stepping on plants.

Fig. 6-10 Field trips are one of the best ways to investigate the earth. These students are collecting information for their stream study.

WHAT YOU HAVE LEARNED

In this chapter you have learned that a community is affected by the physical characteristics of the surrounding region. Landforms, climate, vegetation and soils define the region and affect the way people live their lives.

LOOKING BACK

1. Which do you think affects a community most—landforms, climate, vegetation or soils? Why?

2. Compare the amount of humus you would expect to find in the soil of a maple tree forest, a spruce forest and the prairie grasslands. Explain why the amount differs.

3. Which do you think is more important to a community, its site or its situation? Explain, giving examples.

EXPANDING YOUR LEARNING

There are many things you can learn about your region by going on a field trip. Here are a few suggestions:

4. Are there any rock outcrops in your region? If so, visit the site of the rock outcrop, take samples, then use reference books to identify the types of rocks.

5. Visit your region's weather office. How is weather information gathered? How is the local weather predicted? What causes differences between the weather in your region and neighbouring regions?

6. Visit a forest area. Find out what kinds of trees grow there. Compare this with the types of trees that grow in your school neighbourhood.

7. How do people use the land in the region surrounding your community? Are there farms, mines, lumber mills, quarries or tourist resorts? Visit one of these businesses. How important are the landforms, climate, natural vegetation and soils to these businesses?

UNIT REVIEW

1. Copy the following puzzle in your notebook and complete it by using the clues provided.

a) a comparison between the size of features on a map and those in the real world

b) characteristics of the region surrounding a community

c) a city, a town, or a township

d) partly decayed vegetation that improves the quality of the soil

e) lines on the earth that run east and west

f) a rural municipality

g) the Prime Meridian is one of these lines

h) a community's exact location and details of its physical features

i) modern scientific advances

2. Imagine that you have a pen pal in another country. The pen pal has never been to your community and does not know where your community is. Write a letter to your pen pal describing your community and explaining where it is located.

3. Your pen pal is from the community of Porto Novo in the country of Benin. You do not know where this is. How can you use an atlas to find out?

UNIT III
Exploring Physical Patterns

CHAPTER 7

What Is a Geographic Pattern?

74

Fig. 7-1   The locations you will learn about in this chapter.

WHAT YOU WILL LEARN

Geographers are always interested in the location of things on the surface of the earth. When they see that certain things are found in certain locations, they have found a pattern. For example, there is much more land in the northern half of the world than in the southern half. Most deserts are located on either side of the Equator, along the Tropics of Cancer and Capricorn. These are geographic patterns.

Geographers try to explain the patterns they find. Why are the world's land masses located where they are? Why are there patterns of climate and living things on the earth's surface? Questions like these about the physical patterns of the earth will be introduced in this chapter and explained in the following chapters of this unit.

KEY WORDS

patterns	**sea level**	**relief**
globe	**altitude, elevation**	**continents**
axis		**oceans**

What is a geographic pattern?

It was less than four weeks until Hallowe'en when Alicia realized she needed a costume for Franca's party. She remembered that last year there had been three people in plastic, store-bought Dracula costumes at Jose's party. Alicia did not want to wear the same plastic costume that someone else might wear. She decided to buy a pattern and make her own.

What does making a Hallowe'en costume have to do with geography? This chapter will show that learning geography and working with cloth both make use of patterns. Geographers seek **patterns**.

Alicia found a large piece of checked material that reminded her of the dress on her old Raggedy Ann doll. This gave her an idea for a terrific costume. She located a Raggedy Ann costume pattern and was ready to begin work. She had a large table to work on, the piece of material, her Raggedy Ann doll, the pattern and a calendar. To make sure she would finish the costume in time, Alicia made up a work schedule for herself on the calendar. If she could stick to her work schedule, she would have a one-of-a-kind costume on October 31!

75

Fig. 7-2 What patterns can you find in Alicia's workroom?

Fig. 7-3 A map of Timmins, Ontario. Street maps can show geographic patterns.

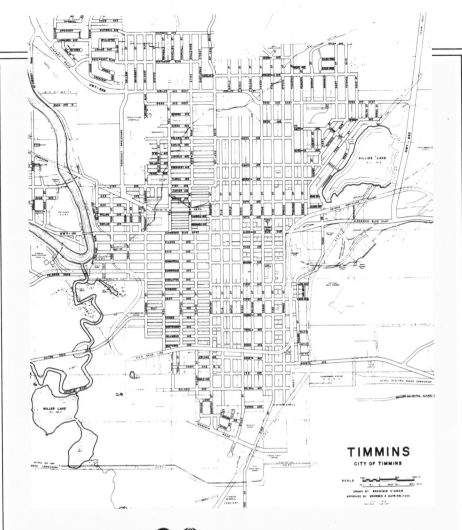

TIMMINS
CITY OF TIMMINS

SCALE

DRAWN BY BRANIMIR VIDMAR
APPROVED BY GEORGES A QUIRION, P ENG

ACTIVITY ONE

Definitions of pattern:

1. Area pattern—the way in which colours, shapes or lines are arranged. For example, on furniture there is often a design in the colours and grain of the wood.

2. Time pattern—a set of actions that is repeated. For example, the seasons follow the same cycle each year.

3. Model pattern—a guide or model of an actual thing. For example, companies design and build a model of every new car before they make the real thing.

1. a) Find two examples of area patterns in Alicia's workroom.

b) What time pattern is she using? Explain her work schedule.

c) Give an example of model patterns that she will be using as she works on the costume.

2. a) Make a simple sketch of your classroom as if you were looking down on it from overhead. Mark where you usually sit.

b) What is the area pattern of desks in your classroom?
i) rows   ii) groups   iii) scattered   iv) other
Explain the pattern.

3. Use Fig. 7-3 to describe the pattern of streets in Timmins.

4. Look at a map of your own community.
a) Is the area pattern like that of Timmins?
b) Describe other area patterns that you see on the map of your community.

5. What do you think is meant by the phrase ''geographic pattern''?

Patterns on the earth

The world around us is very complicated. We need to look for order so that we are not confused by all the places and things that surround us. Finding patterns helps to organize a complicated world. Geographers look for patterns that help us understand the earth and its people.

Colours, shapes and lines are examples of area patterns in geography. For example, in much of the Canadian west the land is divided into large squares, 1.6 km by 1.6 km, called sections. Roads run in a checkerboard pattern. Dark ploughed fields contrast with the lighter colour of growing crops. As you can see in Fig. 7-4, this human-made geographic pattern is striking.

North of the farming regions the area pattern is very different. Fig. 7-4 shows that ancient glaciers have scraped the land deeply. The lake and river pattern left behind tells geographers the direction in which the ice moved.

A section is a type of land survey system in which an area is divided into squares 1.6 km × 1.6 km. In western Canada farms are very large, each averaging about two sections in area.

A glacier is a huge mass of ice. It moves slowly down a valley or across land.

78

Fig. 7-4 Farms in southern Saskatchewan and a section of the Canadian Shield. Describe the area patterns in these photographs.

Geographers also look for time patterns. Alicia worked from a time schedule on her calendar to finish her costume before Hallowe'en. In western Canada wheat farmers follow a yearly pattern of planting, tending and harvesting to bring their crops to market on time. This time pattern is linked to the climate of the west, so it interests geographers. Not all time patterns occur over such a short period. Trees, rivers, communities, the oceans and the continents show patterns of change over long periods of time.

Model patterns are the third kind of pattern geographers use to help them understand the earth. The most basic model used in geography is the **globe**. It represents the shape of the earth in three dimensions and shows the angle at which the earth tilts on its **axis**. The globe model shows how the earth spins on its axis, causing day and night. Some globes also let you feel the height of the world's mountain ranges. The globe is a miniature of the earth, just as the Raggedy Ann doll is a smaller version of the costume Alicia made for herself. In both cases, one is patterned after the other.

The earth's **axis** is an imaginary line through the centre of the earth connecting the North and South Poles.

Fig. 7-5 Two views of the earth. How are they the same and how are they different?

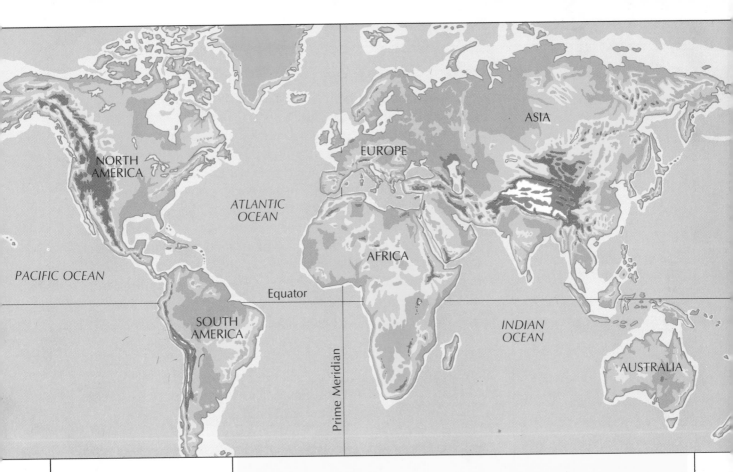

NORTH AMERICA

EUROPE

ASIA

ATLANTIC OCEAN

PACIFIC OCEAN

AFRICA

Equator

SOUTH AMERICA

INDIAN OCEAN

Prime Meridian

AUSTRALIA

Fig. 7-6 Patterns of the world's continents and oceans.

The **continents** are the large land areas into which the surface of the earth is divided.

The **oceans** are large bodies of salt water divided by the large landmasses of the earth.

Patterns are useful in geography. You can remember things more easily when you find area patterns on the earth. For example, on the map of the world in Fig. 7-6 you will be able to find some interesting patterns. You can see several large land masses called **continents**. We call Europe and Asia continents, though they are really opposite ends of one huge landmass. North and South America are also joined, but only by a narrow neck of land. The same is true for Africa and Asia. Only the continents of Australia and Antarctica are not attached to other land.

Fig. 7-6 also shows large bodies of water called **oceans**. The oceans are separated by the continents. However, you can see that three oceans blend together in the Southern Hemisphere. In Activity Two you will use the map in Fig. 7-6 and the table in Fig. 7-7 to find area patterns.

Fig. 7-7 How do the continents and oceans compare in area?

THE AREAS OF THE OCEANS AND CONTINENTS *(in million square kilometres)*					
Arctic	13	Africa	31	Canada	8
Atlantic	89	Antarctica	13	Europe	10
Indian	73	Asia	44	North America	23
Pacific	166	Australia	8	South America	18

ACTIVITY TWO

1. In Fig. 7-7,
   a) which column lists the four oceans?
   b) which name is not an ocean or a continent?
   c) which ocean is the largest? Which is the smallest?
   d) which continent is the largest? Which is the smallest?

2. Use Fig. 7-6 to name
   a) the ocean found only in the Northern Hemisphere.
   b) the continents found only in the Southern Hemisphere.
   c) Draw simple geometric shapes to show the basic pattern of each.

3. a) Look at Fig. 7-6. Which makes up more of the earth's surface, the continents or the oceans?
   b) Check your answer by adding up the continent and the ocean area columns on the statistical table in Fig. 7-7.

4. a) Use Fig. 7-6 to compare the amount of land in the Northern and Southern Hemispheres.
   b) Compare the amount of land in the Eastern and Western Hemispheres.
   c) What overall pattern of continents do you see?

5. Think of some good reasons
   a) why Greenland is not called a continent.
   b) why two names, Europe and Asia, have been given to one landmass.
   c) why all the earth's large islands are close to the continents.

See Chapter 4 for a description of the four hemispheres.

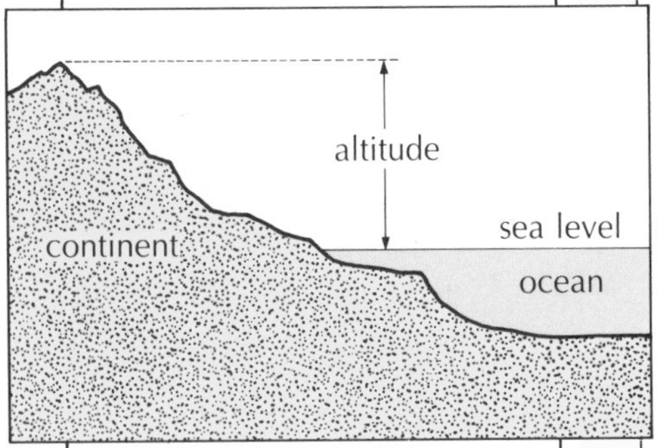

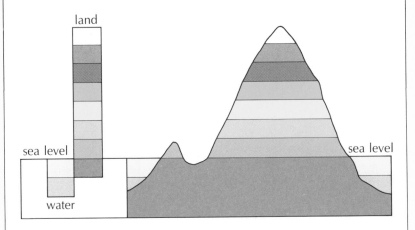

Fig. 7-8   What does altitude measure?

How geographers work: Using colour to show height and depth on maps

Sea level is where the ocean surface and the continents meet. When geographers give the height of land, called the **altitude**, they describe how high the land is compared to the ocean surface. For example, Mount Everest, the highest point on earth, is 8848 m above sea level.

In some parts of the world there are areas which are at altitudes *below* sea level. Death Valley in California, for example, is 87 m below the level of the ocean surface. Altitude can also be called **elevation** or **relief** by geographers.

Some globes have raised areas to let you actually see and feel altitudes. Relief maps show altitude by using different shades of certain colours. Shades of blue usually show water depths. Shades of green show land in areas of low altitude. Yellows and browns show higher land. Purple and white indicate the highest altitudes. Two kinds of relief map legend are shown in Fig. 7-9.

Fig. 7-9   Altitude, or **relief**, is shown on maps by using colours.

1. Find sea level on each of the legends. What does this level mark?

2. Find the highest land shown on each legend. Suggest why this colour is commonly used.

3. Find the deep water shown on each legend. Suggest why this shade is commonly used.

4. Find the land below sea level on each legend. How could there be dry land below the level of the sea?

5. Use these legends with the world relief map in Fig. 7-6 to
   a) locate the highest land in Asia.
   b) find the deeper part of the Pacific Ocean.
   c) describe the elevation of Canada from the Atlantic (east) to the Pacific (west), and north to Hudson Bay.

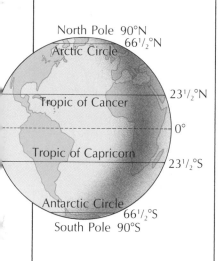

North Pole 90°N
66½°N
Arctic Circle
Tropic of Cancer   23½°N
0°
Tropic of Capricorn   23½°S
Antarctic Circle
66½°S
South Pole 90°S

Fig. 7-10 Some of the earth's important lines of latitude are known as the "Tropics" and the "Circles."

Patterns in the environment

In the unit about your community you learned that the earth is crossed by imaginary lines of latitude and longitude. Look at Fig. 7-10 in the margin, which shows the names of some important lines of latitude and the numerical value of each. Lines of latitude can do more than help us to locate places. They can show patterns of living things such as natural vegetation on different parts of the earth. This is because latitude also indicates the position of the sun over the earth.

There are zones of the earth which are hot and others that are cold. The zone which gets the most heat from the sun is near the Equator, between the Tropic of Cancer and the Tropic of Capricorn. The coldest regions are close to the North Pole and the South Pole. The plants and animals that live in these two temperature zones are very different. Can you give some examples of the living things found in hot and cold environments?

There are also zones of the earth that are wet and others that are dry. Rainforests and hot deserts are the names of these

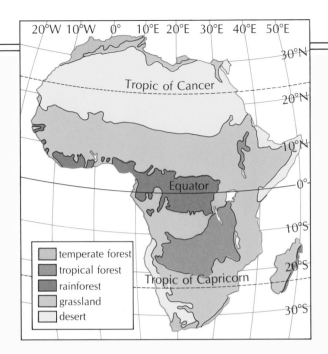

Fig. 7-11 A map of Africa's vegetation patterns. How do they relate to latitude?

opposite regions. You will learn more about these environments in Unit VII. They are each found in a pattern on the earth's surface. Africa shows how latitude is linked to the world pattern of rainforests and hot deserts.

ACTIVITY THREE

1. Look at the map in Fig. 7-11 and the legend that goes with it.
   a) Locate the Equator on the map.
   b) About how many degrees of latitude north of the Equator does Africa extend?

2. What is the major natural vegetation zone found in Africa
   a) along the Equator?
   b) along the Tropic of Cancer?
   c) along the Tropic of Capricorn?
   d) at 35°N latitude?
   e) at 35°S latitude?

3. Locate the 20°E longitude line. Follow this line down the continent from top to bottom.
   a) Explain how the natural vegetation zones repeat themselves.

b) Are there exceptions? Explain.

c) How might elevation affect natural vegetation?

4. Would you expect to see similar vegetation patterns on other continents? Use an atlas to locate a world map of natural vegetation, then find the locations of
   a) rainforests   b) hot deserts

5. How would you go about researching Canada's pattern of natural vegetation?

WHAT YOU HAVE LEARNED

This chapter explained what patterns are and how geographers seek them. Three types of patterns—area, time and model—are sought by geographers. These patterns help them to simplify and to understand the location of things on the earth.

In this chapter you learned about the pattern of land and water on the globe. You should be able to name and locate the seven continents and the four oceans. You practised using relief map legends to find the height of the continents and depths of the oceans. In another activity you looked for natural vegetation patterns in Africa that related to latitude. Now you can name and locate the hemispheres and the major lines of latitude and longitude on a world map.

LOOKING BACK

1. Give an example of each of the three types of pattern in geography:
   a) area pattern
   b) time pattern
   c) model pattern

2. Use an atlas or map of Canada to practise locating the capital cities of the provinces by using latitude and longitude.
   a) What capital is found at these locations:
      - 50°N   97°W   • 45°N   75°W
      - 48°N   53°W

b) Give the latitude and longitude of these capitals:

Edmonton   Halifax   Victoria

3. Use atlas maps that show elevation to find which of the following is higher:

a) in Canada: Lake Superior or Lake Ontario?

b) in North America: New York City or Chicago?

c) in Africa: Egypt or Sudan?

d) in South America: Brazil or Bolivia?

e) in Australia: Canberra or Melbourne?

f) in Eurasia: the Swiss Alps or the Himalayan Range?

EXPANDING YOUR LEARNING

4. Make a simple map of the streets or roads in your immediate neighbourhood. Describe the area pattern you see on your map.

5. Cut the basic shapes of the continents from an outline map. Name each of the continents and place them in the correct map location on a piece of blank paper. Then name the oceans between them.

6. Use the names of the continents and oceans to make a word search puzzle. See if other people can find all the words in your puzzle.

The Changing Continents

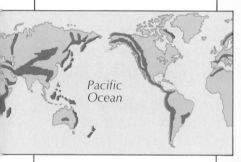

Fig. 8-1   The locations you will learn about in this chapter.

WHAT YOU WILL LEARN

The surface of the earth is always changing. Mountains are pushed up by forces inside the earth. Volcanoes erupt and earthquakes shatter rock. Even the continents themselves move about. As a result, landform patterns are always slowly but steadily changing.

In this chapter you will learn about the earth's changing landform patterns. You will use maps and diagrams to see the patterns of the earth's surface. Drawing a graph will help you to compare the highest mountain on each continent. Finally, you will predict the effect of a distant earthquake on North America by measuring map scale.

KEY WORDS

crust	fold mountain	seismograph
plate	volcanic mountain	fossil
mantle		continental drift
magma	fault	tsunami
volcano	earthquake	core

Fig. 8-2 Canadians Sharon Wood and Dwayne Congdon battled severe storms to reach the top of Mount Everest in May, 1986.

Hillary uses the word plugged to mean that he and Tenzing were moving up the mountain very slowly and with much effort.

How high are the mountains?

How do you feel about heights? Do you like being on balconies in tall buildings or tearing down the track of a roller coaster? Does it bother you to climb a tree or to go up a tall ladder?

Would you like to be a mountain climber? In 1953 Sir Edmund Hillary of Great Britain and Tenzing Norgay of Nepal became the first to reach the top of Mount Everest, the highest mountain on earth at 8848 m. They faced danger and felt fear as they reached the highest point in the world. Hillary described the final climb to the summit in the following section from his book, *Nothing Venture, Nothing Win:*

At 6:30 a.m. we moved off, and taking turns, plugged up the ridge above camp. The ridge narrowed considerably and the breakable crust made plugging tedious and balance difficult. We soon reached the oxygen bottles and were greatly relieved to find about 1100 lbs [7584 kilopascals] pressure in each. The narrow ridge led up to the very impressive steep snow face running to the South Summit.

We commenced plugging up in foot-deep steps with a thin wind crust on top and precious little below for the ice-axe. It was altogether most unsatisfactory and whenever I felt feelings of fear regarding it I'd say to myself, "Forget it! This is Everest and you've got to take a few risks." Tenzing expressed his extreme dislike but made no suggestions regarding turning back. Taking turns we made slow speed up this vast slope . . .

Finally I cut around the back of an extra large hump and then on a tight rope from Tenzing I climbed up a gentle snow ridge to its top. Immediately it was obvious that we had reached our objective. It was 11:30 a.m. and we were on top of Everest . . . Tenzing and I shook hands and then Tenzing threw his arms around my shoulders. It was a great moment!

Fig. 8-3   How high are the highest mountains on each continent?

CONTINENT	HIGHEST POINT	ELEVATION
Africa	Mt. Kilimanjaro	5895 m
Asia	Mt. Everest	8848 m
Antarctica	Vinson Massif	4672 m
Australia	Mt. Kosciusko	2230 m
Europe	Mt. Elbrus	5633 m
North America	Mt. McKinley	6194 m
South America	Mt. Aconcagua	6960 m

Fig. 8-4   At 553 m, Toronto's CN Tower is the world's tallest free-standing structure.

ACTIVITY ONE

1. Use Fig. 8-3 to list the mountains in order from tallest to shortest.

2. Round off the elevations to the nearest hundred metres. (Do this by looking at the last two digits of each elevation. If they are 50 or more, raise the third digit from the left by one. If not, lower it by one. For example, 3210 m becomes 3200 m when it is rounded off, and 3250 m becomes 3300 m.)

3. Draw and label a bar graph to show the mountains from tallest to shortest. Let 1 cm = 1000 m.

4. Make a visual scale for your graph by sketching the CN Tower at the correct size on the graph.

5. Read Sir Edmund Hillary's description of reaching the top of Mount Everest.
   a) What dangers of mountain climbing are described?
   b) What emotions did the climbers feel in the last five hours to the top?
   c) Why do you think mountain climbers and other adventurers do such things?

6. Write a journal entry like Hillary's to describe an adventure you had and how you felt.

How are mountains formed?

There are different types of mountains on the earth. For example, Mount Everest is called a fold mountain. Mount Kilimanjaro in Africa and Mount Aconcagua in South America are volcanic mountains. To understand how each of these landforms is formed you must know the layers of the earth.

Think of the earth as a round egg. Both an egg and the earth have three layers which can be compared. The outer "shell" of the earth is called the **crust**. The crust is a thin layer of rock only about 5 km to 35 km thick in most places. Like a

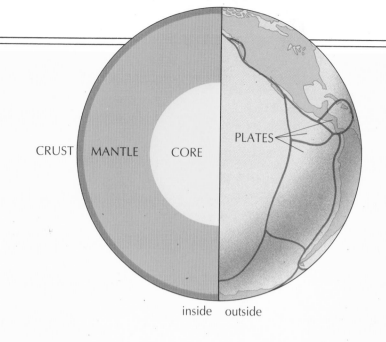

Fig. 8-5 The earth has three layers. The outer layer, the crust, is broken into plates.

CRUST MANTLE CORE

PLATES

inside   outside

Molten means melted, therefore molten rock is rock that has melted due to the high temperatures in the mantle.

cracked eggshell, the earth's crust is broken into many large and small pieces. These pieces are called **plates**.

The other two layers of the earth can also be compared to the layers of an egg. Under the crust is a thick layer called the **mantle**. It consists of **molten** rock called **magma**. This is a zone of thick liquid like the egg white. In the centre of an egg there is the yolk, while the centre of the earth is the **core**. The core is a very hot, dense mass which is solid in the middle. The crust, mantle and core of the earth compare in thickness to the shell, white and yolk of an egg.

Danish geologist Inge Lehmann studied the earth's core in 1936. She helped to convince other scientists that intense heat from the earth's core has melted the rock in the mantle. Molten magma swirls about like boiling water. This causes the plates over the slowly swirling magma to move. When two plates are pushed against one another, rock layers between them are trapped. Solid rock under pressure can slowly bend. Over millions of years the rock layers between colliding plates can be crumpled up into **fold mountains**. Mount Everest and the Rocky Mountains of North America were formed this way.

Other mountains were created by different forces. Often the crust breaks while it is folding. Where the crust is thin, molten rock from the mantle pushes up through the break to erupt as

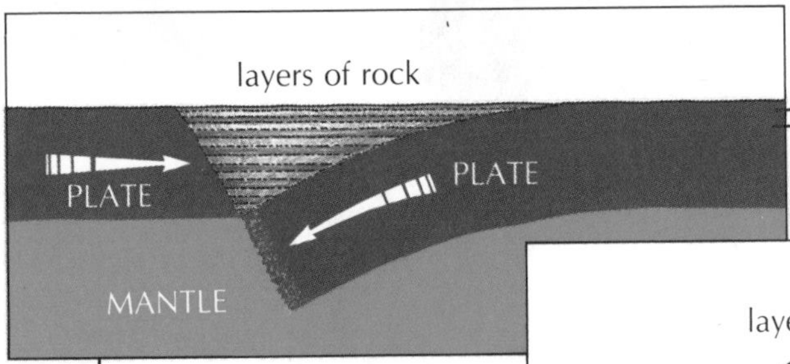

layers of rock

PLATE

PLATE

MANTLE

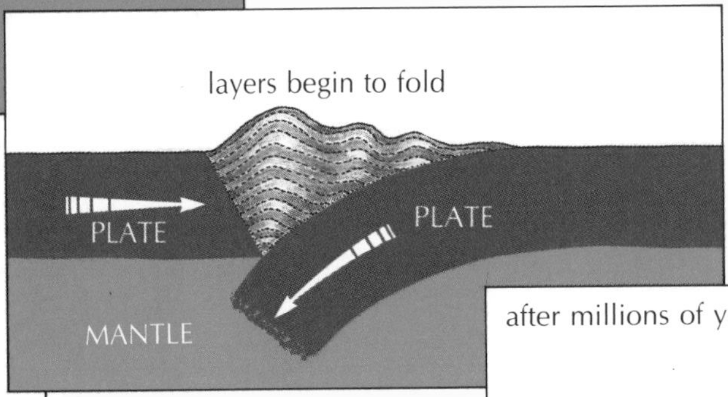

layers begin to fold

PLATE

PLATE

MANTLE

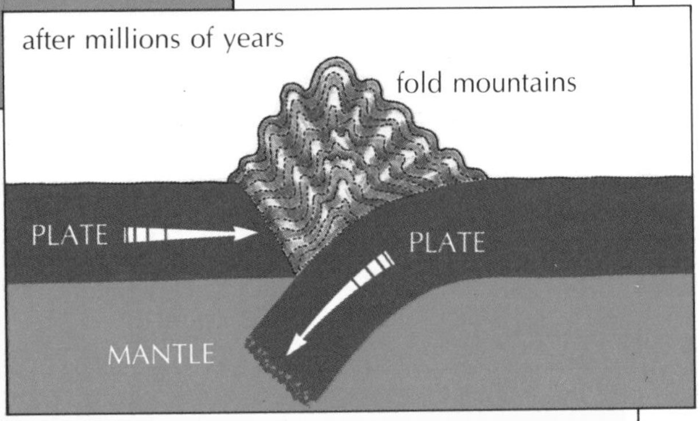

after millions of years

fold mountains

PLATE

PLATE

MANTLE

Fig. 8-6 Fold mountains form very gradually where two plates, moving toward one another, push up layers of rock.

A **volcanic mountain** is one formed by the build-up of layers of molten rock and ash erupting through cracks in the earth's crust or gaps between the plates.

a **volcano**. With each volcanic eruption, another layer of molten rock hardens on the surface, as you can see in Fig. 8-7. The same thing happens when two plates of the earth's crust pull apart, allowing magma to flow to the surface. A **volcanic mountain** is built much faster than a fold mountain. This is how the highest mountains in Africa and South America were built.

Mountains follow clear patterns on the earth. Fig. 8-8 shows that most mountains are found along the edges of continents, near the oceans. This is true for every continent. The Pacific Ocean is almost surrounded by both fold and volcanic mountains. The highest peaks of North and South America and Australia are all very close to the Pacific. So many volcanic mountains surround the Pacific Ocean that it is known as "the Ring of Fire."

ACTIVITY TWO

1. Make a chart to compare the layers of the earth to an egg.

2. Copy the chart in Fig. 8-9 in your notebook and complete

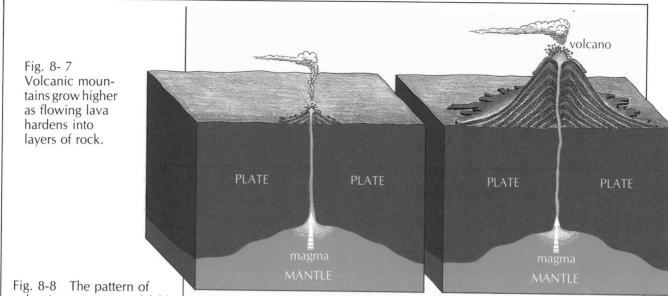

Fig. 8- 7 Volcanic mountains grow higher as flowing lava hardens into layers of rock.

Fig. 8-8 The pattern of volcanic mountains and fold mountains in the world.

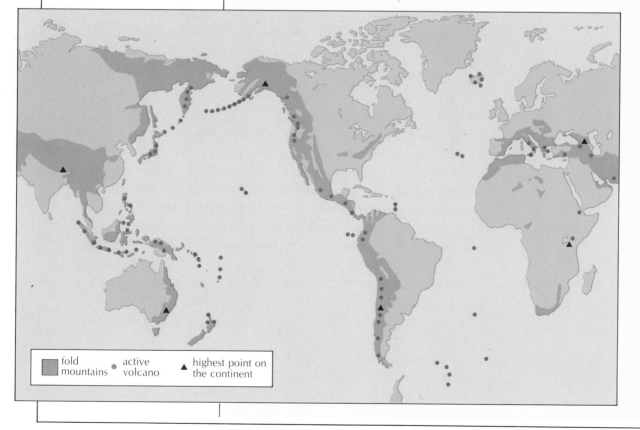

fold mountains   ● active volcano   ▲ highest point on the continent

it to show what happens when there are changes in one of the earth's layers.

CAUSE	EFFECT
• the core gives off heat • two plates move apart • two plates move together • folded rock breaks	

3. Using Fig. 8-8, look for patterns such as
   a) where fold mountains are usually located.
   b) two general types of places where volcanic mountains are found.
   c) the mountain pattern of the Atlantic Ocean. How is it different from the Pacific Ocean?

4. Mountains form where plates move together or apart. Use Fig. 8-8 to suggest the outlines of the earth's major plates.

The quaking earth

The earth is a restless sleeper. The saying "steady as a rock" is not very accurate because the earth's surface is constantly moving.

You have seen that mountains form where plates of the earth move together or apart. Sometimes the pressure on the earth's crust is so great that the rock snaps along a line of weakness. The crack is called a **fault**. There is a sudden release of energy as the pieces of rock move to new positions along the break. This sudden release of energy is called an **earthquake**. The San Andreas Fault is a well-known earthquake zone which slices through California. The city of San Francisco was destroyed by an earthquake in 1906. Two plates are grinding alongside one another in this area.

Earthquakes are very common. One happens somewhere on earth every three minutes, or 180 000 times each year! They are most often found in areas of fold mountains. For example,

Fig. 8-9 What are the effects of each of these events ?

94

An **earthquake** is a movement of a part of the earth's crust that originates below the surface.

Fig. 8-10 Earthquakes and faults occur when rock under pressure cannot bend any further.

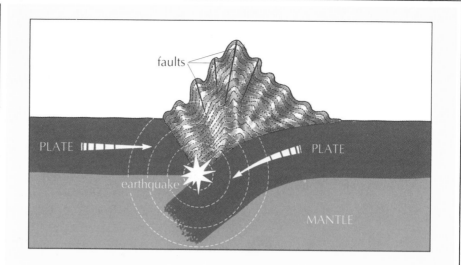

Fig. 8-11 The pattern of earthquakes in the world.

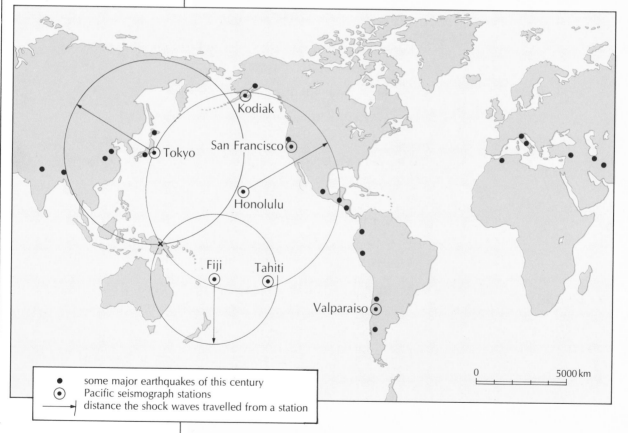

● some major earthquakes of this century
◉ Pacific seismograph stations
→| distance the shock waves travelled from a station

A **seismograph** is a scientific instrument that measures and records the shock waves caused by movements or earthquakes within the earth's crust.

several of the most serious earthquakes in this century occurred in the fold mountain ranges shown on the map in Fig. 8-8. Fortunately, not all earthquakes are so deadly.

Delicate instruments called **seismographs** constantly measure the beat of the earth, much like a heart machine measures heartbeats. A pen on the seismograph machine prints a zig-zag pattern on a slowly turning cylinder. The pen jumps as it records the shock waves that occur when there is an earthquake. Geologists can read the seismograph to learn how strong the shock waves were and how far away the earthquake happened. The shock waves allow scientists to judge how serious the earthquake was or to predict a stronger one. Fig. 8-11 shows how three observation locations permit geologists to find the point at which an earthquake occurred.

ACTIVITY THREE

1. Look at the map in Fig. 8-11 and describe the pattern of earthquakes that is shown.

2. Compare this pattern to the map in Fig. 8-8.
   a) How are the patterns similar?
   b) Why are the patterns similar?

3. Fig. 8-11 shows that geologists in three locations each knew how far away an earthquake had happened.
   a) Find where the earthquake occurred.
   b) Explain your answer.

4. Use the map scale to measure the distance from the earthquake to each of the seven places named.

5. Earthquakes can also shake the ocean floor. This causes a fast-moving wall of water called a **tsunami** (tsoo na′ mē). This sea wave can be more damaging than the original earthquake.

   If a tsunami caused by the earthquake in Fig. 8-11 travels at 800 kilometres per hour, how long will it take to reach each of the seven places? (To calculate this, divide 800 into the distances measured in question 4.)

6. Write a radio or television warning of the approaching tsunami for people on Canada's west coast.

Are the continents moving?

The surface of the earth is constantly changing. Fold mountains are heaved upward and earthquakes shatter solid rock. Volcanoes erupt beside or beneath the oceans. These are obvious changes. Other changes are so gradual that people do not notice them. One such change is called **continental drift**.

Have you ever had a great idea but nobody would listen? This happened to scientist Alfred Wegener. He spent his life trying to convince others that the continents had once been joined together. In 1912 he developed a theory that he called continental drift, but only a few scientists believed him. In his time, people thought that his ideas were strange, but today, people accept much of what Wegener said.

Alfred Wegener used information about geographic patterns, rocks and past climates in his theory. He found that ancient rocks and old mountain ranges in South America and Africa matched when the continents were fitted together. The **fossils** and plant and animal species also matched. Because the plants and animals could not have crossed the Atlantic Ocean, Wegener reasoned that the continents must have moved apart.

Wegener thought that the continents were joined long ago, before the dinosaur age. Unfortunately, he could not explain why or how the continents moved. Scientists in his time did not believe that huge landmasses could move across the earth's surface.

Recent ocean research has proved Wegener's idea correct. Like enormous ships, the continents do travel the earth's surface. You will learn more about this in the next chapter.

WHAT YOU HAVE LEARNED

In this chapter you learned how changes inside the earth cause mountains. As the plates of the crust move, fold mountains are

Fig. 8-12 Were the continents once joined together? Alfred Wegener saw that continents such as Africa and South America could once have been joined.

A **fossil** can be the actual remains of a plant or animal of the past or its imprint, preserved in rock.

gradually forced up. Volcanic mountains form more quickly, in layers. Earthquakes happen very suddenly, often in mountainous areas. The land around the Pacific Ocean is known for all three of these landform changes.

Alfred Wegener saw a pattern in the shape and fit of some of the continents. But scientists in his time did not know enough about the earth to understand how continents could move. Recent exploration of the ocean floor has given us the answer.

LOOKING BACK

1. Identify each of the following:
   a) Inge Lehmann
   b) Alfred Wegener
   c) Pacific "Ring of Fire"
   d) Hillary and Norgay
   e) seismographs

2. Draw and label a simple diagram to show each of the following:
   a) the inside view of a volcano
   b) the layers of the earth
   c) how fold mountains form

3. Use an atlas to find the highest mountain in Canada. Give its name, province or territory, and elevation.

EXPANDING YOUR LEARNING

4. Use an encyclopedia to find out about the Richter scale, used to rate earthquake shock waves.

5. Prepare a report about an earthquake. *National Geographic* is one good source of information. Some ideas for topics are
   • Mexico City, 1985
   • Italy, 1980
   • Guatemala, 1976
   • Nicaragua, 1972
   • Alaska, 1964
   Consider starting your research with these focus questions:
   • What was the exact location of the earthquake?
   • How strong was the shock?
   • Why did it happen?
   • How did it affect people?

Exploring the Ocean Frontier

99

WHAT YOU WILL LEARN

Change is an important part of geography. Weather conditions, for example, change daily and seasonally. Earthquakes and volcanoes change the earth by building new mountains. Continents like South America and Africa drift farther apart.

Until recent times geographers did not know much about some of the changes that affect the earth's surface. For instance, much of our knowledge about the ocean depths is very new. We know now that there are patterns in the valleys and mountains on the sea floor. These patterns help to explain continental drift.

KEY WORDS

mid-ocean ridge	**sea-floor spreading**
ocean trench	

Exploring the ocean frontier

The space shuttle, *Challenger I*, arched upward above the Kennedy Space Centre in Florida. It looked like a successful launch that January day. Then, just after the signal "full throttle" was given, a leaking booster rocket burst into flame. The *Challenger I* blew apart and plunged into the Atlantic Ocean. The entire crew was lost.

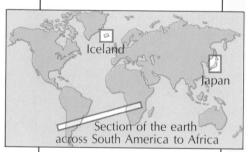

Iceland

Japan

Section of the earth across South America to Africa

Fig. 9-1 The locations you will learn about in this chapter.

Tragedy is sometimes the price of exploration. Space travel is just the latest adventure into the unknown. There have been many others. The Vikings crossed the Atlantic Ocean and landed on Newfoundland. Other adventurers, such as Sir Edmund Hillary and Tenzing Norgay, have explored mountains. This chapter will look at the exploration of another frontier—the oceans. More than 70 percent of the earth's surface is covered by oceans. Yet only in recent times have we learned the secrets of the ocean floor. It is here that Alfred Wegener's theory of continental drift was proved correct.

If you have ever tried to swim underwater, you have felt the need for oxygen. And, if you have ever taken canoe or sailing lessons, you learned that air for breathing can be trapped underneath an overturned boat. This idea was used as early as 33 B.C. to invent the diving bell. The diving bell trapped air so that people could work underwater without surfacing. In this century, we store oxygen in small tanks that scuba divers carry with them as they swim. Mountain climbers use similar oxygen tanks to climb above the oxygen-rich atmosphere. Discovering ways to store oxygen allowed people to go deeper into the ocean than they had been able to before.

Fig. 9-2 An oxygen supply is needed for underwater exploration.

Fig. 9-3 An experiment you can try.

ACTIVITY ONE

1. How do each of the following get enough oxygen?
   a) fish
   c) astronauts in space
   b) scuba divers
   d) mountain climbers

2. Look at the diagram in the margin and try the experiment yourself.
   a) What will happen to the water level in the glasses
      i) when you push them down?
      ii) if you slowly tilt them?
   b) Why does this happen?
   c) Describe this experiment in your notebook.

3. a) How is the diving bell like the experiment in the diagram?
   b) What would happen to the water level inside the bell as the diver worked? Why?
   c) How is the scuba diver's tank an improvement over the diving bell?

How deep are the oceans?

The *Challenger I* space shuttle was not the first craft with that name. More than a hundred years earlier, a British ship called the HMS *Challenger* explored the ocean floor. Between 1872 and 1876, the crew of this ship gathered much new information about the depths of the oceans.

Fig. 9-4 Some ropes from the *Challenger* were lowered more than 8 km. Sinkers of different weights (A) allowed many parts of the sea floor to be tested by bottom samplers (B).

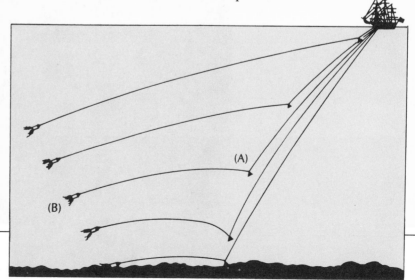

Fig. 9-5 *Alvin*, the deep-water explorer.

HMS *Challenger* travelled around the world and made tests in 360 locations. The crew used long ropes to lower weights, thermometers and bottom samplers to the ocean floor. They discovered more than 700 new kinds of living things. They also found that the depth of the ocean varied from place to place. The ocean floor is made up of mountains and valleys just like the continents.

Today, special deep-water mini-submarines are used to explore the ocean. They are able to operate at depths of almost 4 km. One such mini-sub, *Alvin*, has made thousands of dives. It has been used to explore the **mid-ocean ridge**, a huge undersea mountain chain that circles the globe. *Alvin* is made of light but strong titanium to stand the tremendous weight of water. It is launched from a specially equipped ship.

Mini-submarines like *Alvin* carry floodlights that shine 30 m into the total darkness of the ocean bottom. The floodlights show that life in the deep ocean is different from life in the shallower parts of the ocean.

Most mini-subs cannot explore the deepest parts of the oceans, so people use other eyes to learn about this new frontier. Sonar, ("**so**und **na**vigation **r**anging") bounces sound waves off underwater objects to measure their depth. Sound vibration is sent down through the water until it reflects off an object. The returning sound waves are measured to find out how far they have travelled. Sonar is a very accurate way to measure the depths of the oceans.

Sonar has been used to create detailed maps and profiles of the mountains and valleys under the ocean. It allowed scientists to take accurate measurements of the deepest valleys, called **ocean trenches**. Sonar has also been used to locate the wrecks of ships such as the huge ocean liner, *Titanic*.

A **mid-ocean ridge** is an undersea chain of mountains caused by two pieces of the earth's crust moving apart.

Profiles are side views of the shape of objects or parts of the earth.

Ocean trenches are the deepest parts of the ocean, where one edge of the earth's crust is dragged under another edge.

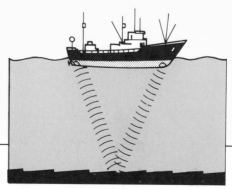

Fig. 9-6
How sonar works.

Fig. 9-8   The ocean trenches.

Fig. 9-7   How deep are the oceans?

OCEAN	DEEPEST POINT	DEPTH
Arctic	Euroasian Basin (Angara Basin)	5 450 m
Atlantic	Puerto Rico Trench	8 605 m
Indian	Java Trench	7 125 m
Pacific	Mariana Trench (Challenger Deep)	10 915 m

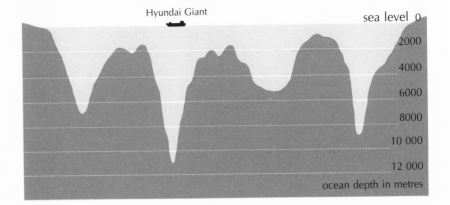

Hyundai Giant

ACTIVITY TWO

1. Prepare a summary chart to compare three different ocean explorers: HMS *Challenger*, *Alvin* and sonar.

2. a) Look at the chart in Fig. 9-7 and compare it to the graph in Fig. 9-8. Find each of the four places from the chart on the graph of ocean depths.

    b) Which method would be used to explore these deeps; mini-subs or sonar? Explain.

3. How deep is the Challenger Deep? How long is the *Hyundai Giant*? (See Fig. 9-9.) Use division to find how many times the *Hyundai Giant* could stand end to end in this ocean trench.

Fig. 9-9 Bulk carriers are among the world's largest ships. For example, the *Hyundai Giant* is 329 m long.

Patterns on the ocean floor

The ocean floor is not flat. There are ocean trenches and mountain chains beneath the water. These mountain chains or ridges circle the earth like the seams on a baseball. There are as many mountains under the oceans as there are on the continents. They total more than 60 000 km in length, long enough to stretch across Canada more than ten times. Even more important, we now know that the ocean floors are changing in size. The floor of the Atlantic Ocean is spreading apart and the floor of the Pacific is squeezing together. These amazing patterns of the ocean floor proved that Wegener's theory of continental drift was correct.

You might think that the oceans are deepest in the middle. The deepest parts, the ocean trenches, are really very close to land. This is especially true in the Pacific Ocean which is almost surrounded by trenches. The Atlantic does not have many. Instead, the Atlantic has a range of mountains through the centre, from top to bottom like a zipper, called the Mid-Atlantic Ridge. The mountain range is exactly halfway between the continents. You can see that patterns on the floors of the Atlantic Ocean and the Pacific Ocean are very different.

Some oceans are shrinking. For example, the Pacific grows narrower each year. Others, like the Atlantic and Indian

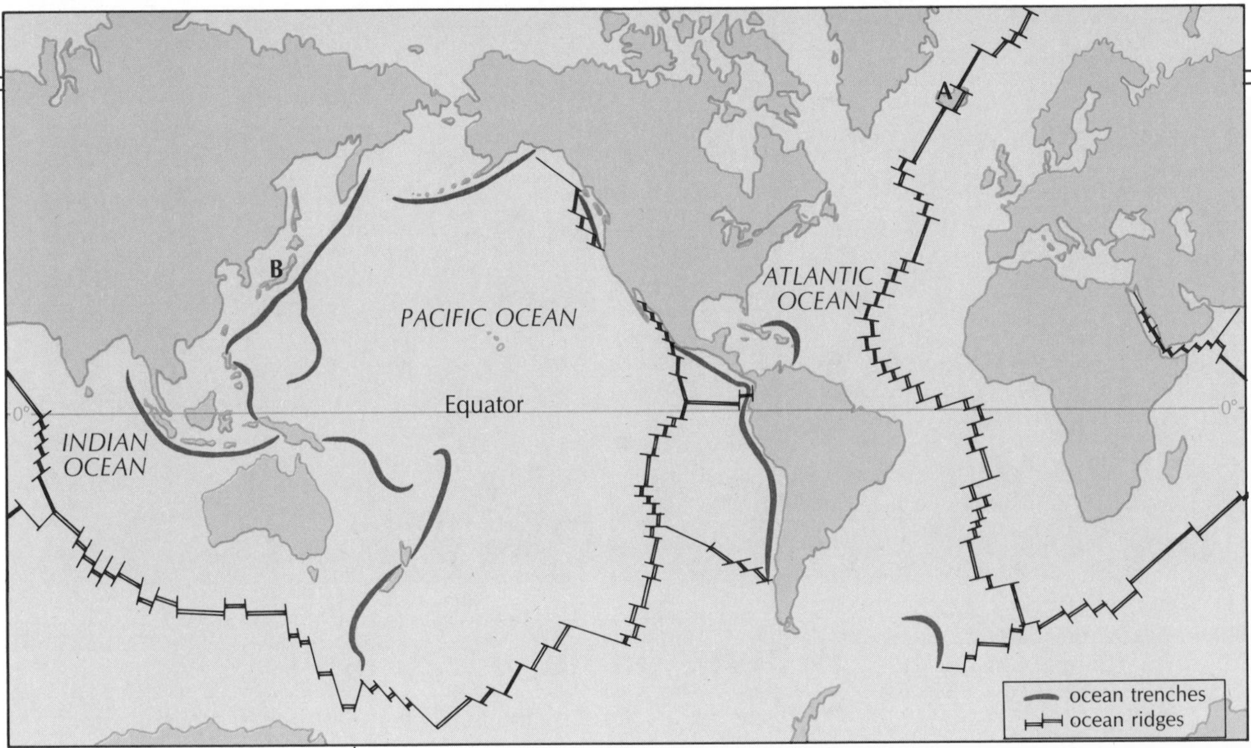

Fig. 9-10 The pattern of ocean trenches and ridges.

Sea-floor spreading is the splitting apart of the ocean floor along the mid-ocean ridges.

Oceans, are becoming wider. Two examples, shown at locations marked A and B on Fig. 9-10, show these changes.

Location A on Fig. 9-10 is Iceland. It is right on the Mid-Atlantic Ridge. When *Alvin* explored this ridge, people discovered that the floor of the Atlantic Ocean is spreading apart at a speed of about 3 cm every year. This process is called **sea-floor spreading**. Two of the plates that make up the earth's crust meet at the Mid-Atlantic Ridge. Scientists believe that these plates are being pulled away from each other by currents in the mantle. As the plates are pulled apart, molten rock pours out from the mantle beneath the plates to fill the gap. Molten rock also erupts in volcanoes along the Mid-Atlantic Ridge, creating new islands such as Surtsey.

ACTIVITY THREE

1. Look at the map of ocean trenches and mountains in Fig. 9-10.
   a) Where are the ocean trenches usually located?

Fig. 9-11 Surtsey, Iceland. Volcanoes erupt in Iceland as the Atlantic sea floor spreads apart. Some of these volcanoes create new islands like Surtsey.

b) Explain the location of the mountains in the Atlantic and Indian Oceans.

c) Compare the Atlantic and Pacific Oceans according to:
   i) size   iii) ocean ridges
   ii) ocean trenches   iv) sea-floor changes

2. In your own words explain why Iceland has active volcanoes. Use Fig. 9-12 to help you.

3. The Atlantic sea floor is spreading by 3 cm per year. How much has it spread
   a) in your lifetime?
   b) since one of your parents was born?
   c) since one of your grandparents was born?

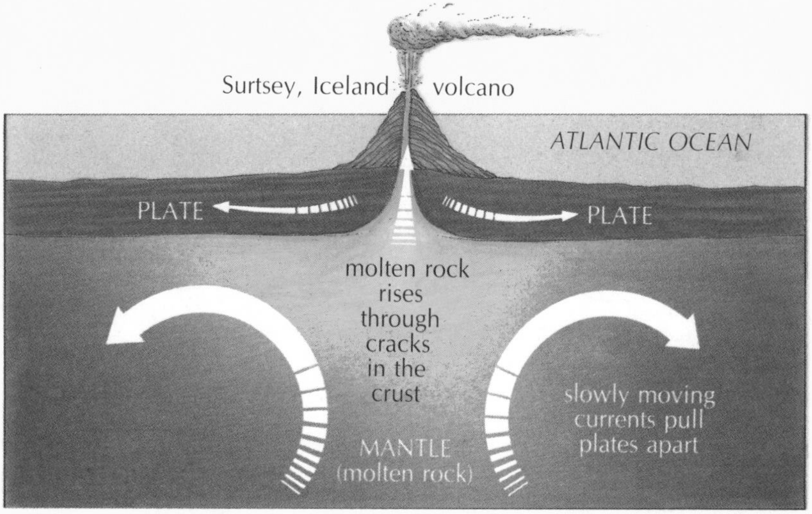

Fig. 9-12 The sea floor under the Atlantic Ocean. Slowly moving currents of molten rock in the earth's mantle pull plates apart, causing the Atlantic Ocean to grow wider.

Surtsey, Iceland volcano

ATLANTIC OCEAN

PLATE ←   → PLATE

molten rock rises through cracks in the crust

slowly moving currents pull plates apart

MANTLE (molten rock)

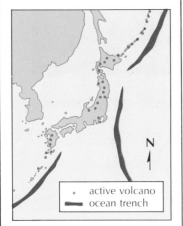

Fig. 9-13 Volcanoes and trenches at Japan.

Fig. 9-14 The sea floor under the Pacific Ocean. Slowly moving currents in the earth's mantle push plates together, causing the Pacific Ocean to shrink.

The shrinking Pacific

The Atlantic Ocean is growing wider. Yet the size of the earth remains about the same. This is because the Pacific Ocean is shrinking in size. Location B on Fig. 9-10 is Japan. This nation sits beside a series of deep ocean trenches where two plates meet. Here the currents in the mantle push the plates together, causing volcanoes and earthquakes. Fig. 9-14 shows how this happens.

The floor of the Pacific Ocean is being pulled down into the molten rock below the earth's crust. It melts there and floats back upward. This molten rock erupts as volcanoes along the edges of the plates. Earthquakes also occur as the plates rub together. This is how the islands of Japan were formed. Volcanoes circle much of the Pacific Ocean because this ocean is shrinking in size.

As we learned in the last chapter, Alfred Wegener developed the idea of continental drift long ago. At that time he did not have enough evidence to explain it. By studying the ocean floor, geographers now understand that the plates of the earth's crust float on the surface of the mantle. The plates carry the continents much like passengers on rafts. As the plates move, the Atlantic spreads apart along the mid-ocean ridge and the Pacific shrinks into the ocean trenches. Wegener was right, the continents of the earth do drift.

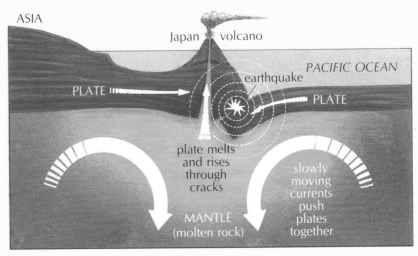

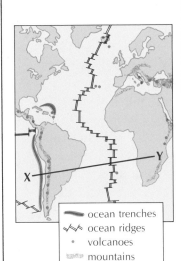

Fig. 9-15   The location of line XY.

Legend:
- ~ ocean trenches
- ^^^ ocean ridges
- • volcanoes
- ~~~ mountains

1. Look at the map of Japan in Fig. 9-13.
   a) Describe the pattern of the following:
      i)   the active volcanoes
      ii) the ocean trenches
      iii) the islands of Japan
   b) What is the overall pattern?
   c) Use Fig. 9-14 to explain why Japan has volcanoes.

2. Look at the diagram in Fig. 9-16.
   a) Use the map in Fig. 9-15 to find the following on the diagram:
      i)   line from X to Y   iv) Atlantic Ocean
      ii) South America   v) Pacific Ocean
      iii) Africa   vi) Mid-Atlantic Ridge
   b) Find these features on the diagram:
      i)   the crust   iv) mid-ocean ridge
      ii) molten currents   v) ocean trench
      iii) volcanoes   vi) the mantle
   c) Describe what happens where two molten currents
      i)   move apart;
      ii) move together.

109

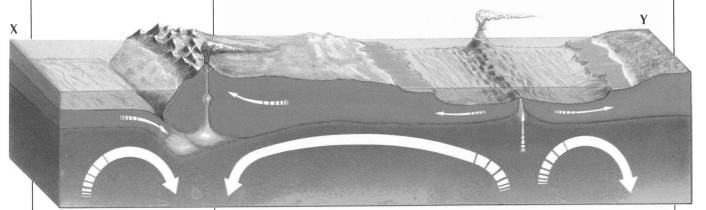

Fig. 9-16   The earth's surface and interior along line XY.

WHAT YOU HAVE LEARNED

There are many changes occurring on the earth's surface. Geographers want to know where these changes are happening and why. They try to understand events and explain why they occur.

Researchers have studied the ocean using ships, mini-submarines and sound waves. In recent years they have found clear patterns of ocean trenches and mid-ocean ridges under the seas. The pattern of these features tells geographers that sea-floor spreading is enlarging some oceans while others shrink in size. The continents do drift, just as Alfred Wegener said earlier in this century.

LOOKING BACK

1. Identify each of these names:
   - a) HMS *Challenger*
   - b) *Alvin*
   - c) *Hyundai Giant*
   - d) Alfred Wegener
   - e) Mid-Atlantic Ridge
   - f) Challenger Deep

2. Make a word maze using vocabulary from this chapter.

3. Explain how ocean research has proved Alfred Wegener's idea of continental drift.

EXPANDING YOUR LEARNING

4. If you could explore the ocean, the mountains or space, which would you choose? Perhaps some other "frontier" of learning interests you more. Write a few paragraphs to explain your interest.

5. a) Find out how adventurers located the wreck of the *Titanic*, 73 years after it sank in 1912.
   b) Prepare a report about the items recovered from the ship.

Does Weather Follow a Pattern?

Fig. 10-1 The locations you will learn about in this chapter.

WHAT YOU WILL LEARN

Weather shows many kinds of patterns. On any one day, the weather varies at different times and in different places. The weather usually follows a pattern from sunrise to sunset, first warming up and then cooling off. Weather patterns also differ from one part of the country to another. Understanding a weather map allows you to predict weather patterns.

Weather also follows a long-term pattern from year to year. This average weather pattern is called climate. The sun is the most important factor in the world pattern of climate.

KEY WORDS

weather	precipitation	sky cover
temperature	air masses	frontal
humidity	wind chill	precipitation
front		

Amal's winter adventure

"**Y**ou sure get warm weather up here!" exclaimed Amal. "I thought that in February Timmins would be a lot colder and snowier than Toronto."

"Well, don't be fooled. It's not usually like this," explained her host Renée. Amal was staying at her home for four days as part of a school exchange visit between the two cities. "Before you leave I'll bet you're going to see some snow and freezing weather."

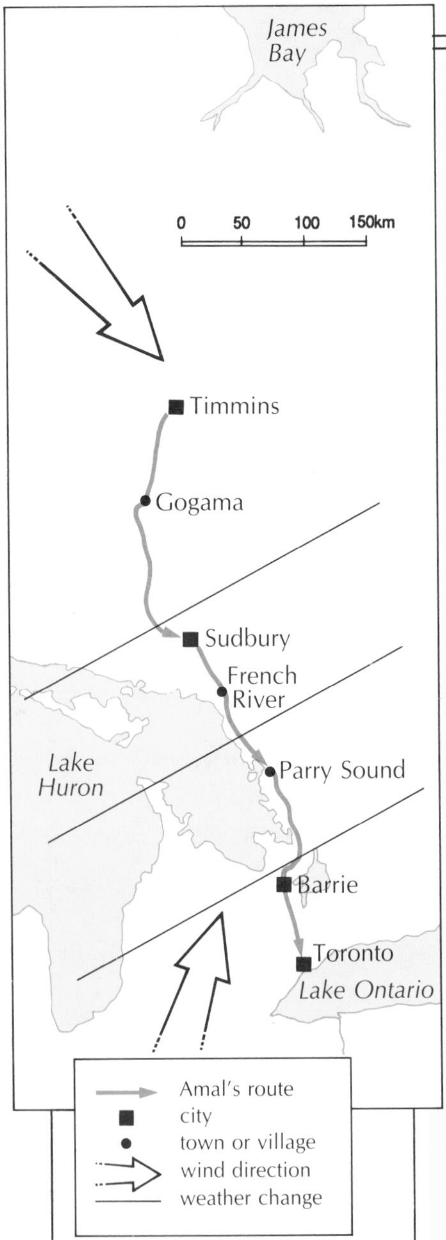

It remained very mild for the weekend. But as the students were boarding the bus to go home on Sunday morning, snow began to swirl in front of a cold wind. By the time they reached Gogama, it was very hard to see. The wind was blowing from the north and west, and the road was covered with snow. Amal began to worry. There were no cars on the road and the bus was moving more and more slowly in the deep snow.

The bus stopped in Sudbury for lunch and a break in the trip, which helped to relieve the tension for a little while. When they started out again, it was still snowing. As they reached French River, the snow changed to sleet, a mixture of rain with snow or ice. The sleet stuck to the bus's windshield wipers and a layer of ice coated the road. Trees were bent under the shining coating of ice. The driver became cranky and yelled at everyone to be quiet. Near Parry Sound night fell, and the sleet turned to heavy rain.

Amal dozed for a while, but she woke up near a highway sign for Barrie. Bright stars gleamed in the winter sky. The highway was crowded with skiers returning from a rainy weekend.

As Amal left the bus in Toronto, she noticed how clear and mild it was. A warm breeze from the south brushed her face. "So Timmins is colder than Toronto," she decided. "And the weather did change just as Renée had said it would."

Fig. 10-2 Amal's route on her winter adventure.

Amal's route — city
■ city
● town or village
⇨ wind direction
— weather change

James Bay

0 50 100 150km

■ Timmins
● Gogama
■ Sudbury
● French River
Lake Huron
● Parry Sound
■ Barrie
■ Toronto
Lake Ontario

Fig. 10-3 A sleet storm coats everything with ice.

Weather and its influences

The weather affects our lives every day. Sometimes the weather is extreme and causes an experience like Amal's winter adventure. Usually the effects of weather are not as dramatic. For example, the **temperature** helps you decide what to wear and what kind of recreation to enjoy. **Sky cover** refers to the amount of sky that is covered by cloud. Whether it is clear, cloudy or raining affects you in the same way as the temperature does. You might decide not to play baseball if it is raining. The wind is the third aspect of weather. Anyone who lives in Canada knows that **wind chill** makes winter temperatures feel much colder.

In the summer, another factor of weather is important. **Humidity**, the amount of moisture in the air, can have a great affect on people, as anyone who has tried to sleep on a humid summer night can tell you. Humidity is usually measured as a percent. A humidity level of 100% means that the air cannot hold any more water. Temperature, sky conditions, wind and humidity are all aspects of weather.

Weather can be defined as the condition of the atmosphere at a particular time and place. The day-to-day conditions of temperature, moisture, sky cover and wind make up the weather.

Wind chill is a measure of the chilling effect of the wind when it is combined with low temperatures on a cold day.

The **weather** refers to the condition of the atmosphere (the layer of air surrounding the earth) at a certain place and time.

Fig. 10-4 Windy days feel colder in the winter and humid days feel hotter in the summer.

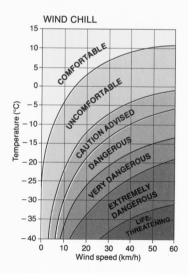

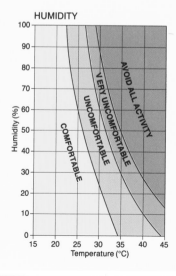

Fig. 10-5 How does the weather affect plants, animals and humans?

These four factors are always changing. Use the photographs in Fig. 10-5 to examine the ways that weather influences people, plants and animals.

Weather is always changing. The weather changes during the day, for example. It normally becomes warmer as the sun rises higher in the sky, then cools when it sets. Weather changes gradually from winter to spring to summer to fall. As Amal learned in her winter adventure, the weather also changes from one place to another. The air gradually got warmer as she travelled from Timmins to Toronto. The weather changed from snow, to sleet, to rain and finally to clear skies.

ACTIVITY ONE 🎲 🌐 📝

1. Look at the map of Amal's trip in Fig. 10-2.
   a) Outline the weather conditions in the four zones of the map using information from the story of Amal's winter adventure.
   b) Suggest what effect the wind direction had on changing the temperature.

2. Give examples of how weather can affect
   a) plants and animals
   b) how people spend money
   c) work and recreation

3. Examine the graphs of wind chill and humidity in Fig. 10-4.
   a) Should you plan a tennis game on a day when the temperature is 35°C and the humidity is 70 percent? Explain your answer.
   b) On a sunny winter day when the temperature is −15°C and the wind chill is 30 kilometres per hour, would it be safe to go skiing? Explain your answer.

4. Use the charts in Fig. 10-4 to explain what the following weather conditions would be:
   a) if the temperature was −30°C and the wind speed 40 kilometres per hour.
   b) if the temperature was 0°C and the wind speed 55 kilometres per hour.
   c) if the temperature was 25°C and the humidity was 90 percent.

Different places, different weather

Canada stretches from the Atlantic Ocean to the Pacific Ocean and from the middle of the Northern Hemisphere almost to the North Pole. Because this is such a huge area, each day the weather is different from one part of Canada to another.

The weather in Canada follows general patterns. Places near the Atlantic and Pacific Oceans get more wet weather than

Precipitation is water falling from clouds in a solid or liquid form. Forms of precipitation include rain, snow, hail and sleet.

A **front** is the leading edge of a new air mass entering an area. The two major types are warm and cold fronts.

places further inland. For example, Prince Rupert, British Columbia, is the wettest place in the country. It gets more than 2.5 metres of **precipitation** a year, mostly as rain. That would fill a room right to the top! No wonder people call Prince Rupert ''the City of Rainbows.''

Winter weather in places near the Atlantic and Pacific Oceans is milder than elsewhere in Canada. On the west coast, the temperature seldom drops below freezing. Winters are colder than this on the Atlantic side of Canada, but they are less cold than in the central part of Canada.

The interior of Canada and the far north enjoy more hours of sunshine and receive less precipitation than the coasts. Cities such as Calgary, Alberta and Regina, Saskatchewan have more dry, clear days than anywhere else in Canada. However, these places can be very hot in the summer, reaching almost 40°C on some days! In the winter, their temperatures are much lower than those of places near the oceans.

Communities located near the Great Lakes have very changeable weather. Two different types of air, led by **fronts**, push into the region, causing cycles of cloud and storms. Sometimes warm, moist air from the Gulf of Mexico moves

Fig. 10-6   Two air masses meet over the Great Lakes. The cold air acts as a wedge, pushing the warm air up.

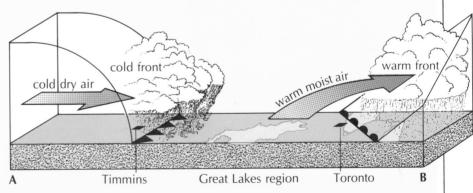

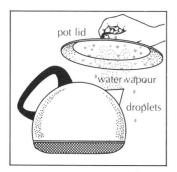

Fig. 10-7 An experiment you can try, which demonstrates why it rains when warm air rises. Be careful—steam burns!

north along a line called a warm front. At other times, cold dry air from the Arctic pushes southward along a cold front. Fig. 10-6 shows these two **air masses** and the weather fronts they bring.

When a new air mass moves into the area, a "battle" begins in the sky. Warm air is lighter than cold air. As a result, when a cold air mass and a warm air mass meet, the lighter, warmer air is forced to rise. The air cools as it rises, causing clouds to form. These clouds can often develop into rain or snow storms. This process is called **frontal precipitation**. It often occurs in the Great Lakes area, where two air masses meet.

A battle between warm air and cold air caused Amal's winter adventure. The weather map for that February day would have been very similar to Fig. 10-6. Cold air from the Arctic caused the snow in Timmins while warm air from the Gulf of Mexico brought the rain to Parry Sound. Further south, in Barrie and Toronto, it was no longer raining and the weather was much warmer. Here Amal felt the influence of the warm air mass from the south. Fig. 10-8 shows how much the weather differs across Canada on any one day.

117

Fig. 10-8 A weather profile and map of Canada for a day in early April.

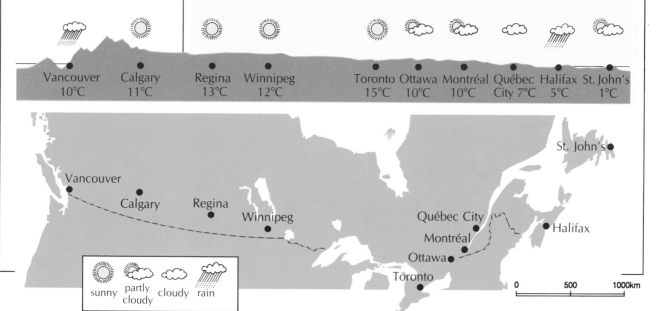

ACTIVITY TWO 📷 🌐 🗒️

1. Use the weather profile for early April in Fig. 10-8 to make a chart showing which cities were experiencing the following weather conditions:
   - the warmest temperature
   - the coldest temperature
   - complete cloud cover
   - rain
   - bright sunshine
2. Use the weather profile and the map in Fig. 10-8 to answer the following questions:
   a) Where are the cities located which are receiving rain?
   b) Where are the cities located which are receiving sunshine?
   c) Explain how the weather changes from Toronto to Québec.

3. Three types of location are shown for the cities in Fig. 10-8 —on the coast, near the Great Lakes, and in the western interior.
   a) Identify the type of location for each city on Fig. 10-8.
   b) Does the weather profile show typical weather for each of the three types of location? Use information from the section ''Different Places, Different Weather'' to help you explain your answers.

How geographers work: Reading a weather map

You will often see weather maps on television and in newspapers. You will find the weather map useful if you learn to read it. For example, it can help you to plan outdoor activities and trips. The weather map can even help you decide what to wear to school. Follow these four steps to understand a weather map like the one shown in Fig. 10-9.

Step A. **Find the location** of the area shown on the map. If the map shows the region where you live, locate your community. This way you can use the information from the map.

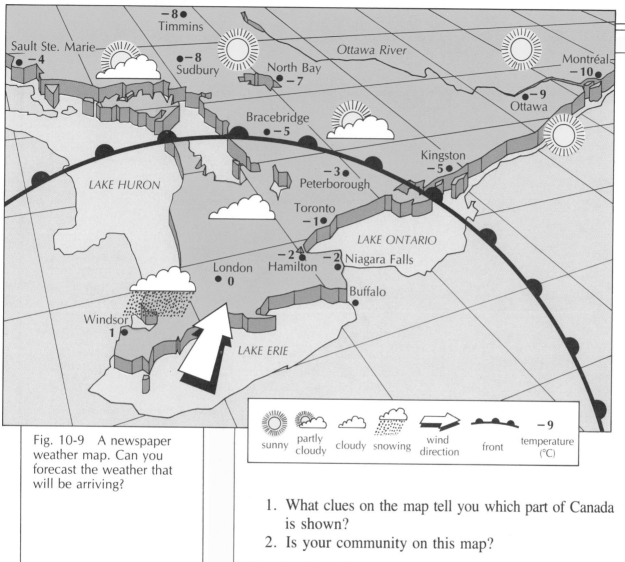

Fig. 10-9 A newspaper weather map. Can you forecast the weather that will be arriving?

1. What clues on the map tell you which part of Canada is shown?
2. Is your community on this map?

Step B. **Identify the meaning** of information shown on the map. Weather maps use symbols and numbers that tell you about the present weather conditions.

3. What do the numbers on the map mean?
4. Use the legend to find the meaning for each of the symbols.

Step C. **Look for patterns** on the map by using the temperatures and symbols. Do the temperatures change from one area on the map to another? Look for a pattern of sky changes. For example, is there a change from clear, sunny skies to cloud and rain?

A forecast is a prediction of what will come. Weather forecasts usually cover a short period of time, such as a day or a week.

5. Find the city that is receiving the following weather:
   (i) clear, −9°C
   (ii) partly cloudy, −3°C
   (iii) cloudy, −1°C
   (iv) precipitation, +1°C
6. Describe the map pattern of
   (i) the temperature from south to north
   (ii) the sky conditions from the southwest to the northeast

Step D. **Predict changes** in the weather by using wind direction and fronts. The wind brings new air masses to an area and often causes changing weather.

7. Find the arrow showing wind direction.
   a) From which direction is it coming?
   b) Will air coming into the area be warmer or cooler? How can you tell?
8. Where will the weather conditions shown at Windsor and London arrive next? Explain the reason for your answer.
9. Write a short weather forecast for either North Bay or Ottawa, similar to one you might hear on television or radio.

Careers in geography: Meteorologist

A meteorologist studies the atmosphere. Some prepare weather forecasts while others research climatic patterns and trends. Meteorologists must have math, science and computer skills for forecasting or research. Most prepare for their careers by completing a Bachelor of Science degree (B.Sc.) at university, with special courses in meteorology.

George Boer has been a meteorologist with Canada's Atmospheric Environment Service for fifteen years.

"I enjoy my research work because meteorology is a study that is useful to people every day. Climatic research and weather forecasting have long been areas of worldwide co-operation. Information

Fig. 10-10 Meteorologist George Boer.

from around the earth goes into each day's forecast. There are many people whose jobs support my work. Observers who collect weather information and technicians who operate or service equipment are important to the meteorologist."

What is climate?

Weather follows patterns over time. Although every community experiences unusual weather occasionally, most communities can expect certain kinds of weather in each season. For example, Canadians can expect the weather to get gradually warmer as winter changes into spring. Wheat farmers in the west can usually expect a rainy season in mid to late spring. Every place has its own "normal" weather for particular times of the year.

Weather follows broad patterns that together are called **climate**. Climate is the average weather conditions of a place or region over a long period of time. It includes average temperature, precipitation, humidity and wind conditions. Climate conditions are the normal conditions for a specific place. The following example shows that daily weather can differ greatly from the average weather conditions, which are recorded over many years. On June 30, 1984, Yellowknife, Northwest Territories got 23 mm of rain. Use Fig. 10-11 to compare this to the average June rainfall in Yellowknife. On December 11, 1984, Yellowknife's temperature was a chilly −44°C! Compare this to the average temperature for December. Unusual weather conditions like these happen in every community. A community might occasionally experience a cold spell, a tornado, a drought or a blizzard, but these occasional events are not considered part of the average climate for that community.

Fig. 10-11 Yellowknife, N.W.T. can experience extreme conditions, including 31°C summer days.

CONDITION	WEATHER (1984)	CLIMATE (1951–1980)
Temperature	Highest: July 27 31°C Lowest: Dec. 11 −44°C	July average: 16°C Dec. average: −24°C
Precipitation	Greatest in 24 hours: June 30 23 mm	Average total for June: 17 mm

WHAT YOU HAVE LEARNED

This chapter showed how much weather affects people and other living things. You have used several types of maps and graphs to find and predict weather patterns. You have read the wind chill and humidity graphs to measure how comfortable you might be if you go out in certain weather conditions. You also learned how to read the symbols, the wind direction and the type of fronts on a map to forecast the weather.

LOOKING BACK

1. a) What is weather?
   b) What four things make up the weather?
   c) How is climate different from weather?

2. a) What kind of weather do you like best? Why?
   b) Write or draw your own weather-related adventure.

EXPANDING YOUR LEARNING

3. Look at a weather map for today in the newspaper or on television.
   a) Prepare a chart to compare the temperatures and sky conditions of four cities in different parts of Canada or your region. What pattern do you see?
   b) Add to the chart the weather predicted for tomorrow at each city.
   c) Use the weather map to explain the factors responsible for the coming weather.

4. Collect photographs or drawings to show the different types of weather conditions around the world. Your collection should show how weather conditions affect living things.

5. Have there been any extreme weather conditions (such as a blizzard, a drought or a storm) which people in your area remember? See what you can find out about them by using interviews or research. Your teacher or school librarian can help you to plan your interviews.

CHAPTER 11

Christmas in Summer: Patterns of Climate

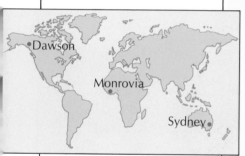

Fig. 11-1 The locations you will learn about in this chapter.

WHAT YOU WILL LEARN

Weather averaged over a number of years is called climate. Places around the world have very different climates. Some are hot while others are cold. Some are wet, while others are dry. These different patterns of climate can be explained.

In this chapter you will learn to draw and interpret climate graphs. You will use the climate graphs of three different areas of the earth to look for patterns. You will see how the sun creates the seasons and world patterns of temperature and precipitation. Finally, you will explore three climatic mysteries to learn about other factors that affect climate patterns.

KEY WORDS

climate graph	condensation	moderated climate
temperature range	convectional precipitation	
equatorial	orbit	temperature
evaporation	ocean current	season

Fig. 11-2 In Sydney, Australia, students often spend their Christmas holidays at the beach.

Christmas in summer

School was finally out for summer vacation. It seemed as if half the people of Sydney had come to the beach. The surf pounded against the shore as Sarah and Allan wiggled their toes in the warm sand.

"So, what is your family doing for Christmas?" Allan asked. "Will you be coming to the beach again?"

Sarah looked at him and sighed. "Tomorrow we're going to my Grandma's place for Christmas. But I think we'll be back in Sydney next week. Maybe I'll see you then."

Some parts of the world do have Christmas during the summer. While you are dreaming of snow, Australians are planning to go to the beach. These opposites are part of the world pattern of climates. Look at the map in Fig. 11-3. It shows three communities that will be compared to one another in this chapter. These communities have very different locations. Monrovia, Liberia is near the Equator, while Dawson, Canada is close to the Arctic Circle. Sydney, Australia is in the Southern Hemisphere, just below the Tropic of Capricorn. Because of their locations, these communities have very different climates.

Fig. 11-3 How are the climates of these three cities different?

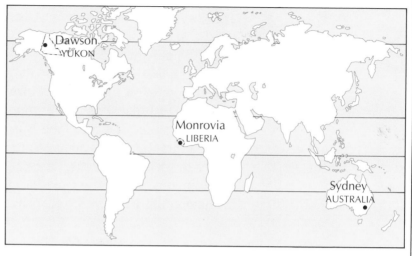

MONROVIA, LIBERIA Elevation 23 m	J	F	M	A	M	J	J	A	S	O	N	D
mm	31	56	97	216	516	973	996	373	744	772	236	130
°C	26	26	27	27	27	25	24	25	25	25	26	26

SYDNEY, AUSTRALIA Elevation 42 m	J	F	M	A	M	J	J	A	S	O	N	D
mm	89	102	127	135	127	117	117	76	73	71	73	73
°C	22	22	21	18	15	13	12	13	15	18	19	21

DAWSON, YUKON Elevation 320 m	J	F	M	A	M	J	J	A	S	O	N	D
mm	17	16	10	10	21	39	47	44	28	29	22	25
°C	−31	−24	−15	−2	8	14	16	13	7	−4	−17	−26

The number table for each community on the map in Fig. 11-3 gives climate information. Along the top, the letters show the months of the year. The first row of numbers shows the average amount of precipitation for each month. For example, Dawson receives 25 mm of precipitation in December on average. The second row of numbers shows the average monthly temperature. Monrovia's temperature averages 26°C in December. Find Sydney's average precipitation and temperature for the month of December.

This climatic information is useful for describing and comparing places. For example, you can estimate the average temperature of a community simply by adding the hottest and coldest months, then dividing by two. Geographers also compare the **temperature range** of places. This is the difference between the hottest and coldest months of the year. For example, if the average temperature in Athens, Greece for January is 10°C , and the average for July is 28°C, the temperature range is 18°C for Athens.

Geographers often draw **climate graphs** to show temperature and precipitation figures. A climate graph combines two types of graph in order to provide important information about a particular place. The bar graph is used to show precipitation and the line graph to show temperature. Climate graphs make it easier to identify patterns. They also make it easier to compare the climates of different places. You will learn to draw a climate graph later in this chapter.

ACTIVITY ONE

1. Use the map in Fig. 11-3 to review
   a) the names of the continents
   b) the names of the oceans
   c) the names of the lines crossing the map

2. What is meant by these terms?
   a) climate
   b) climate graph
   c) precipitation
   d) temperature range

3. Make a chart to compare Monrovia, Sydney and Dawson regarding:
   a) degrees of latitude from the Equator
   b) estimated average temperature
   c) temperature range
   d) total precipitation

4. Use this chart to suggest how distance from the Equator affects
   a) average temperature
   b) temperature range
   c) precipitation

5. Suggest why Sydney is warm enough to have ocean swimming at Christmas.

The effects of the sun

The sun has a great effect on climate. The temperature and precipitation of most places on earth is influenced more by the sun than by any other factor. Our seasonal changes in climate are also due to the sun. Let us look more closely at how the sun effects temperature, precipitation and the seasons.

Temperature

The sun is the source of heat and light which supports life on earth. Some places receive more heat and light than others. Places near the Equator get more heat energy because the sun is directly overhead. There is only one **temperature season** at the Equator. A temperature season is a period of the year with special temperature conditions. In Canada, there are four temperature seasons, from spring to winter.

Figs. 11-4 and 11-5 show how the sun's rays cause different climates in different parts of the earth. Near the Equator, the

Fig. 11-4 Why would average temperatures be higher near the Equator?

Fig. 11-5 An experiment showing how the sun affects temperatures.

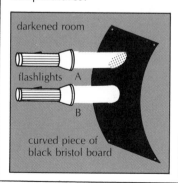

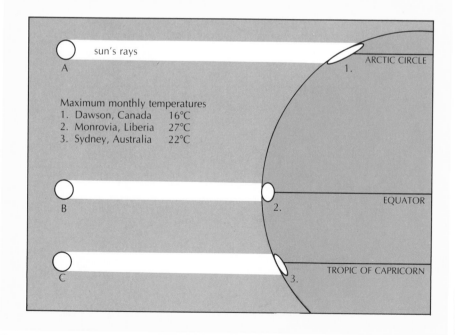

sun's rays

Maximum monthly temperatures
1. Dawson, Canada   16°C
2. Monrovia, Liberia   27°C
3. Sydney, Australia   22°C

A

B

C

ARCTIC CIRCLE
1.

EQUATOR
2.

TROPIC OF CAPRICORN
3.

sun's rays are direct. They are concentrated and intense. At high latitudes, the sun's rays are spread out by the curve of the earth. They hit the earth at an increasingly sharp angle. As a result, the rays are spread over a larger area and the heat they carry is less intense. This is why **equatorial** places are hotter than mid-latitude places. Try the experiment shown in Fig. 11-5 in your classroom.

Equatorial refers to the region or area near the Equator.

Precipitation

Places near the Equator get more rain than most places on earth. High average temperatures and heavy precipitation often go together. Fig. 11-6 shows the world pattern of precipitation. Where are the wettest places on earth located? How much precipitation falls in the northern latitudes?

Near the Equator the sun heats the earth intensely. When the sun rises, it begins to warm the earth. During the day, as

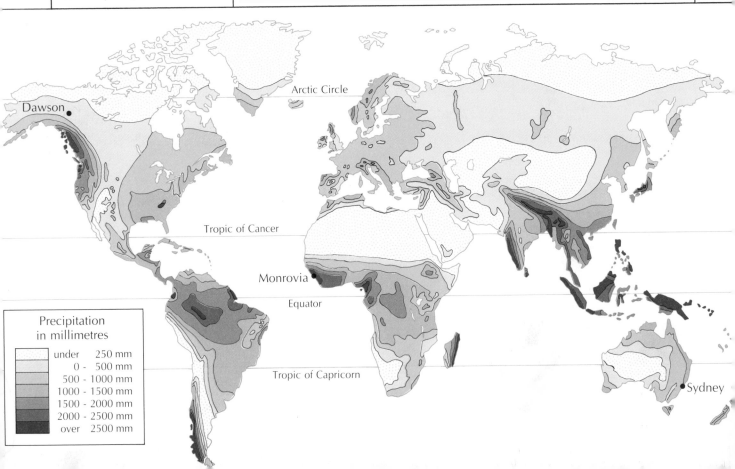

Fig. 11-6 The world pattern of precipitation.

Precipitation
in millimetres

	under 250 mm
	0 - 500 mm
	500 - 1000 mm
	1000 - 1500 mm
	1500 - 2000 mm
	2000 - 2500 mm
	over 2500 mm

Fig. 11-7 What happens to the water and the dish after several hours?

Fig. 11-8 How is convectional precipitation similar to the experiment in Fig. 11-7?

Evaporation is the process in which a substance such as water changes from a liquid to a vapour.

Condensation is the process that is the reverse of evaporation, in which a substance changes from a vapour to a liquid.

the earth grows warm, it warms the air above it. This warm air rises and expands. It carries with it moisture which **evaporates** from the lakes, rivers, land and vegetation. The evaporating moisture cools as it rises higher in the atmosphere. This cooling causes the moisture to **condense** into clouds. By late afternoon, the clouds cannot hold any more moisture, and a brief, heavy rainstorm occurs. The next morning the cycle begins again. As a result, places like Monrovia, Liberia receive more than five metres of precipitation annually. Fig. 11-8 shows this kind of precipitation, called **convectional precipitation**. It occurs where the sun's heat is intense. You can see the process of evaporation by doing the experiment in Figure 11-7 in class.

The seasons

Let us explain why Sydney, Australia has Christmas in summer. Summer is the hottest time of the year at any place in the world. In the Northern Hemisphere summer is from late June until late September. But in the Southern Hemisphere the seasons are reversed—summer is from late December until late March!

Fig. 11-9 Identify the position of the earth that shows summer in the Northern Hemisphere. Which shows summer in the Southern Hemisphere?

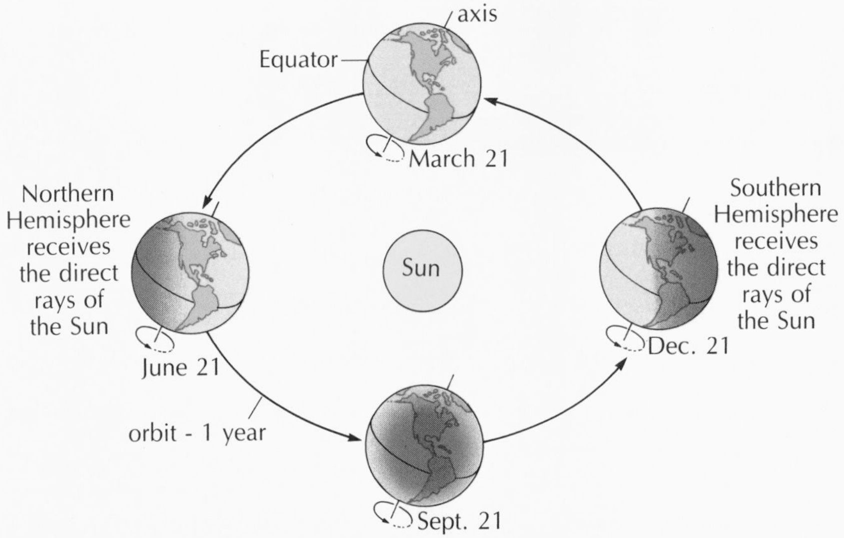

The **orbit** of the earth is the path it follows as it moves around the sun.

This reversal of seasons occurs because of the earth's **orbit**, the path it follows, around the sun. Fig. 11-9 shows how the orbit of the earth around the sun results in the seasons. If you look at a classroom globe you will see that the earth is tilted on its axis. When the earth orbits the sun during the year, first the area north of the Equator gets the direct rays of the sun. This is our summer. Six months later, the area south of the Equator gets the sun's rays directly overhead. This is Australia's summer.

The earth's position as it orbits the sun gives us changing seasons. Some places, like Monrovia, are near the Equator. Their temperatures do not change much all year. But communities like Dawson have great climatic changes from season to season, depending upon how close to the sun they are during the earth's orbit. It is the overhead position of the sun which influences the climate of each place more than any other factor.

ACTIVITY TWO

1. What temperature differences would you notice if you moved to an equatorial region from Canada?

2. How much would you have to grow to equal the five metres of precipitation that Monrovia gets every year?

3. Explain why the seasons are reversed in the Northern and the Southern Hemispheres.

4. Use the new words in this section to make a word search puzzle. Can your classmates find, then define, each term?

How geographers work: Drawing a climate graph

Climate graphs combine temperature and precipitation information for a place on one graph, letting you see climatic patterns easily. The following ten steps describe how to draw a climate graph for Monrovia, Liberia, one of the wettest communities on earth.

1. **Temperature**

   To set up the graph:
   Step 1   Use 40°C and −60°C for the top and bottom of the temperature scale. All places have temperatures within this range.
   Step 2   Make the graph 20 units high. Each unit will represent 5°C. Label the temperature scale on the left side as shown in Fig. 11-10a on the next page.
   Step 3   Draw a line 12 units across from −60°C. Label the months of the year, by letter, in the middle of each unit as shown in Fig. 11-10a.

   To record the temperature data:

   TEMPERATURE DATA FOR MONROVIA, LIBERIA

month	J	F	M	A	M	J	J	A	S	O	N	D
°C	26	26	27	27	26	25	24	25	25	25	26	26

   Step 4   Mark a small dot in the centre of the column for each month to show that month's temperature.

Fig. 11-10   To draw a climate graph for Monrovia, first set up the graph (a), and then record the temperature data (b).

Step 5   Connect the temperature dots with a smooth curving line. Trace over the line with a red pencil crayon. Red is used to represent heat.

Fig. 11-10b shows the completed temperature graph for Monrovia.

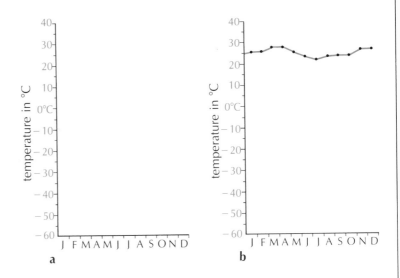

2. **Precipitation**

To set up the graph:

Step 6   Use 0 mm and 1000 mm for the top and bottom of the precipitation scale. Very few places receive more than 1000 mm precipitation in any one month. Put the precipitation scale on the right side of the climate graph.

Step 7   The graph for temperature was 20 units high. Use the same number of units for precipitation, and let each unit represent 50 mm of precipitation. Label it as shown in Fig. 11-11a.

To record the precipitation data:

PRECIPITATION DATA FOR MONROVIA, LIBERIA

month	J	F	M	A	M	J	J	A	S	O	N	D
mm	31	56	97	216	516	973	996	373	744	772	236	130

Step 8   Use a ruler to draw a bar across from the
precipitation scale measurement of 31 mm for
January. Outline the column below the line
to make a bar. Do the same for each month.

Step 9   Shade the bars in with a blue pencil crayon.
Blue is used to represent water.

Step 10   Finish your graph by adding a title and labels
as shown in Fig. 11-11b, which shows the
completed climate graph for Monrovia.

Fig. 11-11   To complete the climate graph, add the precipitation scale (a), the precipitation data and the title of the graph (b).

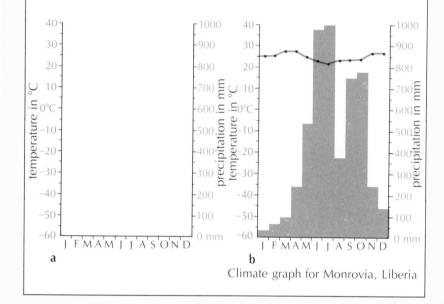

a

b

Climate graph for Monrovia, Liberia

ACTIVITY THREE

1. Look at the graph of temperature for Monrovia in
   Fig. 11-10b.
   a) Describe the pattern of temperature.
   b) How many temperature seasons are there in Monrovia?
   c) How does world location affect Monrovia's temperature?

2. Look at the graph of precipitation for Monrovia in
   Fig. 11-11b.
   a) Describe the overall pattern of precipitation. When is it
      dry? wet? very wet?
   b) What type of precipitation does Monrovia receive? Why?

3. Use the information on Fig. 11-3 and the same graph units to draw and label climate graphs for
   a) Sydney, Australia
   b) Dawson, Canada

4. Look at the completed climate graphs for question 3 and Fig. 11-11b.
   a) Describe the shape of the temperature line for each of the three communities.
   b) Calculate the temperature range for each.
   c) Suggest reasons for the differences.

Solve the climatic mysteries

The sun is the main influence on climate. But several other factors play a role, too. These factors are the clues that help us to solve some of the puzzles in the world pattern of climate. Three of these puzzles are:

1. Some places on the Equator enjoy cool temperatures all year round.
2. Some places near the Arctic Circle are much warmer than places farther south.
3. Some places that share the same latitude have very different temperatures and precipitation levels.

Try to solve each of the three mysteries as a detective would, by looking for clues and patterns. Use your map and graph skills to compare the two communities in each mystery. One has the type of climate you would expect. The other does not. What other climatic influence is at work?

Mystery One: Cool Quito on the Equator

How could a place located on the Equator be cool? Quito (kē′tō), the capital city of Ecuador in South America, is almost exactly on the Equator, where it is usually very hot. But in Quito, temperatures are cool and spring-like all through the year. Not far away, Manaus in Brazil simmers in hot jungles all year long. Both places are located right beneath the overhead sun.

Yet one is very hot and the other is cool. What other climatic influence is at work here?

QUITO, ECUADOR
Elevation 2879 m

month	J	F	M	A	M	J	J	A	S	O	N	D
°C	15	15	15	15	15	14	14	14	14	14	14	15

MANAUS, BRAZIL
Elevation 44 m

month	J	F	M	A	M	J	J	A	S	O	N	D
°C	28	28	28	27	28	28	28	28	29	29	29	28

ACTIVITY FOUR

1. For each of the two places, Manaus and Quito, find
   a) the estimated average temperature.
   b) the temperature range.
   c) the number of temperature seasons.

2. Which place has temperatures more typical of its latitude? Explain.

3. Use the temperature comparison in Fig. 11-12 and the photograph in Fig. 11-13 to look for clues which can explain the temperature differences.

4. Can you explain why Quito is cool and Manaus is hot?

Mystery Two: The Strange Case of Stavanger

Could a place located near the Arctic Circle have mild winters? Normally places as far north as Hudson Bay and Labrador experience long, cold winters. For example, Hopedale, located on the Atlantic coast of Labrador, has an average January temperature of − 16°C. Yet on the other side of the Atlantic, in Stavanger, Norway, there are no months below freezing. How could two places located at similar northern latitudes be so different in temperature? What climate influence is at work here?

Fig. 11-12 The climate data for Mystery One: Quito, Ecuador and Manaus, Brazil.

Fig. 11-13 Quito, the capital of Ecuador. What influences on its climate can you see in this photograph?

Fig. 11-14 The climate data for Mystery Two: Stavanger, Norway and Hopedale, Newfoundland.

STAVANGER AND HOPEDALE TEMPERATURES

month	J	F	M	A	M	J	J	A	S	O	N	D
Stavanger °C	1	1	3	6	10	13	15	15	13	9	6	3
Hopedale °C	−16	−16	−11	−5	1	6	11	11	7	2	−3	−11

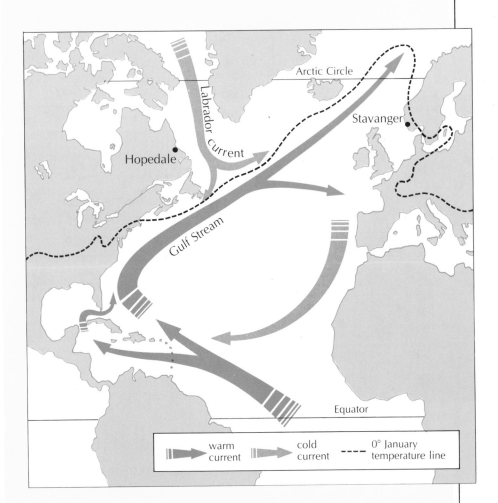

Fig. 11-15 How do ocean currents affect Hopedale and Stavanger, which have similar northern latitudes?

ACTIVITY FIVE

1. For Hopedale, Labrador and Stavanger, Norway, find
   a) the average temperature.
   b) the temperature range.

c) the number of temperature seasons.

d) the season in which the two places differ the most.

2. Which climate is more typical of a far-northern climate? Explain why.

3. Look at the map in Fig. 11-15.
   a) Describe the pattern of the 0°C January temperature line.
   b) Name the **ocean current** which affects this temperature line.

4. Explain Hopedale's cold temperatures and Stavanger's warm weather.

An **ocean current** is a fast-moving stream of water in the ocean.

Mystery Three: Wondering about Winnipeg Winters

Could two cities at the same latitude have winter temperatures more than 20°C different? Both Vancouver, British Columbia and Winnipeg, Manitoba are located at about 50° North latitude. Both have the same amount of sunlight coming their way. However, Winnipeg freezes in average winter temperature of almost −20°C, while Vancouver enjoys mild, rainy winters. Another climatic factor is at work here.

Fig. 11-16   The climate data for Mystery Three: Vancouver, British Columbia and Winnipeg, Manitoba.

WINNIPEG AND VANCOUVER TEMPERATURES

month		J	F	M	A	M	J	J	A	S	O	N	D
Winnipeg	°C	−19	−16	−8	3	11	17	20	18	12	6	−5	−14
Vancouver	°C	3	5	6	9	12	15	17	17	14	10	6	4

WINNIPEG AND VANCOUVER PRECIPITATION

month		J	F	M	A	M	J	J	A	S	O	N	D
Winnipeg	mm	21	18	23	39	66	80	76	76	53	31	25	19
Vancouver	mm	154	115	101	60	52	45	32	41	67	114	150	182

Fig. 11-17 A map of January temperatures in North America. How does Vancouver's position affect its climate?

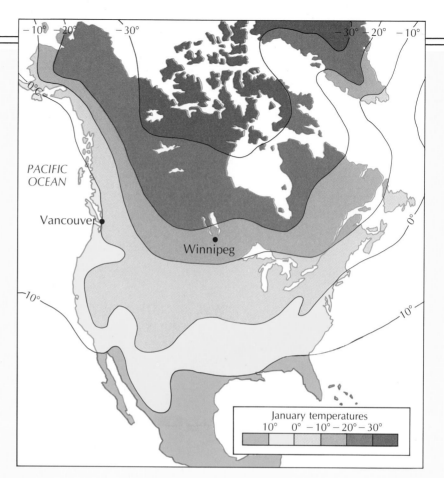

January temperatures
10° 0° −10° −20° −30°

ACTIVITY SIX

1. For each of the two places find
   a) the average temperature.
   b) the temperature range.
   c) the number of temperature seasons.
   d) the total amount of precipitation for one year.

2. Compare winter temperatures and precipitation in the two cities.

3. Look at the pattern of winter temperatures in Fig. 11-17.
   a) Is it warmer by the ocean or in the heart of the continent?
   b) Suggest some reasons for this.

4. Can you explain why winter in Winnipeg is so different from winter in Vancouver?

WHAT YOU HAVE LEARNED

In this chapter you used many math skills. You drew line graphs and bar graphs to show climate in several locations. You estimated average temperature and found temperature range and total precipitation. This information helped you to see world climate patterns.

The sun is the most important factor affecting climatic patterns. The position and intensity of the sun are the main influences on temperature, precipitation and the seasons. Other factors, such as elevation, location and ocean currents, can also have important influences.

LOOKING BACK

1. Use the information in Fig. 11-18, showing precipitation and temperature measurements for Buenos Aires, to find
   a) the total precipitation.
   b) the estimated average temperature.
   c) the temperature range.

2. a) Draw and label a climate graph of Buenos Aires.
   b) Which hemisphere is this place in, the Northern or the Southern? How can you tell?

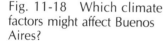

Fig. 11-18 Which climate factors might affect Buenos Aires?

BUENOS AIRES

month	J	F	M	A	M	J	J	A	S	O	N	D
mm	79	71	109	89	76	61	56	61	79	86	84	99
°C	23	23	21	17	13	9	10	11	13	15	19	22

EXPANDING YOUR LEARNING

3. Locate Buenos Aires in an atlas or on a wall map. Which of these factors would have an important affect on the climate of this city? Explain your choices.
   a) elevation   c) ocean currents
   b) location   d) mountain barriers

4. Use an atlas or wall map to find
   a) two places similar to Quito that are near the Equator yet remain cool year-round.
   b) two places similar to Stavanger that are at high latitudes yet remain mild in winter.
   c) two places similar to Winnipeg that have cold winters because they are in the heart of a continent.

SOLUTIONS TO THE THREE CLIMATIC MYSTERIES

Mystery One: Cool Quito

The higher the altitude, or elevation, the colder it becomes. This is because at high altitudes, the atmosphere becomes "thinner." It contains less oxygen, carbon dioxide and other gases. These gases act as a "lid" to hold in the heat of the sun. With less oxygen at high altitudes, the atmosphere cannot hold in as much of the sun's heat. Therefore, as the atmosphere becomes thinner, air temperatures fall by about 2°C per 300 m of altitude.

The Andes Mountains are located all along the west side of South America. Quito's high elevation of 2879 m is the reason that it is so much cooler here than in Manaus at 44 m.

Mystery Two: Strange Stavanger

The ocean waters are not still. Waves and tides cause the ocean to rise and fall. Large steady motions called currents move the surface water from one side of the oceans to the other and back again. Ocean currents are much like the movements in the molten mantle of the earth. There are several factors that cause ocean currents, including the winds that blow near the earth's surface, differences in water temperature, and the amount of salt in the water.

A strong warm current called the Gulf Stream begins in the Caribbean Sea. As it moves across the Atlantic Ocean it is known as the North Atlantic Drift. It crosses the ocean, bringing a warm climate to northwest Europe and Norway. Ocean currents are why Stavanger is so much warmer than Hopedale.

Mystery Three: Winter in Winnipeg

On a bright summer day, which is hotter, the beach or the water? If you dig a few centimetres into the sand what happens to the sand's temperature? Later in the evening, how would the temperatures of the beach and the water compare?

The beach can only absorb the sun's heat to a very shallow depth, so it heats up quickly. A few centimetres below the surface the sand is cooler. Almost as soon as the sun sets, the beach cools off, but the water itself changes little in temperature.

Land and water heat up and cool off at different rates. This is because land is solid while water is transparent. The heat of the sun can penetrate oceans much deeper than it does the continents. Oceans warm up slowly, but deeply. Because of this stored heat, oceans cool off more slowly than continents do. A location by the ocean is the reason that Vancouver has the mild winters of a **moderated climate**, while Winnipeg has cold winters.

A **moderated climate** describes the climate of a place by a large body of water. The influence of the water prevents extremes of temperature, keeping the place warmer in winter and cooler in summer.

North America's Rainforest

Fig. 12-1   The location you will learn about in this chapter.

WHAT YOU WILL LEARN

A region is a part of the earth with distinctive characteristics. The Pacific Coast of North America is a region that has unique links between the environment and the people who live there. The coastal mountains and the ocean create a climate with warm temperatures and heavy rainfall. Towering forests have grown in this environment, causing controversy over logging here. Loggers want to cut the trees, while others seek to protect some of the forest.

This is the last chapter of this unit. You will use many of the ideas and skills that you learned earlier in the unit. Knowledge about landforms and climate, as well as the skills you use to interpret map and graph patterns, will help you understand the Pacific Coast region.

KEY WORDS

rainforest	**rain shadow**	**coniferous**
prevailing wind	**orographic precipitation**	

Fig. 12-2   Look for evidence of lumbering, farming and gravel mining here in British Columbia's Skeena River valley.

Rainforests are areas of lush vegetation found in hot tropical areas of the earth. Rainforests receive at least 1800 mm of precipitation annually.

The wettest places on earth

"Class," Mrs. Twillingate began, "in this chapter we will learn how climate affects vegetation and industry on North America's Pacific Coast, one of the wettest regions of the world. This is a very interesting region," she continued. "It is the warmest part of Canada and receives more than 2.5 metres of precipitation every year. Because of this warmth and moisture, the natural vegetation thrives. The trees are huge, some as tall as a thirty-storey building. Most places in the world that get this much precipitation are in tropical areas, close to the Equator. These areas are known as **rainforests**. They are very distinctive areas, and you will learn about them in Unit VII.

"The Pacific Coast region of North America is not a tropical rainforest, but it shares an important characteristic with the tropics. You can see this characteristic in Fig. 12-3, which shows some of the wettest places on earth. Most of these places have high temperatures all year round. Only Prince Rupert has cooler temperatures. Compare the latitudes of these wet places to find out why the Pacific Coast has the high precipitation levels without the high temperatures."

Fig. 12-3 This graph explains why the Pacific Coast is sometimes called North America's "rainforest."

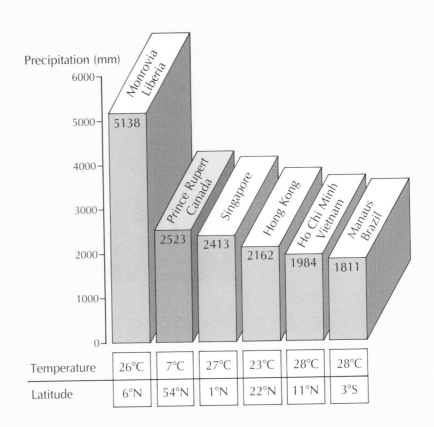

	Monrovia Liberia	Prince Rupert Canada	Singapore	Hong Kong	Ho Chi Minh Vietnam	Manaus Brazil
Precipitation (mm)	5138	2523	2413	2162	1984	1811
Temperature	26°C	7°C	27°C	23°C	28°C	28°C
Latitude	6°N	54°N	1°N	22°N	11°N	3°S

Fig. 12-4 How do the climate conditions of the two Princes compare?

PRINCE RUPERT, BRITISH COLUMBIA
Elevation 34 m

	J	F	M	A	M	J	J	A	S	O	N	D
mm	228	222	201	190	140	130	103	158	233	367	268	284
°C	0	2	3	5	8	11	13	13	11	8	4	2

PRINCE GEORGE, BRITISH COLUMBIA
Elevation 676 m

	J	F	M	A	M	J	J	A	S	O	N	D
mm	57	39	37	27	47	67	60	68	59	59	51	57
°C	−12	−6	−2	4	9	13	15	14	10	5	−3	−8

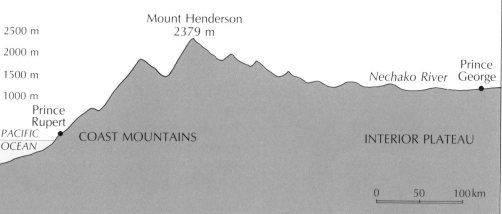

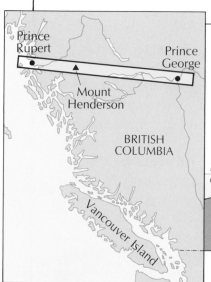

Fig. 12-5 A profile of British Columbia along the 54°N line of latitude, from Prince Rupert to Prince George.

Refer to Chapters 10 and 11 for a review of climate factors.

ACTIVITY ONE

1. Use Fig. 12-4 to compare the climate of Prince George and Prince Rupert, British Columbia. Calculate the following information:
   a) total precipitation per year
   b) estimated average temperature per year
   c) temperature range

2. Draw a chart comparing winter and summer conditions between the two Princes.

3. Use Fig. 12-5 to explain how each of the following factors cause climate differences between the two Princes:
   a) the Pacific Ocean
   b) Prince George's location
   c) elevation

4. a) Which of the two Princes would have larger trees?
   b) Give two reasons for your answer.

5. Which of these two places would you prefer to live in? Explain your choice.

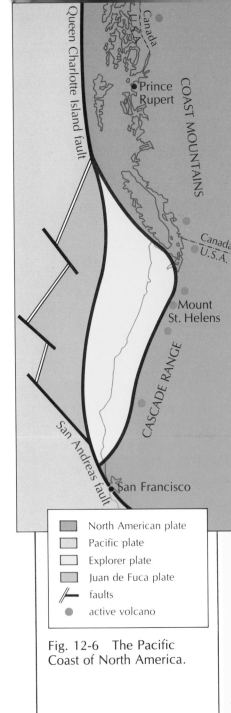

Queen Charlotte Island fault

Canada
U.S.

● Prince
Rupert

COAST MOUNTAINS

Canada
U.S.A.

Mount
St. Helens

CASCADE RANGE

San Andreas fault

● San Francisco

☐ North American plate
☐ Pacific plate
☐ Explorer plate
☐ Juan de Fuca plate
╱╱ faults
● active volcano

Fig. 12-6 The Pacific Coast of North America.

Researching the Pacific Coast

Mrs. Twillingate decided to have her class do the teaching on this topic. She divided the class into groups of four. Each person in the group was responsible for researching a subtopic and presenting it to the rest of the group. This way students would learn from each other.

The subject of these reports was the link between the physical environment and human activity on the Pacific Coast, North America's "rainforest." The class was to study how landforms and climate affect vegetation and people. The four subtopics to be studied were:
• how the mountains formed
• why it rains so much
• trees of the coast forest
• logging and conservation
Here is what one group learned.

Darren's Report: How the Mountains Formed

"It's a good thing we learned about the moving plates of the earth's crust before I picked this topic," said Darren. "Otherwise, I wouldn't have understood all this information about faults, volcanoes and plates. When I knew that this region was part of the Pacific "Ring of Fire" it was easier. I know why there are mountains along the coast.

"Look closely at the map as I explain it. First, you can see that the map has four coloured areas, two large and two small. They are divided by heavy black lines. These are the pieces, or plates, of the earth's crust, divided by faults. Two main faults run along the Pacific Coast under the sea floor—the San Andreas fault in the south and the Queen Charlotte Island fault in the north. The Pacific and the North American Plates meet here, so this is an active earthquake zone.

"Now look along the coast beside these faults," Darren continued. "You can see the Coast Mountains in Canada and the Cascade Range in the United States. These volcanic mountain chains were formed in a similar way. In the Cascade Range, there are several active volcanoes along the fault that divides the small Explorer Plate from the large North American Plate. The currents under the earth's crust pull the smaller plate under the large plate, and a line of volcanoes is the result. One volcano in the Cascade Range, Mount St. Helens, erupted in 1980. You can see the volcanoes on the map, just below the border between Canada and the United States. Volcanic eruptions over millions of years created the mountains along the Pacific Coast," Darren concluded.

ACTIVITY TWO

1. Define the following words:
   a) plate
   b) fault
   c) earthquake
   d) volcano

2. What is happening to the Explorer Plate? Draw a simple sketch to illustrate your answer.

3. Why is there a line of volcanic mountains along the Pacific Coast? Use Fig. 12-6 to explain your answer.

4. Suggest how these mountains might affect the weather and climate of British Columbia.

Mai Lin's Report: Why It Rains So Much

"My topic was about all the precipitation on the Pacific Coast," Mai Lin said. "It is closely related to Darren's report, because the mountains are the reason it rains so much there. But it is a different kind of precipitation from the frontal and convectional precipitation we learned about earlier in this unit.

"Remember in Activity One when we compared the two Princes, Rupert and George? Prince Rupert on the coast has four times more precipitation than Prince George in the interior. The two Princes are separated by the Coast Mountains. We saw that it was wettest on the ocean side of the mountains. Well, here's a diagram I found that explains why.

"Winds regularly blow across the Pacific Ocean at this latitude. They are called **prevailing winds**. They pick up

Refer to Chapters 8 and 9 for a review of this information.

A **prevailing wind** is one that usually blows from the same direction.

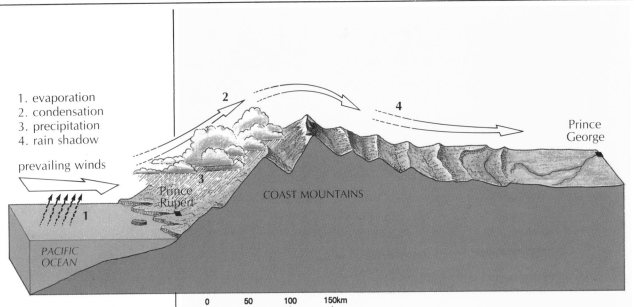

1. evaporation
2. condensation
3. precipitation
4. rain shadow

prevailing winds

PACIFIC OCEAN

Prince Rupert

COAST MOUNTAINS

Prince George

0   50   100   150km

148

Fig. 12-7 This is how orographic precipitation occurs.

A **rain shadow** is an area on the "lee," or protected, side of a mountain range. This area receives less precipitation than the side that faces winds carrying moisture.

moisture from the water through evaporation. When the moist winds arrive at the coast, they are forced to rise over the Coast Mountains. As the air rises it becomes cooler because of the higher altitude, and moisture in the air condenses to form clouds. When the clouds can hold no more moisture, rain or snow falls on the Pacific side of the Coast Range. In this case, the cycle of evaporation, condensation and precipitation is influenced by the mountains. This type of precipitation is called **orographic precipitation**."

"But why is it fairly dry in Prince George?" Darren asked. "I mean, it isn't too far from the coast."

"The east side of the Coast Range is much drier," Mai Lin explained. "Some of the mountains here are almost 4000 metres high. The air that passes over these mountains no longer contains much moisture. It has been lost before the air reaches Prince George. The winds are dry, leaving Prince George in what is called a **rain shadow**.

"All precipitation is caused by moist air rising, then cooling and forming clouds. In orographic precipitation, the mountains are the reason the air rises. And that's exactly what happens in Canada and the United States along the Pacific Coast."

ACTIVITY THREE

1. What do each of these words mean?
   a) evaporation
   c) condensation
   b) prevailing winds
   d) rain shadow

2. Use Fig. 12-7 to explain
   a) why it is raining at location 3.
   b) why it is dry at location 4.

3. Using a chart, compare the three different types of precipitation—orographic, convectional and frontal.

Sarah's Report: Trees of the Coast Forest

Sarah began her report with enthusiasm. "It's really amazing how big the trees can grow along the Pacific Coast! The huge trees that grow on the West Coast are all **coniferous**, which means that they are softwoods with needle-shaped leaves, and they reproduce by dropping cones. This region is so wet and mild that trees this big aren't found anywhere else in North America. Look at this table and photograph to see what I mean.

"The California redwood is the giant of them all," Sarah pointed to the chart. "These trees grow higher than a 30-storey

Fig. 12-8 Giant trees of North America. Coniferous trees such as the western red cedar grow to great heights in the warm, wet climate of the Pacific Coast.

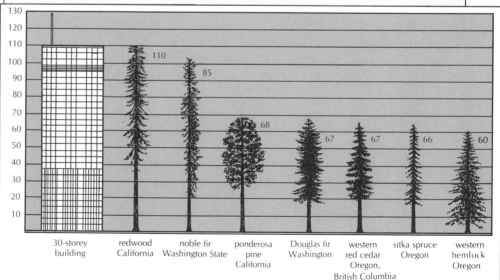

building and are more than ten metres around at the base of the trunk. They grow best on the wet slopes facing the Pacific Ocean. Scientists have calculated that the oldest living redwood is 3500 years old. Loggers prize these trees because of their size and their attractive light red wood. Most of the original forest has now been cut down, but redwoods are still being harvested. In fact, they rank fourth in California's lumber production. But the biggest redwoods are protected in state and national parks in the Eureka area of northern California. They are such unusual trees that I wish there were more being saved.

"The Douglas fir is another tree the loggers want. They grow very quickly and reach heights of 100 metres. Wood from this tree has few knots because there are not many large branches. Their size, straightness and lack of knots make the Douglas fir important to logging companies. This tree grows along slightly drier sections of the Pacific Coast from Canada to Mexico and inland to the Rocky Mountains."

ACTIVITY FOUR

1. Compare the California redwood and Douglas fir in a chart. Include the following:
   a) height
   b) location(s)
   c) commercial advantages
   d) amount of precipitation required

2. a) Use a full page to draw and label a bar graph of the giant trees in Fig. 12-8.
   b) Measure your own height in metres and add it to your graph. Use division to find how many times taller a redwood or a Douglas fir is than you are.

3. Use an atlas to find the locations of the states or provinces named in Fig. 12-8. Explain the reason for the pattern you find.

4. Write a paragraph describing how trees are important for more reasons than logging.

The term "board feet" is used in the United States as a measure of lumber volume. One board foot is a piece of wood 30 cm long by 30 cm wide by 2.5 cm thick.

Fig. 12-9 The leading lumber-producing states and provinces.

Tim's Report: Logging and Conservation

"Look what I found!" Tim exclaimed. "This chart shows how important the Pacific Coast forest is to both the United States and Canada. The leading forestry provinces and states—British Columbia, Oregon, Washington and California—are all on the Pacific Ocean. And they don't just lead their countries in forest production, they are far ahead of the other provinces and states. It's too bad each country records different kinds of figures, though. You can't compare board feet to dollars to see who produces the most. But you can see that logging creates many jobs in the Pacific Coast rainforest.

UNITED STATES Lumber Cut Billions of Board Feet, 1983		CANADA Logging—Value in Millions of Dollars, 1984	
Oregon	7.1	British Columbia	$2675
Washington	4.6	Québec	937
California	3.8	Ontario	923
Idaho	2.0	New Brunswick	370
Georgia	2.0	Nova Scotia	132

"Not everybody is happy about the industry. The Haida people of British Columbia held protests to try to stop loggers from clear-cutting islands off the coast, where their ancestors lived. Clear-cutting is a method of logging in which every tree in a stand of timber is cut down.

"You see," Tim explained, "for thousands of years, the tall western red cedar was a basic part of Haida daily life. For example, these giant trees were important to the Haida's economy. The Haida used the cedars to make 15-metre ocean-going canoes for trading, fishing and hunting. The cedars were also used to make totem poles, boxes, masks and other objects. These objects were often carved with the crest of each family or clan, because family history was important to the Haida. Many cultures use symbols to identify clans and families."

Fig. 12-10 Miles Richardson (right) and members of the Haida Nation, some in mourning paint, protest logging on Lyell Island, British Columbia, in November, 1985.

Fig. 12-11 Why are the Haida concerned about the logging on Lyell Island?

''The fate of the land parallels the fate of the culture,'' states Miles Richardson, young leader of the Council of the Haida Nation. And the land is at risk; the last of the old-growth cedars—the Haida stuff of life—have been falling to the logger's chain saw.

These giant cedars, symbols of the natural world that nurtured Haida culture, are the focus of the fight. Loggers armed with permits from British Columbia's Ministry of Forests have moved on the last of the virgin stands on Lyell Island, in the so-called South Moresby Wilderness south of Skidegate.

The face-off began in the autumn of 1985, when a small armada of fishing boats and helicopters brought blanket-cloaked Haida elders like 67-year-old Ethel Jones and parka-clad younger Indians to blockade a logging road on Lyell Island's Sedgwick Bay. Seventy-two people were taken into custody during the months-long confrontation. Strengthened by ''the faces of our young boys who thought they were fighting all by themselves,'' Ethel Jones was arrested by her own nephew, a Mountie, who wept as he led her away.

ACTIVITY FIVE

1. What do these terms mean?
   a) forestry   b) board feet   c) clear-cutting

2. Use Fig. 12-9 to identify and explain the pattern of the forest industry in North America.

3. Use an atlas to locate the Queen Charlotte Islands off British Columbia.

4. Use Fig. 12-10 and 12-11 to answer the following questions:
   a) Which trees are the focus of this dispute?
   b) Identify the two sides in the dispute.
   c) What conflict has occurred?

5. Write a one-paragraph news bulletin about the dispute on Lyell Island. Use the W5 approach—Who? What? Where? When? Why?

WHAT YOU HAVE LEARNED

This chapter gathered together many topics you learned in this unit. You saw how physical and human patterns are related in one region.

You learned that the Pacific Coast mountains formed along faults in the earth's crust. The height of these mountains, combined with moist prevailing winds blowing over the ocean and in across the mountains, causes orographic precipitation. Huge coniferous trees grow in the wet, mild climate of the region. The Pacific states and provinces are the leading lumbering areas of North America, but many people are trying to protect the West Coast giants from logging.

LOOKING BACK

1. a) What are the major characteristics of the land, climate and vegetation in the Pacific Coast region?
   b) Explain why each of these characteristics is found in the region.

2. Draw and label simple sketches to compare three types of precipitation: frontal, convectional and orographic.

3. a) Use an atlas to find other parts of the world where heavy precipitation is caused by winds blowing first over oceans and then against coastal mountains.
   b) Compare their latitude to the Pacific Coast.

EXPANDING YOUR LEARNING

4. Research Haida culture. Begin by selecting a few important focus questions. Draw sketches to show three ways that the Haida use the huge cedars.

5. Visit a lumber or building centre to find out how lumber from the Pacific forests is made into the following building products:
   a) cedar shakes
   b) plywood
   c) rot-resistant
   d) windows and doors
   e) pressure-treated lumber

UNIT REVIEW

This unit explored physical patterns of landforms and climate. These patterns form distinctive regions like the Pacific Coast of North America. Not everyone agrees on how the earth's surface should be used in such regions. The logging conflict on Lyell Island, British Columbia shows that environmental questions can be complicated. At least four different points of view had to be weighed.

1. Read the four different points of view presented in the following articles with a group of students.

2. Summarize one point of view in your own words.

3. Discuss how the four viewpoints differ.

4. What is your own viewpoint on the issue? Explain your position.

5. The proposed national park was actually agreed to in September of 1987. What promises would each of the four people want before they would agree?

The four viewpoints

1. Logging Contractor

"It's the uncertainty that kills you," logging contractor Frank Beban told me, his back quite literally against the wall in the coffee shop of the Beban-owned Sandspit Inn. Beban's concern was real—and immediate. He held the timber-cutting contract with Western Forest Products, the company that was granted Tree Farm License No. 24 permitting logging of contested Lyell Island. It was Beban's crews—Indians among them—that had been stopped by the Haida blockade at Sedgwick Bay. An affable bear of a man, Beban claims that without the jobs that logging provides, even more of the younger Haida would be forced to migrate to the mainland. "Half the Haida in Skidegate are in logging," Beban says.

2. Haida Leader

In their massive dugout cedar canoes the Haida had long raided and traded with mainland and Vancouver Island tribes—Tlingit, Tsimshian, Kwakiutl—and, later, with European traders in Victoria. During the brief summers they turned the treacherous 60 miles [96 km] across the Hecate Strait and the 200 miles [322 km] south to Vancouver Island into Haida freeways. During the dark stormy winters they gathered in cedar houses and elaborated their rich culture with art, stories, and ceremony. With the bounty of the forests and teeming tidal zone, the Haida had the building blocks of civilization.

Miles Richardson, the young college-educated activist who in 1985 assumed the presidency of the Council of the Haida Nation, has little sympathy for Beban's view. "We're not talking about 70 logging jobs," he stressed. "We're talking about forever. The issue is not logging versus 'eco-nuts.' It's our

A blockade is a barrier.

An activist is someone who takes action on social or political issues.

To sustain means to continue.

156

To expedite means to speed up or make easier.

A moratorium is a delay or pause in action.

An unprecedented action is one never done before.

Aesthetics are a measure of natural beauty.

ability to sustain our culture. And that lies in our relationship—as a people with a 10 000-year history—to the land and the sea and their resources.''

3. Provincial Premier

As international pressure grew, the first glimpse of serious provincial sympathy for the conservation option was revealed in the Speech from the Throne this March by new British Columbia Premier William Vander Zalm: "We will attempt to expedite the federal-provincial negotiations for establishment of a national park on South Moresby that will generate economic benefits for all British Columbia.''

Later that month the provincial government announced a six-week moratorium on new cutting permits in South Moresby, while logging continued at breakneck pace on the contested slopes.

4. Federal Environment Minister

"Jobs lost would be more than compensated by establishment of a national park and increased tourism,'' said Tom McMillan, expressing the commitment of the federal government in Ottawa to preserving South Moresby "for Canadians yet unborn and for the international community.''

But where does Lyell Island fit into the plan? "If it's a park, it's a wilderness park, and you can't have it facing clear-cut logging,'' asserted Minister McMillan. Yet this spring logging crews ripped through Lyell Island with unprecedented speed, leaving ravaged slopes visible from the core area of the proposed park, bringing the region closer daily to disqualification as a park by Parks Canada's aesthetics guidelines.

"We've put our money on the table to compensate the loggers,'' stated McMillan, determined to preserve cutting boundaries that would include Lyell Island and to push for a national park that would bring new prosperity to the entire province.

UNIT IV
The Earth's Riches

What Is a Natural Resource?

Fig. 13-1   The location you will learn about in this chapter.

Kapuskasing

WHAT YOU WILL LEARN

People rely on the earth to provide much of what they need. We call the products of the earth natural resources. Nature provides water, soil, forest, animal, mineral and energy resources.

This chapter will introduce the idea of natural resources. You will look at your own use of resources. You will also see that some communities are based on a resource. The rest of this unit will explore natural resources that are gathered in different places around the world.

KEY WORDS

natural resource	**renewable resource**	**hydroelectric power**
metallic minerals		
recycling	**non-renewable resource**	

How do we use natural resources?

How good is your memory? Take a close look at the ten things on the top of the desk in Fig. 13-2. Say the name of each item to yourself. Now cover the picture and see how many of the items you can remember.

How did you do? One good way to remember things is to

Fig. 13-2 Which natural resources would you need to make these objects?

Metallic minerals are deposits of metals such as gold, copper or iron, found in rock.

put them into groups. Look at the drawing again. You could group the objects according to the materials they are made from, which include wood, metal, plastic or paper.

You could also group the objects in the picture based on the resource from which each is made. Some items have been made from trees and some from **metallic minerals** like iron. Anything plastic is made from oil. Glue is based on the skin and bones of animals. Each of these original materials is a **natural resource**. Natural resources are materials found in nature that are useful to people or that people need to live. Water, forests and minerals are examples of natural resources.

Natural resources satisfy human needs and wants. We need food, water, clothing and shelter. We cannot live without these things. There are also things we want, but could live without. Examples include special foods, clothing styles, a new bike or a home computer. A computer itself is not a natural resource but natural resources are needed for the metal, silica chips and plastic used to make it. Natural resources, therefore, are the basic things in nature from which other goods are made. There are seven different natural resources:

- air
- minerals
- animals
- soil
- water
- forests
- energy

Fig. 13-3 People rely on natural resources to satisfy their needs. Can you identify the natural resources shown in these photographs?

Fig. 13-4 Try the Resources Survey—are you "resource-wise"?

NATURAL RESOURCES SURVEY

How do you use natural resources? Answer each of the following questions in your notebook, using Y for Yes, N for No, or U for Unsure.

1. I turn the lights out when I leave my room.
2. I throw away food from my lunch.
3. We save things for recycling at home.
4. I prefer computer games to board games.
5. I write on both sides of my notepaper.
6. I use a lot of hot water for a bath or shower.
7. I would rather have my old bike fixed than get a new one.
8. I would rather get a ride in a car than walk or ride a bike a few blocks.
9. I would rather eat at home than at a "fast food" outlet.
10. I would rather receive my purchase in colourful plastic bags than in paper ones.

ACTIVITY ONE

1. Write a definition for natural resources in your notebook.

2. Use Fig. 13-3 to answer the following questions:
   a) Locate examples of natural resources that are shown in the photographs.
   b) Identify how people use the resources shown in the photographs.

3. Do the Natural Resources Survey in Fig. 13-4, then score your answers in your notebook. For the odd-numbered questions, each Yes equals two points, each Unsure equals one point, and each No equals zero points. For the even-numbered questions, give every Yes zero points, every Unsure one point and every No two points.
   a) Into which category do you fall?

Points	
16-20	Resource-wise
11-15	Becoming resource-wise
0-10	Resource-waster

b) Identify which natural resource each of the questions is about.

4. "Natural resources have no limit. People are smart enough to find new ones if we start to run out of resources." What is your opinion on this statement? Discuss it with your classmates, defending your position.

Learning the three Rs

The question of resource use is an important one. Many people think that we are being careless with our natural resources, and that we may run out of some resources in the future. Questions about the three Rs of resource use— Recycling, Resource waste and Renewable resources, are often in the news.

1. Recycling

Questions 3 and 7 in the Natural Resources Survey were worth two points for a Yes answer because recycling and repairing save resources. **Recycling** things means using them again, often

Recycling means using things over again or finding new uses for them. Recycling helps prevent the waste of these materials and the resources they are made from.

Fig. 13-5 Many communities encourage people to recycle materials rather than to throw them away.

—— RECYCLING ——

A BONUS FOR YOU!

• Local Employment
• Savings on landfill costs and pollution problems
• Assisting all to save our natural resources
  Where and When?

During the week at your curb
Richmond Hill Recycling Corporation operates a curbside pick-up program to coincide with your regular garbage day. Please keep your recyclables about 3 feet away from your garbage to make it easier to see.

Newsprint: tied and bundled, boxed or bagged
Glass Bottles: of ALL types. Labels may be left on bottles
                    and jars – *but PLEASE RINSE*
Pop Cans: as is
Tin Cans: labels removed and flattened
Motor Oil: in suitable closed containers
Saturday Mornings at the Recycling Depot
          Pugsley Ave. (Old Town Maintenance Yard)
          from 10 a.m. to noon

in some other form. Items made from natural resources can often be melted down or cleaned up and reused.

Repairing things rather than buying new ones also saves natural resources. Recycling and repairing help the environment in another way too, by reducing the amount of garbage we produce. Finding places to dispose of garbage is a serious problem for many communities.

2. Resource waste

If you gave a Yes answer to question 9 in the survey, you lost two points. "Fast foods" are foods that are ready when you arrive at the store. They are packaged using cardboard, styrofoam containers or cups, and similar products. After you have eaten, you throw away all the packaging. Sometimes you even throw away some of the food. The chart in Fig. 13-6 shows how this wastes resources.

Fig. 13-6   Did you know that "fast foods" are wasteful?

FOREST RESOURCES	PLANT OR ANIMAL RESOURCES	MINERAL RESOURCES	ENERGY RESOURCES
– paper cups – cardboard – serviettes – paper tray liner – wooden forks or stir-sticks	– unused ketchup packets – unused relish packets – unused mustard packets – uneaten food Note: Any food not sold is thrown out after ten minutes under the warming lamps.	– plastic straws – plastic lids – plastic containers for burger "fixings" – styrofoam burger containers – unused salt	– used to make the packaging – used to keep the food warm until you buy it – used to collect and dispose of the waste – used to gather more resources for more packaging

Fig. 13-7   How do these liquid resources differ?

3. Renewable resources

When you shop, you are usually given plastic bags to carry your purchases. Plastic bags do not rip easily and have convenient carrying handles. Most stores use them rather than paper bags. Plastic bags are made from oil, while paper bags are produced from trees. Why might the use of plastic instead of

paper be a form of resource waste? This is an example of an important question in the use of our natural resources.

Natural resources that can replace themselves in a reasonable length of time are called **renewable resources**. These resources can be renewed by nature. They include animal, plant, forest and water resources. Mineral resources such as metals, coal, oil and gas are called **non-renewable resources**. Nature cannot replace these resources quickly. Millions of years must pass before these minerals can form. Once we have used them up, we cannot expect they will be renewed. This is why you received more points on the survey if you used paper bags instead of plastic bags.

ACTIVITY TWO 📷 ✏️

1. What are the advantages of recycling or repairing?

2. a) Use Fig. 13-5 to identify the items that are recycled in this community.
   b) What natural resource does each of these items represent?

3. How might some of the waste associated with "fast foods" be avoided?

4. a) What would we have to give up to have less waste?
   b) Would you be willing to give up what was necessary?

5. a) Identify the natural resource shown in each photograph in Fig. 13-7.
   b) List three uses for each resource.
   c) Which resource is renewable? Which is non-renewable?

6. Explain the difficulty in using non-renewable resources.

How geographers work: Reading topographic maps

Some maps are used to show the things that are found on the earth's surface. Such maps are called topographic maps. Two things found naturally on the earth's surface are water and land. On a topographic map, everything coloured blue represents water; almost everything else is land, which is usually a shade of brown or green. Sometimes farmed areas or cleared lands are shown in white. Other features on the earth's surface that have been made by humans are shown by symbols that often have the same shapes as the objects they represent. These symbols are usually red or black. Fig. 13-8 shows some common topographic symbols.

Using the topographic map in Fig. 13-8, identify five symbols that represent natural features on the earth's surface, and five that represent human-made features.

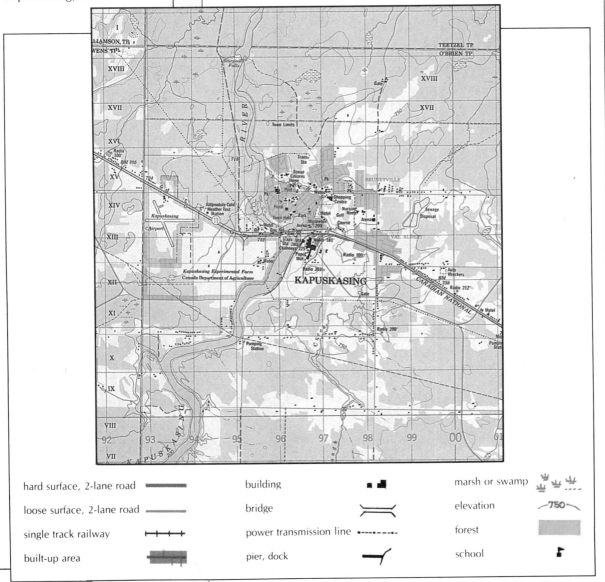

Fig. 13-8   A topographic map and map symbols for Kapuskasing, Ontario.

hard surface, 2-lane road		building		marsh or swamp	
loose surface, 2-lane road		bridge		elevation	
single track railway		power transmission line		forest	
built-up area		pier, dock		school	

0   1   2km

Communities and natural resources

Are natural resources found in your community? Are raw materials made into manufactured goods near where you live? Many communities rely on natural resources for jobs. Let us look at one such community, then you can explore your own.

Craig Schwindt works for Kimberly-Clark of Canada Ltd., a company that makes paper products in Kapuskasing. Kapuskasing is a town of 12 000 people, located in Northern Ontario. Craig can tell you how important forest resources are to Kapuskasing.

"You may not have heard of Kimberly-Clark," said Craig, "but you have likely heard of KLEENEX facial tissues. KLEENEX facial tissues are our largest-selling product and we make them in twenty different countries. We make many other types of paper goods, too, from disposable diapers to newsprint. We make newsprint here at Kapuskasing.

"Kapuskasing has always relied heavily on forest resources. It is part of a huge area covering northern Manitoba, Ontario,

167

Newsprint is a type of thin paper made from wood pulp that is used for the printing of newspapers.

Fig. 13-9 Look closely to find the Kimberly-Clark mill beside the river on this photo and on the topographic map. In which view is the mill larger?

Softwood is a light, loosely grained wood. Pine and spruce are examples of softwood trees.

Hydroelectric power is a form of electricity that is produced by a water-driven turbine. Hydroelectric power plants are often found at the base of a waterfall.

Québec and the Atlantic provinces that is covered by spruce forests. This softwood tree is ideal for making paper products.

"In 1922, the Spruce Falls Power and Paper Company opened a mill to make pulp from wood. The mill brought 500 jobs to the tiny village of Kapuskasing. Many more workers were needed to cut and haul trees to the Kapuskasing River during the winter. In the spring the logs were floated downstream to the mill.

"In 1928, Kimberly-Clark built a paper mill in Kapuskasing to make newsprint. It also built a large **hydroelectric power** plant at Smoky Falls, 80 km north of Kapuskasing. Over the years, the mill has grown bigger and bigger as the world demanded more Canadian paper. Today we produce about 40 boxcar-loads of newsprint a day."

Craig Schwindt has shown us how the community of Kapuskasing depends on natural resources. Are natural resources important to your community?

ACTIVITY THREE

1. a) Using the map in Fig. 13-8, locate the Spruce Falls paper mill.
   b) How could you guess that it is important to the town?

2. Using Fig. 13-8, locate each of the following. How is each important to the paper mill?
   a) town of Kapuskasing
   b) Canadian National Railroad
   c) Kapuskasing River

3. A. 1910 – Railway reaches Kapuskasing. Village founded.
   B. 1913 – Canadian paper allowed to enter U.S. tax-free.
   C. 1922 – Spruce Falls pulp mill opens.
   D. 1928 – Kimberly-Clark paper mill and Smoky Falls power plant open.
   E. 1945 – Wadding mill to make KLEENEX opens.
   F. 1951 – Newsprint mill doubles output.
   G. 1966 – De-barking and wood-chipping mill added.
   H. 1982 – Economy is poor, wadding mill closes.

Make a timeline of these events.
  (i) Draw a line ten centimetres long across a page in your notebook. This line will represent the years 1900 to 2000. Divide the line into ten equal sections (one centimetre for each section). Label each ten-year division.
  (ii) Use the letters A to H to record the eight events at the correct locations along the line. Make a legend to explain what each letter represents.
  (iii) Add your own year of birth and that of one of your parents or grandparents.
  (iv) Complete your timeline by adding a title.

4. a) How would event B affect the forest industry?
   b) How would event H affect the town of Kapuskasing?

5. Find out about natural resources in your community or another community nearby. The following are useful sources of information:
   • atlases and road maps
   • topographic maps
   • local history books or a historical society
   • the local Chamber of Commerce
   • the local conservation authority
   Prepare a sketch map of your community that includes any natural resources the community may use. Record the information you found on a timeline similar to the one you drew in question 3.

WHAT YOU HAVE LEARNED

This chapter introduced you to natural resources. You have seen that people require the products of the earth to satisfy their needs and wants. Sometimes satisfying our wants leads us to waste resources. Recycling and reducing our use of non-renewable products will help to conserve our natural resources.

   You learned how natural resources can affect a community by examining Kapuskasing, Ontario. Many Canadian communities are similar to Kapuskasing. They have grown because they gather natural resources or because they manufacture products made from them. You have also learned to use maps and timelines to show the location and growth of your own community.

Careers in geography: Forester

There are many demands on Canadian forests. Foresters are responsible for managing them for wood production, wildlife habitats and recreation. Each forester is in charge of an area, and looks after the planting, weeding, thinning and harvesting of the trees in that area.

Becoming a registered professional forester requires four years of university, studying forest economics, forest and wildlife management, soil science, computing, and ecology, plus two years of work experience.

Silvia Strobl is a forester working for the Ontario Ministry of Natural Resources.

She is using a technique called intensive forest management. This involves planting genetically-improved seedlings in good soil, near the wood mills. The growing trees are also fertilized, so they will produce wood much faster than "normal" trees. Using this method means that less land will have to be logged, therefore more land can be reserved for recreation and wildlife.

"Intensive forest management can contribute a great deal towards effectively managing our forest resources for the future."

Fig. 13-10 Foresters must try to manage our forest resources to produce the most benefits.

LOOKING BACK

1. a) What is a natural resource?
   b) Name seven types of natural resources identified in this chapter.

2. a) Print the words NATURAL RESOURCES in your notebook. Can you connect all seven types of natural resources to these words?
   Example: NATURAL RESOURCES

   I

   R
   b) Make up a word search that contains all seven natural resources. See if your classmates can find these words.

3. Have your family and friends try the Natural Resources Survey. How do their scores compare with your own? Explain to them why certain answers receive more points.

EXPANDING YOUR LEARNING

4. Find out more about the following focus questions:
   a) How does your community dispose of waste?
   b) How do people in your community recycle some natural resources?
   c) What are the advantages of using refillable pop containers instead of disposable ones?

5. Obtain a topographic map for your community. Locate and identify the important landmarks and roads using the symbols you have learned.

Wheat Farming "Down Under"

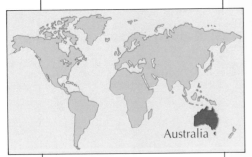

Fig. 14-1 The location you will learn about in this chapter.

WHAT YOU WILL LEARN

The world is made up of many regions. Each region is a special part of the earth. It is special because it has distinctive characteristics in the way people and the environment are linked. Regions make studying the world easier because they are smaller areas, and can be compared to other such areas.

This chapter will look at wheat farming in one region of the world—Australia. You will learn why it is an excellent place in which to grow wheat. You will see how one particular farm works, how wheat is grown and who buys the wheat.

KEY WORDS

export	mid-latitudes	quotas
competitors	irrigation	

Wheat for the world

Advertising has helped the hamburger become a favourite food world-wide, and the popularity of the hamburger helps to support Canada's farm industries. Beef and wheat are important parts of every hamburger, so Canada's beef and wheat farmers benefit from our liking for hamburgers. The extra trimmings—cheese, pickles, mustard, tomatoes, onions and lettuce—help dairy producers and vegetable growers in the same way.

Fig. 14-2   Canada is one of the world's largest wheat exporting countries.

To **export** means to send a product outside the country in which it was produced for sale in another country.

In business, **competitors** are people or countries trying to sell the same products.

Farmers sell many of their products to people within Canada. They also **export** their products to the rest of the world. Canada is among the world leaders in the export of both wheat and beef. Canada's major **competitors** in the production of wheat and beef are Australia and Argentina. In this chapter we will examine one of Canada's competitors in wheat exports— Australia, the land "down under."

Fig. 14-3   The world's ten leading beef-producing countries and their populations. How are the four countries indicated similar?

COUNTRY	POPULATION (in millions)	BEEF PRODUCTION (1984) (in million tonnes)
U.S.A.	236	10.0
U.S.S.R. (1980)	273	6.7
Argentina	30	2.9
Brazil	134	2.5
China	1034	2.5
France	55	2.0
Australia	15	1.6
West Germany	61	1.4
Canada	25	1.2
New Zealand	3	.5

Fig. 14-4   The world's five leading wheat exporters.

COUNTRY	AMOUNT OF WHEAT EXPORTED *(in milllion tonnes)*	
	1980	1984
USA	35.8	38.9
Canada	16.8	21.8
Australia	14.9	11.6
France	9.9	14.0
Argentina	4.5	9.6

ACTIVITY ONE

1. Using Fig. 14-3, determine where Canada ranks in world beef production.

2. a) In Fig. 14-3, what four countries lead the world in beef production? Suggest two reasons why China does not export beef.
   b) Compare the size of the population of the four leading beef producers to the other countries on the list.
   c) Suggest a reason why they are exporters of beef.

3. Which countries appear in both Fig. 14-3 and Fig. 14-4?

4. Using Fig. 14-4 and an atlas,
   a) locate each country on an outline map of the world.
   b) compare each country's location in relation to the Equator.
   c) compare the sizes of the countries in terms of area and population.

5. Name the country in Fig. 14-4 that had a severe drought in 1982-83. How can you tell?

An introduction to Australia

"**G**'day mate! I'll be showing you around a huge wheat farm in Western Australia. First let me tell you about my country. Like Canada, Australia was once occupied only by Native peoples. Australia's Native peoples are the Aborigines. Now, however, people of British ancestry make up about 95% of the population. You can see the British influence when you look at the names of our major cities and states. We also have many names that come from the language of the Aborigines.

"Our two countries are similar in many ways. Both are very large, yet they have fairly small populations. Both are located in the **mid-latitudes**, away from the Equator. There are also huge areas in both countries in which few people live and few crops can grow. In Australia, these areas, called the outback, are hot and dry. There are other huge areas of land in both countries where grain is grown; so much, in fact, that we compete with each other to sell the extra grain we produce on the world market.

"Right, mate. I'll talk to you again soon when I show you one of these wheat-growing areas."

The **mid-latitudes** refers to the areas of the earth located between the Tropic of Cancer and the Arctic Circle, and between the Tropic of Capricorn and the Antarctic Circle.

CANADA	AUSTRALIA
Ottawa	Geelong
Chicoutimi	Wollongong
Saskatoon	Toowoomba
Inuvik	Wagga Wagga

Fig. 14-5 Many place names in Canada and Australia reflect the languages of the Native peoples of each country.

Fig. 14-6 Australia's states, territories and major cities.

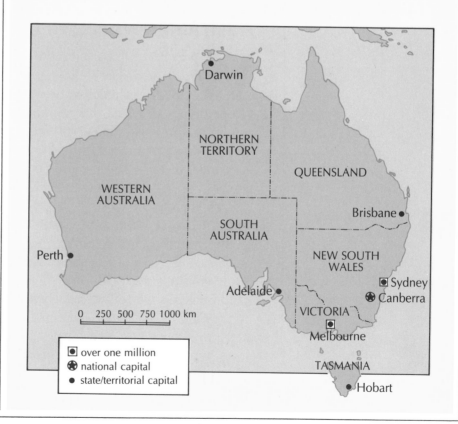

ACTIVITY TWO

1. Copy the chart in Fig. 14-5 into your notebook. Using an atlas or wall maps, find three or more names to add to each list.

2. Use an atlas to list the names of some Canadian cities that show the influence of the British and French inhabitants of Canada.

3. Use Fig. 14-6 to identify
   a) the largest state or territory.
   b) the smallest state or territory.

4. In what part of Australia are most cities found?

5. Find three similarities between Australia and Canada.

The location and climate of Australia's wheatlands

Wheat is a grassland crop which can be grown in fairly dry areas (areas that receive only 400 to 800 millimetres of precipitation yearly). Scientists have developed types of wheat that are able to survive harsh weather conditions. In Australia, wheat is planted during the winter season. To grow successfully, the wheat must be able to resist occasional drought and it must ripen before the hot summer begins. Fig. 14-7 shows the two wheat belts in Australia.

Each summer in Western Australia is very dry, but in the winter the winds shift north. These winds blow across the Indian Ocean from May to September and come up against the low mountains of Western Australia. Orographic precipitation results, as the moist air rises and forms clouds. Enough of this precipitation reaches the rolling hills behind the town of Geraldton, north of Perth, to allow wheat and other grains to grow and sheep to survive. As well, crops are grown in some of the dry areas by using **irrigation**, the process of watering crops or other plants by using sprinklers, canals or wells. Wells are dug in this area to provide a source of water for irrigation.

Fig. 14-7 What is the link between Australia's precipitation patterns and its wheat belts?

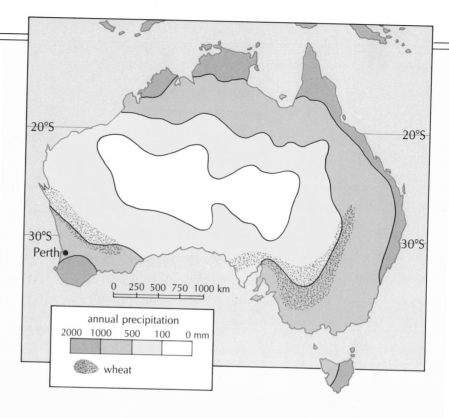

PERTH, AUSTRALIA
Elevation 60 m

	J	F	M	A	M	J	J	A	S	O	N	D
mm	8	10	20	43	130	180	170	149	86	56	20	13
°C	20	20	18	15	13	10	9	11	13	14	16	18

Fig. 14-8 Climate data for the city of Perth. What do these figures show?

ACTIVITY THREE 🌐 📝 🏛️

1. Using Fig. 14-7, identify the patterns of precipitation. How much rain falls
   a) in the interior?
   b) on the coast?

2. Identify where Australian wheat is grown as shown on Fig. 14-7. What is
   a) the approximate latitude?
   b) the approximate amount of precipitation?

3. Suggest why wheat is not grown in
   a) the interior.
   b) the north.

4. Use Fig. 14-8 and 14-9 to answer the following questions about the climate for the city of Perth:
   a) When is it hot and dry?
   b) When is it cool and wet?
   c) Suggest why wheat is planted in May instead of September.

5. Use the map in Fig. 14-9 to answer the following:
   a) Why does it rain in the Perth area?
   b) How much precipitation is needed to grow wheat?
   c) Find the location of the wheat-growing area on this map by comparing it to Fig. 14-7.

6. Why is it hot in Australia in January?

Fig. 14-9   The wheat belt in Western Australia.

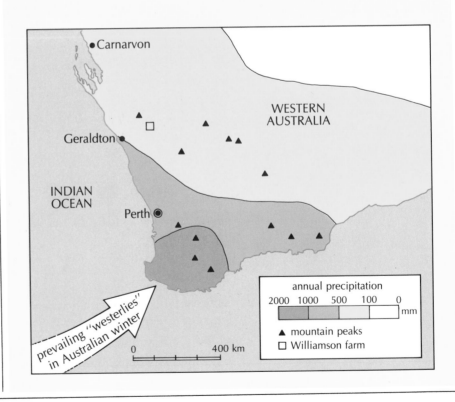

A visit to an Australian wheat farm

"G'day again, mate. I said I'd show you a wheat-growing area. This is the Williamson Farm in Western Australia. (See Fig. 14-9.) We'll have to see it by truck because it covers 25 000 hectares. That's an area nearly 15 kilometres square! The farm is so large that the family who owns it lives in several different farmsteads scattered across the property. Look at the map in Fig. 14-11 to see just how big it really is.

"In addition to growing wheat, they also raise sheep. This makes the farm less dependent on one crop and gives the wheat fields a chance to "rest" by becoming pastureland for a while. I believe you Canadians usually leave your wheat fields

Farmsteads are a cluster of farm buildings, houses and barns. More than one farmstead may be found on a large farm.

Fig. 14-10 Why do many Australian wheat farmers also raise sheep?

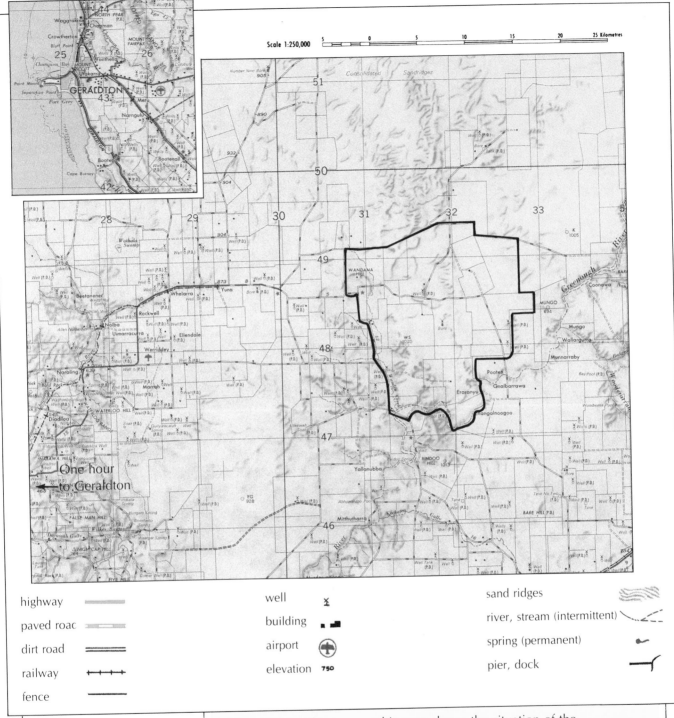

Fig. 14-11 This topographic map shows the situation of the Williamson Farm, near Geraldton, Australia.

unplanted or ''fallow'' for a year or so to allow the soil to recover.

"Western Australia grows more wheat than any other area in Australia. The wheat farmers have a very busy year. During the hot, dry weather in January and February we have to be sure to keep the sheep watered. Fields must be ploughed and planted in the autumn. Oats are planted in April, and barley and wheat are planted in May.

"When the grain crops are planted we spend our time looking after the sheep. New lambs are born in June. By mid-winter (July and August) the sheep are turned out to graze. Just before shearing time in September, we have to spray the weeds in the grain fields. Professional shearers travel about from farm to farm. Using electric clippers, they shear the wool from each sheep in two or three minutes.

"Crops are harvested in late spring—oats in October, barley and wheat in November. December is spent taking the grain to market. By Christmas everyone is ready for a holiday in this place!"

ACTIVITY FOUR

Using Fig. 14-11, answer the following questions:
1. List three examples of
   a) aboriginal place names.
   b) British place names.

2. a) Use the legend to locate the following:
   • a hilly area on the west side of the map
   • a sandy area on the north side of the map
   • the Greenough River
   • the Williamson Farm
3. a) How many of each of the following are shown on the Williamson Farm?
   • farmsteads
   • wells
   • fenced fields
   b) What is the purpose of the wells?

Shearing is cutting or clipping the wool from sheep or other animals.

4. Use the map scale to measure the maximum size of the Williamson Farm in kilometres
   a) from north to south.
   b) from east to west.

5. List evidence on the map that suggests that this is a fairly dry area.

6. Why are the farmers ready for a rest in December?

Wheat growing and marketing

Australia has a Wheat Board that sets **quotas** on the amount of wheat farmers can grow. This board began in 1969 because there was such a large crop of wheat that year. Farmers could not sell all their crops because there was too much wheat produced, and this caused the price of wheat to drop. Ever since, the Wheat Board has used quotas to limit the amount of wheat that each farmer can grow. Many farmers grow crops such as barley and oats, or graze more sheep on their pastures instead.

This affects how much money the farmers can get for their products. There is another factor involved, however, and that factor is the world demand for each of these products. Farmers produce as much of their product as people want to buy.

Fig. 14-12 Australian wheat sales in 1980. These countries are the biggest customers for wheat exported from Australia.

COUNTRY	POPULATION (in millions)	AUSTRALIAN WHEAT BOUGHT (in millions of Australian dollars)
China	1034	453
U.S.S.R.	273	432
Egypt	47	251
Iraq	15	179
Japan	120	147

ACTIVITY FIVE

1. a) What are quotas?
   b) How do quotas affect farmers?

2. a) Look at Fig. 14-11 and find four different types of transportation at Geraldton.
   b) Why do railways and highways lead to ports?

3. Suggest three different ways in which Geraldton serves the Williamson Farm.

4. Locate the countries in Fig. 14-12 on a map of the world.
   a) Identify two main regions of the world in which they are located.
   b) Which two of these countries would be the easiest to reach from Geraldton?

5. Find out to which of these countries Canada usually sells wheat.

6. China and the U.S.S.R. grow large amounts of wheat. Why do they also import it?

WHAT YOU HAVE LEARNED

In this chapter you have learned about one particular region of the world—Australia. You have seen that Canada and Australia are similar in three ways: their position in relation to the Equator; their cultural backgrounds; and their relatively small populations in relation to the size of each country. You have visited an Australian farm, and you have seen that there is more to farming than just planting and harvesting. The amount grown and sold depends on outside forces such as the Wheat Marketing Boards and world demand for the product. Are Canadian farmers affected by similar considerations?

LOOKING BACK

1. Define each of the following words:
   - farmstead
   - outback
   - quotas
   - irrigation
   - fallow

2. What effect has each of the following had on the Williamson Farm?
   a) the introduction of sheep
   b) Wheat Board quotas

3. Draw a circle calendar. First, draw a large circle and divide it into 12 equal parts. Start with the month of January at the top and mark on it the work that is done on the Williamson Farm in January, then complete the calendar by filling in the work done in each month of the year.

EXPANDING YOUR LEARNING

4. Create a brochure describing the Williamson Farm and the surrounding area to encourage people to come and visit the area.

5. Research the seasonal cycle of wheat production on a Canadian Prairie farm. How is it affected by the climate?

15

Beef Ranching in Argentina

WHAT YOU WILL LEARN

A regional study looks at how people and their environment are linked in one part of the earth. Patterns found in one region can be compared with other areas.

In this chapter, you will learn about beef ranching in Argentina, in the plains region called the Pampas. At one large ranch named the Estancia San Martín, you will see that beef production in Argentina is a big business. Finally, you will look into the future to see if these large ranches will be able to keep up in the world markets.

Fig. 15-1 The location you will learn about in this chapter.

KEY WORDS

import	market	Pampas
parent material		
estancia		

Hamburger geography

The last chapter introduced wheat farming by using the hamburger. This product has an even more important influence on beef ranching. Canadians and Americans each eat about 35 kg of beef every year, much of it as hamburgers. Stacked one on top of another, this number of hamburgers would almost reach the moon! Did you know that the hamburger got its name from geography?

Fig. 15-2 Guaranteed 100% pure beef patty on a sesame seed bun. Couldn't you go for one right now?

A **market** is a central place where products and livestock may be brought and sold.

To **import** products means to bring them from other countries into one's own country.

hamburger (ham′ ber gər) n., a flat cake of ground beef that is fried or broiled and usually served on a roll or a bun. The word ''hamburger'' comes from Hamburger steak or Hamburg steak, named after the city of Hamburg in Germany. No one knows why hamburgers came to be named after this city in Germany.

Let us look at some other ''hamburger geography.'' Where does the beef for one of North America's favourite foods come from? Beef does not stay fresh very long. It can be refrigerated or frozen, but this is quite expensive. It is easiest to ship live animals to **market.** Most Canadian hamburgers are made with all-Canadian beef. That is because Canada produces more beef cattle than it needs. The United States is the largest producer of beef in the world, but Americans eat more beef than their farmers raise. Look at Fig. 15-3. Which of these countries can export live cattle to the United States most easily?

North America **imports** beef from South America, especially Argentina and Brazil. These countries are too far away to ship their animals live. Because of the high cost of refrigeration,

COUNTRY	BEEF PRODUCTION (in million tonnes)
Canada	1.2
U.S.A.	10.0
Mexico	.8
Venezuela	.4
Brazil	2.5
Argentina	2.9

Fig. 15-3   Beef production in North and South America.

Fig. 15-4   Competition in beef production.

A duty is a tax paid to the government on goods coming into the country (imports) or being sent to another country (exports).

most Argentine beef does not arrive fresh, but is shipped in cans or as processed meat. Therefore, you are more likely to eat it in your sandwiches than in your hamburgers.

U.S. cattle producers cool demand for duty on Canadian imports

WINNIPEG (CP)—Cattle producers south of the border have cooled their demands for duties on Canadian cattle exports to the United States, says the vice-president of the Canadian Cattlemen's Association.

Charlie Gracey said that Canadian prices for beef are now rising due to shortages of beef. This means that Canadian beef is no longer cheaper to buy than U.S. beef, therefore the Canadian beef imports no longer threaten the sales of U.S. beef.

Also, U.S. cattle producers are now more concerned with Mexican cattle exports which have been flooding into southern U.S. states for the past year. About one million cattle were trucked into the U.S. from Mexico last year, Gracey said.

Last year, about 251 000 cattle were exported to the U.S. from Canada. American cattle producers had been calling for an import duty to help fight off Canadian competition.

ACTIVITY ONE

1. a) Locate the countries in Fig. 15-3 in an atlas or on a map.
   b) Use Fig. 15-3 to find out how much beef is produced by each country.

2. Draw and label an outline map showing the countries in Fig. 15-3 and the amount of beef each produces.

3. Where does Canada rank in beef production?

4. Do Canada's hamburgers contain beef from Argentina? Why or why not?

5. Read the newspaper article in Fig. 15-4. Who competes with U.S. cattle ranchers?

6. What is an import duty?

7. Give two reasons why U.S. ranchers no longer want a duty on Canadian beef cattle.

8. Do you think import duties to protect American farmers are fair to Canadian farmers? Explain your answer.

Argentina: The people and the environment

Argentina is the home of people from many different cultures. People of Native, Spanish and Italian backgrounds and many other European cultures are represented in the population. The Spanish influence can be seen in the place names.

Buenos Aires is the capital of Argentina, and the largest port in the country. This city is one of the world's largest, with a population of almost 12 million people. More than one third of the people of Argentina live in Buenos Aires. Most of the remaining two thirds live in the fertile district called the **Pampas**, which lies west and south of the capital.

Argentina's richest resource is its farmland. The crops and the animals of the Pampas provide the country with food and exports. The Pampas has fertile soils and a climate suited to both crop and livestock farming. Decaying natural grasses have built up a thick layer of humus in the topsoil. Beneath this thick layer is a base of fine wind-blown deposits called **parent material.**

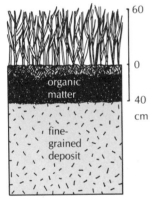

Fig. 15-5 A soil profile of the Pampas region.

Parent material is the rock from which soil is formed.

Fig. 15-7 Argentina, showing the Pampas, cities and transportation lines.

Estancias are ranches in Argentina that cover vast areas.

BAHÍA BLANCA
Elevation 29 m

	J	F	M	A	M	J	J	A	S	O	N	D
mm	48	63	59	56	36	15	24	16	43	70	47	54
°C	24	22	20	17	13	10	9	10	12	15	20	23

Fig. 15-6   Climate information for Bahía Blanca, a city on the edge of the Pampas.

ACTIVITY TWO

1. a) What is humus?   b) What is parent material?

2. What is the origin of each of these layers?

3. What part of Canada is most like the Pampas?

4. a) Locate Bahía Blanca on the map of Argentina in Fig. 15-7.
   b) Suggest why inland parts of the Pampas are drier than Bahía Blanca.

5. Use Fig. 15-6 to draw and label a climate graph for Bahía Blanca.
   a) Which months are the warmest?
   b) Which months are cool and dry?

Raising beef in Argentina

When Spanish colonists came to the Pampas in the late 1700s, they began to raise cattle. They produced beef for the local area on large ranches. When refrigeration was invented around 1876, frozen beef could be shipped to British markets. Therefore, cattle ranching became more profitable, and the size of the ranches increased.

Argentina's large cattle ranches are called **estancias.** There are different kinds of estancias. This is because the land in different parts of the Pampas has many uses. In the north and east sections of the Pampas, the wet soil conditions allow only the natural grasses to grow. These grasses provide grazing for

Fig. 15-8 Land use on the Pampas.

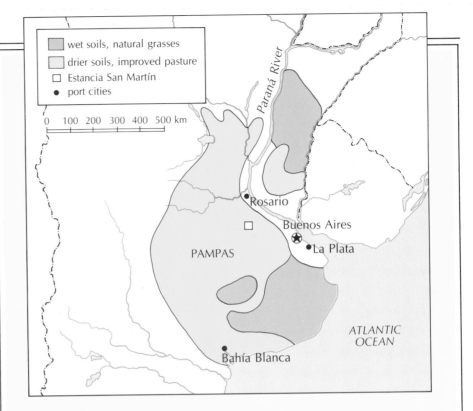

calves. Young cattle are raised in this area. When they are older and almost ready for market, they are shipped to the south and west to be fattened. Because there is less rainfall here than in the north, the soil is more fertile and provides better grazing pastures for the cattle. The animals are then shipped from the south and west to major ports for market.

In the next activity, you will use a topographic map to study the operation of one large ranch, the Estancia San Martín.

Fig. 15-9 In Argentina, the cowboys are called gauchos.

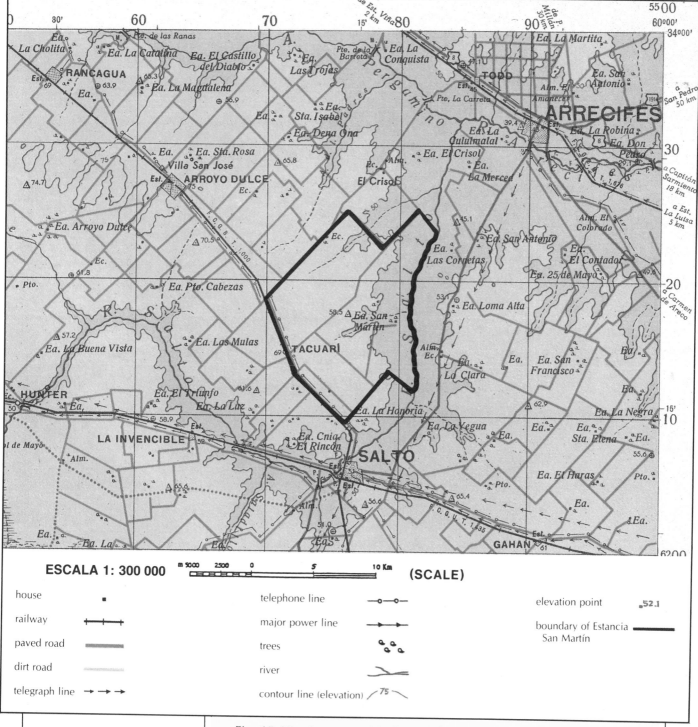

Fig. 15-10   A topographical map of the Estancia San Martín, on the Pampas.

ACTIVITY THREE 🌐 📝

1. a) Use the map in Fig. 15-8 to locate the land that is less fertile.
   b) Locate the better grazing areas on the Pampas.

2. Use the map in Fig. 15-8 to find out what area the Estancia San Martín is in.

3. Use the map and legend in Fig. 15-10 to locate the following:
   a) the Pergamino River   c) a small city
   b) the River Salto   d) a large town

4. The small numbers with a △ or ⊕ beside them indicate the height of the land in metres. Find some of these symbols near the centre of the map. Are the numbers similar or different? Does this show that the land is flat or hilly?

5. Find the Estancia (Ea) San Martín on Fig. 15-10. Why would each of the following be valuable to this ranch?
   a) the River Salto
   b) the railroad
   c) the dirt roads
   d) the trees planted by the farmsteads

6. a) Use the map scale on Fig. 15-10 to measure the maximum length and width of the estancia.
   b) Suggest the names of other ranches that might be as big as the Estancia San Martín.

The future of the estancia

There are two different kinds of farms on the Argentine Pampas—estancias and smaller farms. The estancias are huge beef ranches that cover more than half the Pampas region. They are usually owned by wealthy families who live in Buenos Aires. Most estancias have remained in the same family for many generations. The families employ managers to operate the ranch or they rent sections of the land to tenant farmers.

Tenant farmers are farmers who live and work on land they rent from the landowner.

Fig. 15-11 Estancia San Martín. An aerial photograph of the owner's farmstead.

Argentine farm experts are worried. Many estancias are not being used as well as they could be. In the past generation or so there has been little effort to fertilize and improve the pastures. The soil, which was once very fertile, is becoming less nourishing for the cattle. New breeds of cattle are not being developed. Farm experts say that the owners should invest more in their ranches. The owners say they cannot afford to do so, because they must pay heavy taxes. They also say that they are having trouble selling their beef to North America and Europe because they face so much competition from other countries, such as Canada. The estancia faces an uncertain future.

ACTIVITY FOUR

1. Fig. 15-11 is a photograph of the Estancia San Martín. How would you describe the Argentine Pampas as shown in this photograph?

2. List evidence you see in Fig. 15-11 that this is a large and prosperous estancia.

3. a) How can you tell that this estancia also raises grain crops?
   b) Why would it be wise to produce both crops and cattle?

4. Locate the following features in Fig. 15-11:
   a) the horizon
   b) the farm lane leading toward the road
   c) a horse barn along this lane
   d) other treed lanes leading out of the fields
   e) a roofed enclosure for feeding and watering cattle
   f) managers' and workers' houses on the property
   g) a windmill waterpump behind the owner's house

5. From what you have learned, evaluate the problems the estancias face. Do you think these problems can be solved?

WHAT YOU HAVE LEARNED

In this chapter, you have learned about beef production in Argentina. You have seen that the market for beef is very competitive. You learned the Argentine Pampas is an area well-suited for farming because of a thick layer of humus in the soil, which promotes plant growth. Finally, you looked at the estancias as big businesses that are having difficulty competing in the world market for beef.

LOOKING BACK

1. What do the following terms mean?
   a) gaucho
   b) estancia
   c) to import

2. Explain the importance of each of the following:
   a) humus
   b) the north and east sections of the Pampas
   c) the south and west sections of the Pampas

3. On a map of the Pampas, trace the movement of cattle from birth to export.

EXPANDING YOUR LEARNING

4. a) Find a world map showing income levels of countries.
   b) Decide whether or not there are potential buyers for Argentina's beef outside Europe and North America.

5. Prepare a short report recommending what the Argentine ranchers should do about the problems of investment and markets.

6. Design and prepare a poster or brochure that could be used to attract increased sales and investment in beef.

7. Visit the canned meat section of your grocery store. Look on the cans to find where these products originate. Locate these countries on a map of the world.

8. Would you like to work on a farm similar to the Estancia San Martín? Explain your reasons.

South Africa: Mineral Storehouse

196

Fig. 16-1   The location you will learn about in this chapter.

WHAT YOU WILL LEARN

The major focus of this chapter is also on a particular region. By looking at the unique features of the region, you will be able to understand more about its resources.

In this chapter, you will look at the gold-rich region of South Africa. You will see that gold is a non-renewable resource, and learn how it is mined in South Africa. Finally, you will learn a little about the South African government's policy of apartheid.

KEY WORDS

fossil fuels	reefs	stope
apartheid	troy ounce	reserve

Our world's resources

Think for a moment about the natural resources you have learned about in this unit. First you looked at a paper mill in northern Ontario, then at a wheat farm in Western Australia, and in the previous chapter you studied a cattle ranch in Argentina. What do all these resources—trees, grain, and cattle— have in common? All are living things that are able to reproduce, or renew themselves. Therefore, they are renewable resources.

Gold is the most easily shaped and stretched metal. One troy ounce (30 grams) can be spun into a thin wire strand eight kilometres long.

Gold is very rare. If all the gold ever mined were melted down, it would only fill a 20-room school.

Gold is usually found in seams, or reefs, in the earth's crust. Two thirds of the world's present supply is found near Johannesburg in the Republic of South Africa.

Gold coins are a popular investment. In 1956, Canada's 14-karat Maple Leaf coin made up 70% of gold coin sales in the world.

Large amounts of gold float in the oceans. Approximately ten billion tons of fine gold flakes are suspended in the ocean waters. At present, we cannot afford to "mine" this gold.

Gold is sometimes found in chunks called nuggets. The "Welcome Stranger" nugget, found in Australia in 1872, was 99% pure gold and weighed almost 100 kilograms!

Gold film is used to coat glass on buildings such as the Royal Bank Plaza. It cools the building in summer by reflecting 90% of the sun's heat.

Gold is very valuable. The price rises and falls regularly, but it reached a high of $855 for one troy ounce (30 grams) in 1980.

Fig. 16-2 Golden nuggets: facts about gold.

Fossil fuels are resources such as coal and oil that were formed millions of years ago from the fossils of sea creatures.

Other natural resources are not renewable. Oil, for example, requires millions of years to form. It originates as the crushed shells of tiny animals that lived in ancient seas. Once it is brought to the earth's surface and used, oil is gone forever. Coal is another **fossil fuel** that is not renewable.

Metallic minerals such as iron, copper, lead and zinc are another kind of non-renewable resource. They were formed over millions of years during ancient periods of volcanic activity.

Today, some metallic minerals, such as gold, silver, and platinum, are found only in rare pockets, and are therefore of great value. Once they are removed from the earth, they cannot be replaced within a reasonable time by natural means. Gold is one of the rarest and most valuable of these non-renewable resources.

ACTIVITY ONE

1. Is gold a renewable resource? Explain why or why not.

2. Use the information in Fig. 16-2 to explain
   a) why gold is so expensive.
   b) how gold can be used.
   c) where gold can be found.

3. Find out the meaning for each of these terms related to gold:
   - placer mining
   - karat
   - bullion
   - assay
   - gold rush

4. Gold is often measured by the **troy ounce**, a weight measurement used for gold and silver that equals approximately 30 grams. The price of gold per troy ounce is announced every day in the newspapers, and on radio and television.
   a) Follow the price every day for a week to find out if it is rising or falling.
   b) Plot your results on a bar graph.
   c) Explain the reasons for the changes in the price of gold.

Gold in South Africa

South Africa is an incredible storehouse of mineral wealth. It leads the world in the mining of several precious metals. Fig. 16-3 and 16-4 show how many of the earth's valuable minerals are found in South Africa.

South Africa's gold is found in the Transvaal, the state north of the Vaal River. Dutch settlers, who called themselves Afrikaaners, came to this area in the 1830s. The settlers forced

Fig. 16-3 This graph shows South Africa's percentage of the world's reserves of six minerals. A **reserve** is the amount of a mineral resource that we are able to recover from the earth.

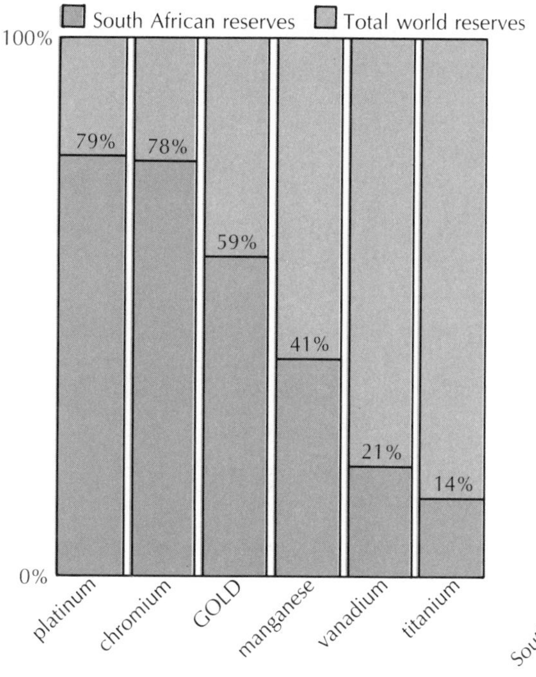

□ South African reserves □ Total world reserves

100%

79% 78%

59%

41%

21%

14%

0%

platinum chromium GOLD manganese vanadium titanium

Fig. 16-4 How the world's gold reserves are divided, by percent. What percent of the world's gold do the top five countries share?

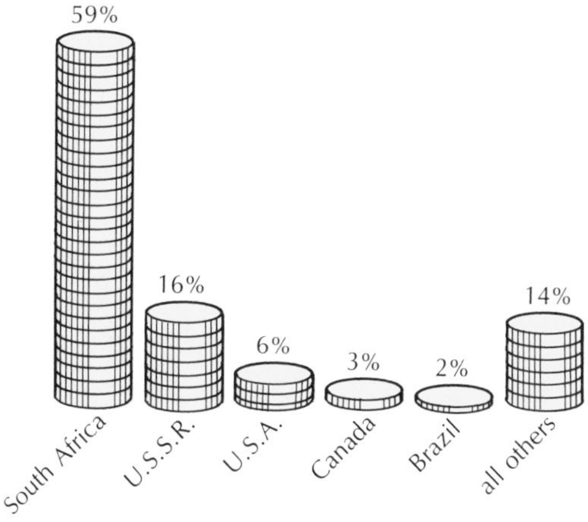

59%

16%

6% 3% 2%

14%

South Africa U.S.S.R. U.S.A. Canada Brazil all others

Fig. 16-5 The Republic of South Africa.

□ Transvaal
⊛ capital
• major city

0 100 200 300 km

Limpopo River

Pretoria

Johannesburg SWAZILAND

Vaal River

Orange River

LESOTHO

Durban

REPUBLIC OF SOUTH AFRICA

ATLANTIC OCEAN

INDIAN OCEAN

⊛ Cape Town Port Elizabeth

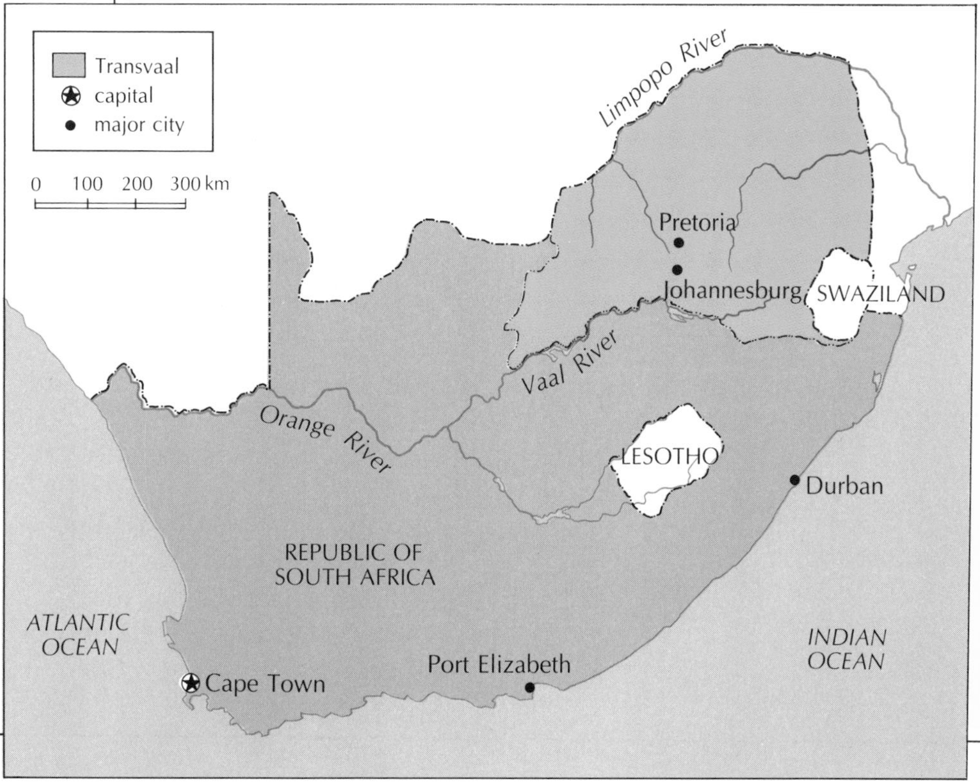

Fig. 16-6 Crossroads is an illegal camp outside Cape Town, built to allow city workers to live with their families.

Fig. 16-7 The policy of apartheid requires separating people according to their race.

the Africans who lived in the area to leave, in much the same way as the European settlers did to North America's Native peoples. In 1884, a huge ridge of gold was discovered in the Transvaal and the community of Johannesburg grew up beside the gold deposits. Today, Johannesburg is the fourth largest city on the African continent, with 1.9 million people.

Although Johannesburg has grown rich on the gold mines located close to it, this wealth is not shared by all South Africans. In 1948, the South African government began a policy called **apartheid.** Under the apartheid system, South Africans are divided by law into groups on the basis of race. The government has defined four groups—Whites, Africans, Coloureds (mixed race) and Asians. The whites, who make up less than 17% of the population, control the government and the economy. Africans, who make up over 70% of the population, face many restrictions. They are only allowed to live in certain areas. These areas are often locations too far from the cities they work in to allow Africans to live at home with their families. African workers are only able to work at certain jobs, and are paid much less than white workers, as you can see in Fig. 16-8. People and governments around the world are trying to get the South African government to change its policies. So far there has been little success.

WAGES IN SELECTED INDUSTRIES *(Average monthly wage in U.S. dollars)*		
Industry	*Africans*	*Whites*
Mining (1983)	$260	$1 395
Manufacturing (1983)	$320	$1 290
Agriculture (1980)	$28-40	N.A.
Unemployed (1984)	est. 25%	N.A.

Fig. 16-8   Monthly wages, in United States dollars, for workers in three South African industries.

ACTIVITY TWO

1. Use a dictionary to match South Africa's six leading precious metals, shown in Fig. 16-3, to the following descriptions and uses.
   a) A hard silvery metal that does not rust or become dull. It is used on car bumpers and trim.
   b) A heavy yellow metal used to make jewellery and coins.
   c) A brittle silver-grey metal used in the making of steel.
   d) A soft metal similar to silver, but that does not tarnish. It is used in the making of jewellery and watches.
   e) A silver-grey metal that is strong and very light. It is used in the aircraft and space industries.
   f) A greyish metal that is easily workable. Most often it is used to make steel.

2. Use the photographs in Fig. 16-6 and 16-7 to help you to explain what is meant by the term apartheid.

3. Use the scale in Fig. 16-5 to measure the following:
   a) the distance from Cape Town to Johannesburg
   b) the length of the country—Cape Town to north Transvaal
   c) the width of the country—Durban to the mouth of the Orange River.

4. Discuss possible reasons for the system of apartheid in South Africa. Collect newspaper articles on current events in South Africa and speculate on what you think might happen in the future.

5. Use Fig. 16-8 to answer the following questions:
   a) How many times greater are the earnings of the whites working in mining compared to the Africans working in mining?

b) From what you have learned, why is this so?

c) How much would Africans working on a farm earn in one year?

Mining in South Africa

South African gold mining is similar in many ways to Canadian gold mining in Val d'Or, Québec or Yellowknife, Northwest Territories. One difference, however, is the depth of the mine shafts. Shafts in Johannesburg's gold mines are much deeper than those in Canada, extending more than three kilometres below the surface of the earth. Because

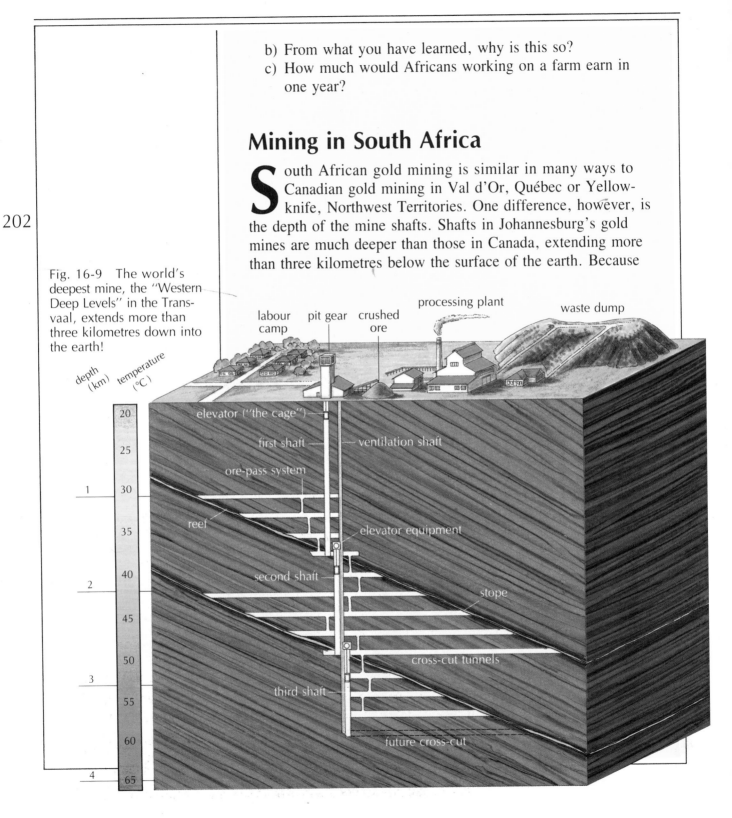

Fig. 16-9 The world's deepest mine, the "Western Deep Levels" in the Transvaal, extends more than three kilometres down into the earth!

depth (km)   temperature (°C)

labour camp   pit gear   crushed ore   processing plant   waste dump

elevator ("the cage")
first shaft — ventilation shaft
ore-pass system
reef
elevator equipment
second shaft
stope
cross-cut tunnels
third shaft
future cross-cut

Reefs are veins of metallic minerals found beneath the surface of the earth. For example, gold is a mineral found in reefs.

Fig. 16-10   Miners working a stope in a gold mine 2.5 km below the surface. Find this area on Fig. 16-9.

the mine shafts are so deep, temperatures are extremely high, even when cool air is pumped down into the shafts from the surface. Only very fit and healthy miners can work in conditions much below a depth of one and one-half kilometres.

In both Canadian and South African mines, new mine tunnels are blasted out at night, so the dust settles by the time the miners go down to work in the morning. Horizontal cross-cut tunnels are cut at different depths across the vertical shaft to get to the gold **reefs** where the ore is drilled. The drilling area, or working face, is called a **stope**. It is very hot and humid at the stope. Water sprays from the end of the drills in order to prevent sparks, which could cause the dust to explode. South African miners often have to sit down to drill, working their drills with their feet, because the seam of gold may only be 30 to 50 centimetres wide.

The chunks of rock that are blasted and drilled out are then pushed by small scoop-loaders to openings in the mine floor. These openings lead to the ''ore-pass system,'' a chamber through which rocks crash down to the very bottom of the mine. Now broken and crushed, the rock is lifted to the surface to be processed. Gold mines in South Africa produce about one troy ounce (30 grams) of gold from every two tonnes of ore, while some Canadian gold mines must mine nine tonnes of ore to produce the same troy ounce of gold.

ACTIVITY THREE

1. What are the similarities and differences in gold mining between South Africa and Canada?

2. Look at Fig. 16-9, the diagram of the Western Deep Level Mine. Find the following and explain the meaning or purpose of each:
   - reefs
   - shafts
   - stope
   - cross-cuts
   - pit gear
   - ore-pass system

3. Look at the drawing in Fig. 16-10 of the miners working a stope.
   a) Explain what is happening in the drawing.
   b) Where is the gold reef?
   c) Where does the ore go from here?

4. Find the location of the drawing (Fig. 16-10) in the mine diagram (Fig.16-9).
   a) At what depth are the miners working?
   b) What would the temperature be there without ventilation?
   c) Write an accurate description of the route these miners followed from the labour camp using mining vocabulary.

WHAT YOU HAVE LEARNED

You have seen that gold, other metallic minerals and fossil fuels are non-renewable resources because they require special conditions and a time period of millions of years to form. Therefore, these mineral resources are very valuable. You have seen how gold is mined in South Africa. Finally, you have some understanding of the problems faced by the miners themselves in South Africa as they work under the apartheid system.

LOOKING BACK

1. Explain why certain resources, such as gold, are non-renewable.

2. Define the following terms:
   a) troy ounce   b) reefs   c) apartheid

3. Imagine you are a miner working in the Western Deep Level Mine. Describe the working conditions you experience.

EXPANDING YOUR LEARNING

THE MINERS

This dungeon
Makes the mind weary
Kneaded with the sight of
A million stones
Passing through my hands
I see the flesh sticking like hair
On thorns
Against the grating rocks
Of these hills dug for gold.
And life is bitter here.
Crawling through the day
In a sleepwalker's dream.
Frightening the night away with my snores.
I dream of the diminished breath
Of miners planted in the stones—
The world is not at ease
But quakes under the march of our boots
Tramping the dust under our feet . . .

Click, clack, our picks knock for life
Until the eyes are dazed
Counting the rubble of scattered stones.
Day and night are one.
But I know each day dawns
And the heated sun licks every shrub dry
While we who burrow the earth
Tame the dust with our lungs.
. . . .

And so
Clap, scrape
With our hands manacled
With weariness
We mine
All our lives
Till the mind is numb
And ceases to ask. . . .

Mafika Mbali
South African poet

Fig. 16-11 How does this poem make you feel about mining in South Africa?

4. Read the poem *The Miners* and answer the following questions:
   a) What is "this dungeon" in the first line?
   b) Which phrase names the mineral being mined here?
   c) Name three dangers of mining mentioned in this poem.
   d) Find phrases that show how the miner feels.
   e) How does the poet make the mine seem to be a prison?

The Fall of the Hull Fishing Fleet

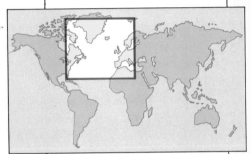

Fig. 17-1 The locations you will learn about in this chapter.

WHAT YOU WILL LEARN

People and places interact with one another in many ways. This interaction can change over time. It can also be affected by the introduction of new technology, by changes in the supply of resources or in the demand for them, and by the decisions that governments make.

In this chapter you will see both positive and negative effects of the interaction between people and their environment, by learning about the Hull fishing fleet. You will learn where fish are found and what has caused their numbers to drop over the years. You will also learn about various government policies to protect fishing fleets and fishing grounds.

KEY WORDS

supply	**marine pastures**	**food chain**
demand	**phytoplankton**	**trawlers**
nautical mile	**zooplankton**	

Fishing: A resource industry

Have you ever been in business delivering papers or selling lemonade? If so, you offered a product for sale, the papers or the lemonade. Resource businesses, like lumbering, farming, mining and fishing also offer a product for sale.

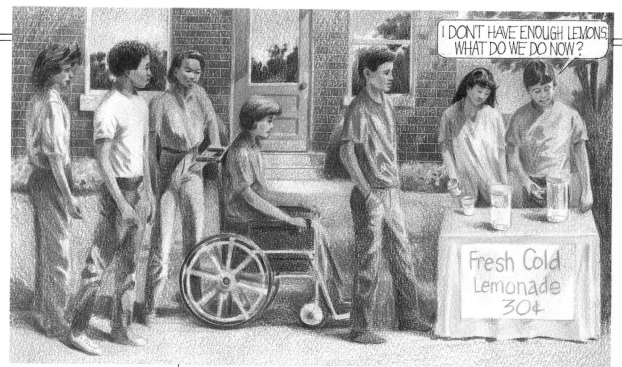

Fig. 17-2 What difficulty is this business facing?

Supply, in economics, is the amount of a particular product or service offered for sale.

Demand, in economics, is the amount of a particular product or service that people want to buy.

When running your own business, you need a supply of your product and people to create a demand for it. In much the same way, resource businesses depend on a steady **supply** of their resource and a steady **demand** for their product in order to flourish. They also face competition from other businesses, as you would if someone set up a business similar to yours. In addition, resource businesses can be affected by political events, war and new technology.

In this chapter, we will look at the fishing industry. It is a good example of how resource businesses operate. The fishing industry has experienced many changes in recent years.

ACTIVITY ONE

1. a) What is meant by the terms "supply" and "demand"?
   b) How does each affect resource businesses?

2. What other factors affect resource businesses?

3. With a group of students, plan a small business.
   a) Choose a product to sell (for example, T-shirts, hats or boxes of chocolates).

b) Identify
  • what you need to get started
  • how much to charge
  • where to locate your business
  • who will buy your product

Where the fish are

The world has an abundant supply of fish. Over 70 percent of the world is covered by oceans, although fish are not found in all parts of the oceans. There are two areas where fish are plentiful. The first area is along the coastlines of continents. Rivers wash minerals from the land into the sea along

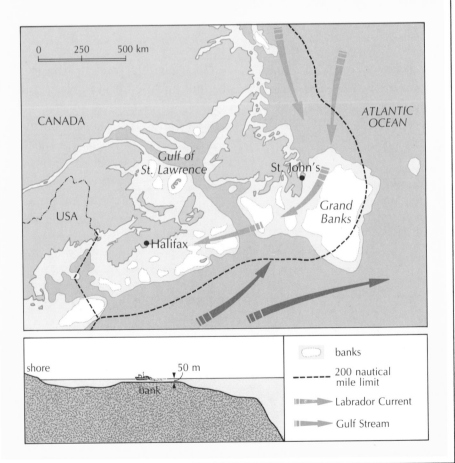

Fig. 17-3 There are large fish populations on the Grand Banks of Atlantic Canada because of the shallow waters and the mixing ocean currents.

Fig. 17-4 The ocean food chain.

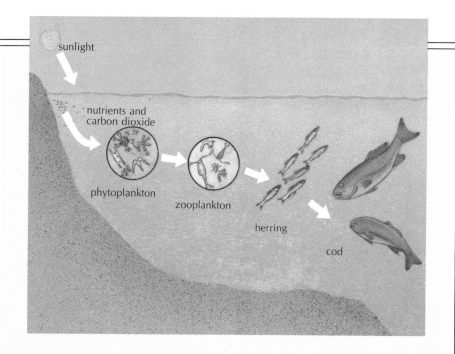

sunlight

nutrients and carbon dioxide

phytoplankton

zooplankton

herring

cod

A **food chain** is the sequence of plants and animals which depend on each other for food.

the coastlines. These minerals are nutrients that fertilize the plant life in the ocean, creating good feeding grounds for fish.

The second area where fish are abundant is where cold and warm ocean currents mix. An example is the Grand Banks off the coast of Newfoundland. The cold Labrador Current mixes with the warm Gulf Stream in this area. As well, the sea is shallow here. Where the currents meet, they cause the nutrients from the ocean floor to rise to the surface. The Grand Banks are one of the richest fishing areas in the Atlantic Ocean.

The mineral nutrients that are washed into the ocean by rivers combine with sunlight and carbon dioxide to produce **marine pastures** alive with billions of tiny plants called **phytoplankton**. These plants are eaten by tiny animals called **zooplankton**. Small fish, like herring or sardines, eat the zooplankton. In turn, the small fish are eaten by larger fish, such as cod. This **food chain** can produce an abundance of fish if left undisturbed.

Fish are a very important source of food for the world. In 1983, more than 75 million tonnes of fish were caught world-wide. Most of the fish is used as food for people. About 25 percent is used for oil or feed for animals. Japan and the U.S.S.R. lead the world in the amount of fish caught per year. Canada ranks fifteenth.

210

Fig. 17-5   The fishing grounds of the North Atlantic Ocean.

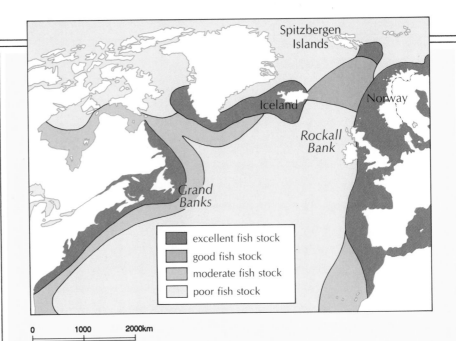

excellent fish stock
good fish stock
moderate fish stock
poor fish stock

0   1000   2000km

Fig. 17-6   What role does Canada play in fishing?

CANADIAN FISH FACTS

• Fishing is not a major national industry. Only one Canadian worker in 350 works in commercial fishing.

• Canada produces a lot of fish, well over one billion tonnes in 1983.

• Canadians do not eat much fish. We average about five kg each per year, compared to over 70 kg of meat.

• Canada is a major fish exporter. We exported four billion dollars worth in 1985.

ACTIVITY TWO

1. a) Define the following terms:
   • food chain
   • nutrients
   • marine pastures
   • phytoplankton
   • zooplankton
   b) Use the diagram in Fig. 17-4 to explain the ocean food chain.

2. Identify one important fact about each of the following:
   • the Grand Banks
   • the Gulf Stream
   • the Labrador Current

3. Use the map in Fig. 17-5 to
   a) describe the pattern of the North Atlantic Ocean's fish stocks.
   b) give two reasons to explain why these areas have large fish stocks.

4. Use Fig. 17-6 to answer the following:
   a) Why is fishing not a major industry in Canada even though we produce over one billion tonnes of fish per year?
   b) What happens to the fish we do not eat ourselves?

5. Using the information in Fig. 17-5, draw a chart to identify where fish are found in abundance and why this is so.

Changes in the fishing industry

Thirty years ago, the British fishing industry was very profitable. The twin seaports of Hull and Grimsby on the North Sea, for example, were home to a large fleet of fishing boats. Hull and Grimsby caught as much fish as all the other British ports combined. Large diesel-powered boats called **trawlers** travelled from Hull and Grimsby to fishing grounds all over the North Atlantic. Canada's Grand Banks, Rockall Bank, the Spitsbergen Islands of Iceland and the coast of Norway were all favourite fishing spots for the fleet. After a week or more of fishing, the trawlers returned to England, their holds full of cod, haddock, herring and other fish. Full holds meant full employment in the ports where the fish were processed. Hull specialized in marketing fresh fish. In Grimsby, the fish were frozen for shipment to more distant customers.

Today, however, the ports of Hull and Grimsby lie idle. What has happened to this once-thriving fishing industry? Read the article in Fig. 17-8 to learn about a few of the changes that have caused this.

There are other reasons for the decline of the Hull fleet. The most important one is over-fishing in the North Atlantic Ocean. Modern fishing boats use very fine steel mesh nets that drag along the ocean floor, scooping up far more fish than was possible before. In addition, modern fishing fleets now have "fish

Fig. 17-7   The ports of Hull and Grimsby in Great Britain.

Trawlers are fishing boats designed to drag large nets behind them as they move. Some trawlers are large diesel-powered boats that can remain at sea for long periods of time.

Government-sponsored fishing sinking British trawlers

British trawler companies are in trouble because of cheap fish imports from Europe. Fourteen deep sea trawlers have been taken out of service, reducing Britain's deep sea fleet to less than 130 trawlers, a drop of 370 since the mid-1970s.

J. Marr and Son, of Grimsby, will take eight ships out of service, putting about 100 men out of work. Another company, Lindsay Trawlers of Grimsby, will cut its fleet by six vessels.

Imports are being blamed for the disastrous fall in fish prices. Increases in the price of fuel oil, and the financial aid given by European governments to support their fleets are given as other causes of this fall. Without immediate government action, the British trawling fleet will disappear.

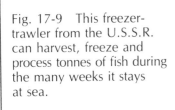

Fig. 17-8   Difficulties in the British fishing industry.

Fig. 17-9   This freezer-trawler from the U.S.S.R. can harvest, freeze and process tonnes of fish during the many weeks it stays at sea.

factories.'' These are large boats that clean and process the fish as soon as they are caught. No longer do fishing fleets have to return to their home ports to have the fish processed before they spoil. As a result of these developments in technology, the oceans were being over-fished and the supply of fish was declining.

ACTIVITY THREE

1. Examine the article in Fig. 17-8.
   a) How many British trawlers have been taken out of service since the mid-1970s?
   b) Which fish business was hurt the most at Hull?
   c) What three reasons are given for the drop in the British fishing industry?
   d) Why are fish prices down?
   e) If you could advise the British government, what advice would you give them?

2. Would Grimsby have lost as many trawlers as Hull? Explain your answer.

The law of the sea

A development in international law also affected the prosperity of the Hull fleet. In the past, countries claimed control of a narrow, five kilometre zone of the ocean along their coasts. This was the distance that a cannon could fire from land out to sea.

Fig. 17-10   Canada arrested these crew members of a French fishing boat from Saint-Pierre and Miquelon for over-fishing in Newfoundland waters in April, 1988.

A **nautical mile** is the standard unit of measurement for distance at sea, equal to approximately 1852 m.

In 1982, following a Law of the Sea Conference, coastal nations began to claim a 200 **nautical mile** zone along their coasts. This larger coastal waters zone allows countries more control over the amount of fishing that is done in their waters. Each country grants only limited fishing rights within their zone to the fishing fleets of other countries, and takes action if the fleets exceed these limits. Canada, for example, will seize the cargo of ships that over-fish in our waters.

The new boundaries had a great impact on the amount of fishing done. It became more difficult for fishing fleets like the Hull fleet to take home huge catches. However, the new boundaries helped nations to protect their supply of fish.

As a result of Canada's new fishing zones and its control of the amount of fishing, the Grand Banks and Labrador coast are now producing more fish than ever. The same is true for the fishing grounds controlled by Norway and Iceland. There is unemployment in Hull and Grimsby, but over-fishing in the North Atlantic Ocean has ended.

ACTIVITY FOUR

1. Why was the distance a cannonball could travel used to measure coastal boundaries in the past?

2. Why were the coastal zones of nations changed in 1982?

3. Use the map in Fig. 17-5 to see the effect of the new zones. Locate the 200 nautical mile boundary. How many times farther from land than the 5 km limit is the new limit?

4. In your opinion, which is more important:
   a) that countries relying on fish for food have access to fishing grounds?
   b) that the supply of fish around the world be protected?
   Explain the reasons for your decision.

WHAT YOU HAVE LEARNED

In this chapter you have learned about the conditions that make some areas of the ocean rich in fish. You have learned how the British fishing fleets from Hull and Grimsby travelled the North Atlantic Ocean. Over-fishing, new territorial limits for nations and other factors have combined to harm the British fishing industry. At the same time, new coastal boundaries have helped to restore the fish population of the North Atlantic.

LOOKING BACK

1. Describe the conditions that make the Grand Banks such a good area for fish.

2. What problems have been caused by increasing technological improvements in fishing?

3. a) Explain the problems created for the fishing industry by the 200 nautical mile limit imposed by most countries on the Atlantic.
   b) What are the advantages of this same limit?

EXPANDING YOUR LEARNING

4. Construct a word search which uses at least eight new words from this chapter.

5. Research the Greenpeace Foundation. How has Greenpeace brought attention to the problem of over-fishing?

6. Visit a local fish store or supermarket. Use observation and interview skills to
   a) find out what types of fish come fresh, frozen and canned. Where does each type come from?
   b) compare the prices of different types of fish by making a bar graph.
   c) prepare a report to trace the route followed as fish move from source to market. Include a map.

7. Look at a map of Canada's East Coast region. Locate the islands of Saint-Pierre and Miquelon.
   a) Identify the country that rules these islands.
   b) Speculate on the problems in trying to enforce the 200 nautical mile limit in this area.

UNIT REVIEW

1. Draw a chart to compare the wheat-growing areas of Australia, Argentina and Canada. Use the following headings:
   • natural resources   • climate   • population
   • wheat exports and beef production   • size of farms

2. a) What is the difference between a renewable and a non-renewable resource?
   b) Give three examples of each and explain why they are or are not renewable.

3. Use your imagination to plan, sketch and explain the operation of a futuristic machine that is able to collect the gold flakes floating in the oceans of the world.

4. Write a poem or story describing the life of a miner in South Africa.

5. Design a poster to advertise the need for resource conservation.

6. With a group in your class create a commercial to show the need for recycling our waste products.

7. Write a paragraph that expresses your opinion on the following statement: "The oceans are filled with enough fish to provide an endless supply of food."

8. Try your luck in the resource business. Play the game on pages 218-219, and go out with the Hull fleet. The game represents the real conditions and events that affected the Hull fleet during one fishing season.

Follow the fleet!

Object of the game

Collect at least ten metric tonnes of fish in each of the three fishing grounds (North America, Arctic, and northern and southern Europe) before returning to Hull.

Movement

Each square on the game board represents one day of travel by a trawler. Start at Hull or Grimsby. Move one space at a time in any direction.

Fishing Tonnage

1) The colours of the ocean squares show how good the fishing is. The darker the colour of the square, the more fish you can catch there.
   - 3 tonnes—excellent fish stock
   - 2 tonnes—good fish stock
   - 1 tonne —moderate fish stock
   - 0   —poor fish stock
   - Inside coastal fishing zone—1 tonne per square, regardless of fishing quality
2) The solid line along the coasts shows the coastal boundaries. You are limited to a maximum catch of one tonne inside any boundary, no matter how large the fish stocks are. Britain's boundary is not marked because the Hull fishing fleet enjoys the right to fish in its own waters.
3) You must ''fish'' on a new square in each turn. You may not move back and forth between the same two squares.
4) Keep track of your fish catch with a score sheet. You need at least ten metric tonnes from each of the three different fishing grounds.

Chance Squares

The lettered squares are Chance Squares. They represent events, good and bad, that happened to the Hull fishing fleet. Do not look at the legend for these squares on page 220 until you land on one of these squares.

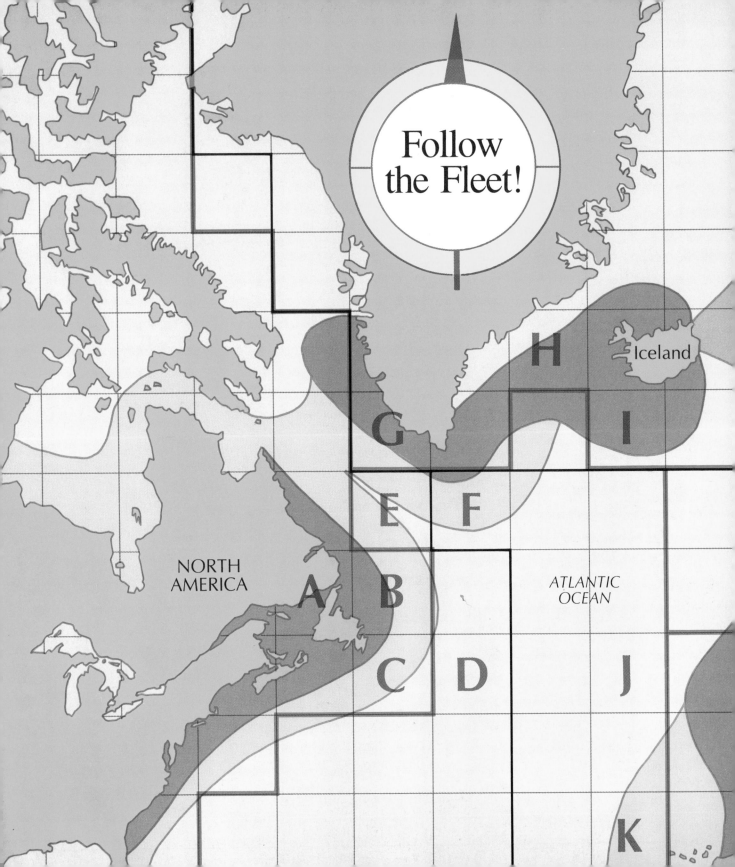

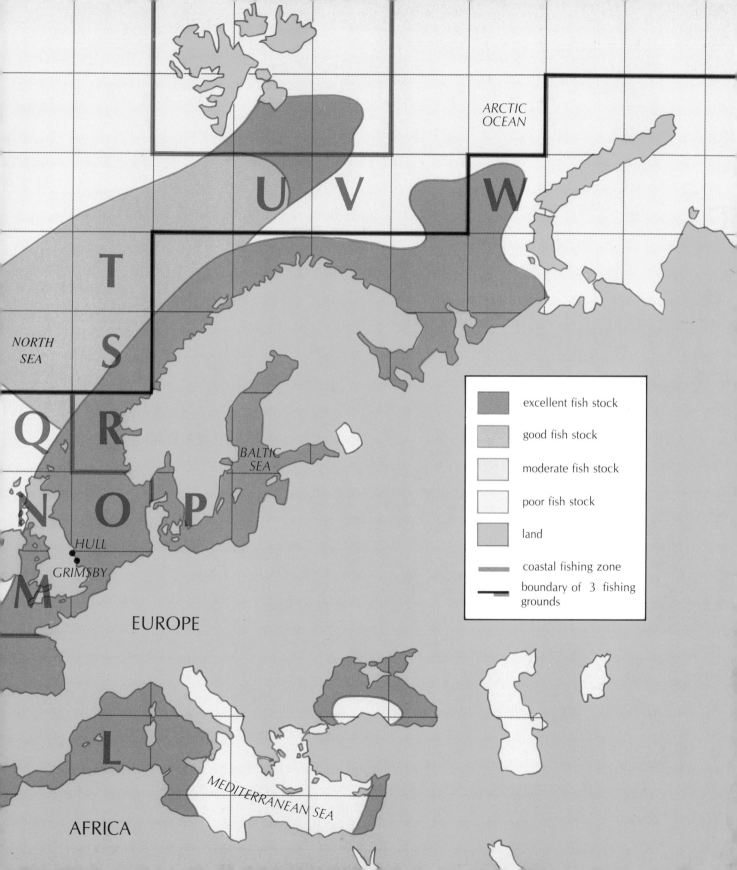

ARCTIC
OCEAN

U V W

NORTH
SEA

T

S

Q R

N O P

BALTIC
SEA

HULL
GRIMSBY

M

EUROPE

L

MEDITERRANEAN SEA

AFRICA

excellent fish stock

good fish stock

moderate fish stock

poor fish stock

land

coastal fishing zone

boundary of 3 fishing
grounds

LETTER ON SQUARE	CHANCE AND RESULT
A	Canada-France boundary dispute. Lose a turn.
B	Strict regulations on the amount of fishing improve Grand Banks. Add three tonnes.
C	Canadian authorities board your boat. Miss a turn.
D	Growing world demand for fish oil. Add three tonnes.
E	Labrador coast over-fished by Spanish fleet. Lose three tonnes.
F	Hit an iceberg. Lose Arctic tonnes. Return to Hull and start again.
G	Over-fishing in hard-to-patrol waters has reduced the number of fish. Lose three tonnes.
H	Caught over-fishing. Lose Arctic tonnes.
I	Damaged by Icelandic gunboat. Keep points but return to Hull for repairs.
J	World fuel prices drop. Take an extra turn.
K	Industrial nations over-fish off Africa. Lose three tonnes.
L	Mediterranean Sea polluted. Lose three tonnes.
M	English Channel oil spill ruins sea bed. Lose three tonnes.
N	British government reduces business tax. Take an extra turn.
O	North Sea herring fishery collapses. Lose three tonnes.
P	Industrial pollution fouls Baltic fishery. Lose three tonnes.
Q	European competition receives government help. Miss a turn.
R	Caught over-fishing in Norwegian waters. Lose European tonnes.
S	Demand for fish rises after nuclear accident. Add three tonnes.
T	Japanese fleet over-fishes mackerel. Lose three tonnes.
U	Growing demand for fish meal as livestock feed. Add three tonnes.
V	Favourable Arctic Ocean weather this season. Take an extra turn.
W	Caught in Soviet waters. Return to Hull. No tonnes in European fishery.

UNIT V

Environments in the News

What Is a Natural Disaster?

Fig. 18-1 The location you will learn about in this chapter.

WHAT YOU WILL LEARN

Our environment is the entire world around us. We, as humans, both live in and form part of this environment. We are affected by our environment, but we also affect it by acting on it and changing it. Natural disasters occur frequently within this environment. They affect how and where people live.

In this chapter we will look at some students' discoveries about what natural disasters are and how they affect peoples' lives.

KEY WORDS

flood plain	natural disaster	volcanic eruption
hurricane	tornado	

A class trip

Naleema's Grade 7 class was enjoying a nature walk and stream study along the Humber River in Étienne Brûlé Park. As they were looking for different forms of plant and animal life, Jin-min and Peter noticed that there were no buildings closer than 100 metres from the river. At the same time, Naleema and Maria were trying to check the rate of flow of the river using a stopwatch and a ping-pong ball. They found this difficult because there were so many small dams.

Fig. 18-2 What steps have been taken to prevent future flooding of the Humber River?

Fig. 18-3 Why are there no buildings near the Humber River?

Naleema and Jin-min both ran up to Mr. Tanel, their teacher, speaking at once. "Why are there no buildings near the river?" asked Jin-min.

"And why are there so many dams in the river?" added Naleema.

Mr. Tanel explained that in 1954 there had been a terrible storm called Hurricane Hazel that had flooded the entire Humber River valley. Many houses had been washed into the river and many lives had been lost. After the flood, building was no longer allowed directly beside the river. The area next to the river is the river's **flood plain**, the part of a river valley that is covered with water when the river floods. At times during Hurricane Hazel, the Humber River had risen to more than ten metres, completely covering its flood plain.

Mr. Tanel then turned to Naleema. He told her that the many small dams were part of an elaborate flood control system that was built after Hurricane Hazel.

The day ended and as the class returned to their school, the students talked excitedly about their discoveries. Everyone was interested in learning more about natural disasters, so the class decided to study three types—**hurricanes, tornadoes** and **volcanic eruptions**.

ACTIVITY ONE 📷 🔊

1. Study the photograph at the beginning of this unit carefully. Name this disaster and list three characteristics of it.

2. What was the cause of this disaster?

3. How could the disaster have been prevented?

4. Describe the steps taken following Hurricane Hazel to prevent another such disaster.

5. Suggest other types of events that have some of the same characteristics as Hurricane Hazel and the disaster in the opening photograph.

What is a natural disaster?

The next day in class, Mr. Tanel explained that Hurricane Hazel was a **natural disaster**. A natural disaster is an event in nature that causes tremendous damage and loss of life. He asked the students to suggest other types of natural disasters. The list that they developed included:

- hurricanes
- tornadoes
- tsunamis
- avalanches
- cyclones
- forest fires
- volcanic eruptions
- earthquakes
- rock or mud slides
- blizzards

"What makes these disasters different from airplane crashes or sinking ships?" asked Jessica. "These events cause death and destruction too." Mr. Tanel explained that disasters such as airplane crashes were not the result of a natural occurrence. Natural disasters occur as the result of an event in nature, rather than as a result of the actions of people.

ACTIVITY TWO 📖 📝

1. Define the term "natural disaster."

2. List ten types of natural disasters.

Fig. 18-4 In 1954, Hurricane Hazel struck Ontario, causing severe damage and the loss of many lives.

3. Why is a natural disaster different from an airplane crash?

4 a) Have any natural disasters occurred in or near your community? Ask your parents to describe any they may remember.

 b) Choose one natural disaster you have heard about. What type of natural disaster was it?

 c) Write a paragraph about this disaster, describing the causes and the effects. What steps were taken to prevent this type of disaster from causing damage in the future? Try to find newspaper clippings or magazine articles about the disaster, or interview someone who remembers this event.

World disasters

Natural disasters can occur anywhere in the world and at any time. However, there seem to be certain patterns to some of these events. Figure 18-5, 18-6 and 18-7 show the three main types of natural disasters: earthquakes, hurricanes, and floods, or tsunamis. Can you see any patterns to these natural disasters? Compare the locations in which they occur, and the times of the year. In other parts of the world, hurricanes have different names: in India and Southeast Asia, they are known as tropical cyclones, and in the Pacific Ocean, China and Japan, these storms are known as typhoons.

Fig. 18-5 The ten worst earthquakes in history.

DATE	LOCATION	NUMBER OF DEATHS
20 May 556	Antioch, Syria	250 000
24 Jan. 1556	Shaanxi, China	830 000
11 Oct. 1737	Calcutta, India	300 000
28 Dec. 1908	Messina, Italy	83 000
16 Dec. 1920	Gansu, China	100 000
1 Sept. 1923	Tokyo, Japan	99 330
22 May 1927	Nan-shan, China	200 000
26 Dec. 1932	Gansu, China	70 000
31 May 1935	Quetta, India	50 000
31 May 1970	Northern Peru	66 794

Fig. 18-6   The ten worst hurricanes, typhoons and cyclones since 1900.

DATE	LOCATION	NUMBER OF DEATHS
8 Sept. 1900	Galveston, Texas	6 000
20 Oct. 1926	Cuba	600
12-17 Sept. 1928	West Indies and Florida	4 000
3 Sept. 1930	Dominican Republic	2 000
21 Sept. 1938	New England, U.S.A.	600
15-16 Oct. 1942	Bengal, India	11 000
22-28 Sept. 1955	Caribbean	500
4-8 Oct. 1963	Cuba and Haiti	6 000
19-20 Sept. 1974	Honduras	2 000
30 Aug.-7 Sept. 1979	Eastern United States	1 100

Fig. 18-7   The ten worst floods and tsunamis since 1887.

DATE	LOCATION	NUMBER OF DEATHS
Oct. 1887	Huang He River, China	900 000
31 May 1889	Johnstown, Pennsylvania	2 200
8 Sept. 1900	Galveston, Texas	5 000
1911	Chang Jiang River, China	100 000
Aug. 1931	Huang He River, China	3 700 000
1939	Northern China	200 000
10 Oct. 1960	Bangladesh	6 000
31 Oct. 1960	Bangladesh	4 000
12 Aug. 1974	Monty-Long, Bangladesh	2 500
11 Aug. 1979	Mowi, India	15 000

ACTIVITY THREE 🌐 📶

1. Use an atlas to locate the places in Figs. 18-5, 18-6 and 18-7. Mark the information on an outline map of the world. Use red dots to mark the locations of earthquakes, black for hurricanes, typhoons or cyclones and blue for floods and tsunamis.

2. Rank the number of deaths listed in each chart from highest to lowest.

3. Look at the months of the year in each chart. Can you see any patterns? If so, what might explain these patterns?

4. Refer back to your world map in question 1 and look for patterns of natural disasters. Do certain disasters occur more frequently in some parts of the world than in others?

Careers in geography: Seismologist

Seismologists study earthquakes. They usually work with a team of other scientists and technicians to locate the earthquake and to assess its size on the Richter scale. The work of the team is useful to engineers who design earthquake-resistant buildings.

Seismologists take university courses leading to a degree in science or engineering, and usually have special training in geophysics. They use geology, physics, mathematics and computer science, and they write reports on their findings. Other members of the team include experts in geology, computer science, engineering and telecommunications, and technicians with community college training.

Maurice Lamontagne is a seismologist with Energy, Mines and Resources, Canada.

''I believe that most seismologists are naturally curious and attracted by non-routine work and outdoor activities.''

WHAT YOU HAVE LEARNED

There are many different types of disasters, but those that occur naturally seem to cause the greatest number of deaths. Natural disasters are events in nature that cause tremendous damage and loss of life. They occur in specific areas during particular periods of the year.

LOOKING BACK

1. List the characteristics of natural disasters.

2. In what parts of the world do the disasters listed in this chapter occur most frequently?

EXPANDING YOUR LEARNING

3. Why do you think that people continue to live in areas that have suffered much damage caused by natural disasters?

The Eye of the Storm

228

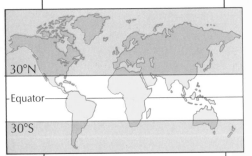

Fig. 19-1   The locations you will learn about in this chapter.

WHAT YOU WILL LEARN

Hurricanes occur in particular regions of the world on both sides of the Equator. They follow well-established patterns in their movement, and they happen during particular times of the year. There are also patterns of movement within the hurricanes themselves, caused by convectional heating.

In this chapter, we will learn what hurricanes are, where they occur and what causes them. In addition, we will see how people deal with hurricanes in various locations.

KEY WORDS

hurricane	**Beaufort scale**	**eye**
anemometer	**storm surge**	**convectional heating**
reservoir	**control dam**	

Hurricanes: What are they?

There was a definite air of anticipation in Mr. Tanel's geography class. They were getting ready to learn more about the hurricane, one of the most deadly and destructive of all natural disasters.

What exactly is a **hurricane**? It is the name given to the violent wind storms of the West Indies and the Gulf of Mexico. In other regions of the world this type of wind storm is known by other names:

Fig. 19-3   A satellite photograph of Hurricane Diana in September, 1984, as it approached the east coast of the U.S.A.

Fig. 19-2   Damage caused by hurricanes can be severe. These houses were washed away by the flooded Humber River during Hurricane Hazel in 1954.

baguio — Philippines   typhoon   — Pacific
cyclone — Indian Ocean   willy-willies — Australia

For a storm to be considered a hurricane, it must have winds over 120 kilometres per hour. The **Beaufort scale** is used to measure the speed, or velocity, of the wind. It is shown in Fig. 19-4. To use the scale, compare the wind conditions to the descriptions on the scale. Force 4 on the Beaufort scale is described as a moderate breeze, which raises dust and moves small branches. Therefore, if the breeze on a beautiful summer day moves small tree branches, the wind speed would equal Force 4. By looking at this scale you can see how fierce the winds of hurricanes are. The winds often reach a velocity as high as 240 kilometres per hour.

Hurricanes have a distinctive pattern. They are about 800 km in diameter, and the winds move in a circular motion, rotating around the centre of the hurricane, called the **eye**. The eye has

Fig. 19-4 The Beaufort scale measures wind speed.

BEAUFORT FORCE	VELOCITY (in kilometres per hour)	DESCRIPTION OF WIND SPEED	EFFECTS OF THE WIND
0	less than 1	Calm	Smoke rises vertically
1	2-5	Light air	Wind direction shown by smoke
2	6-12	Light breeze	Wind felt on face; leaves rustle
3	13-20	Gentle breeze	Twigs in constant motion
4	21-29	Moderate breeze	Raises dust; moves small branches
5	30-39	Fresh breeze	Small trees sway; wavelets form
6	40-50	Stong breeze	Large branches in motion
7	51-61	Near gale	Whole trees in motion
8	62-74	Gale	Breaks twigs off trees; walking difficult
9	75-87	Strong gale	Slight damage (roof shingles may blow off)
10	88-101	Storm	Trees uprooted (roofs may be blown off; windows broken)
11	102-119	Violent storm	Rarely experienced inland; small buildings destroyed; cars overturned
12	>120	Hurricane	Rare except in the tropics; whole buildings destroyed; ships turned over
13	133-148		
14	149-165		
15	166-183		
16	184-201		
17	202-218		

no winds and is often sunny, but it is only about 50 km in diameter.

In the Northern Hemisphere, the winds rotate around the eye in a counter-clockwise direction. In the Southern Hemisphere, they rotate in a clockwise direction. This moving mass of air reaches a height of three kilometres.

ACTIVITY ONE

1. What is a hurricane?

2. What other names are given to this type of storm?

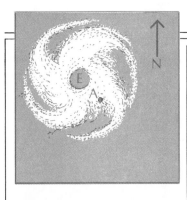

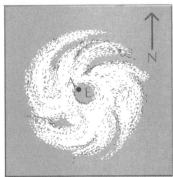

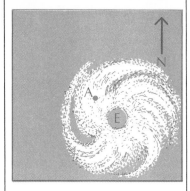

Fig. 19-5   The movement of winds in a hurricane as it passes over a point (**A**).

3. a) How could you use the Beaufort scale to find out the speed of wind on a given day? How accurate do you think this would be?

   b) Check today's weather report. What is the wind velocity? Where would it be on the Beaufort scale?

   c) Do the following exercise for a week: Determine the velocity of the wind each day using the Beaufort scale. Check your findings either by checking with your local weather bureau or by using an **anemometer**, an instrument that measures wind speed.

4. What is the eye of the hurricane?

5. Speculate on why the winds rotate differently in the Northern and Southern Hemispheres.

6. Look at each of the three diagrams in Fig. 19-5. Which direction is the wind coming from as it passes over point **A**?

Hurricanes: Location, cause and characteristics

If we look at the map of the world in Fig. 19-6, we can identify the patterns of hurricanes—where they occur on earth and the directions they move in.

Hurricanes form in the tropics over large bodies of water, within the 8° and 15° lines of latitude on either side of the Equator. In the Northern Hemisphere, they travel west until they reach the 25°N to 30°N line of latitude. Then they usually change course and travel east. The hurricanes in the Southern Hemisphere travel to the west until they reach 25°S to 30°S latitude, and then they also turn to the east.

What causes hurricanes to form? They are caused by convectional heating combined with winds that blow in a spiral pattern. In Chapter 11, you learned how convectional precipitation occurs. In the same manner, the sun causes **convectional heating** over the oceans. The warm, moist air at the water's surface is lighter than the surrounding air, and it rises. It is replaced by cooler, heavier air which sometimes blows inward

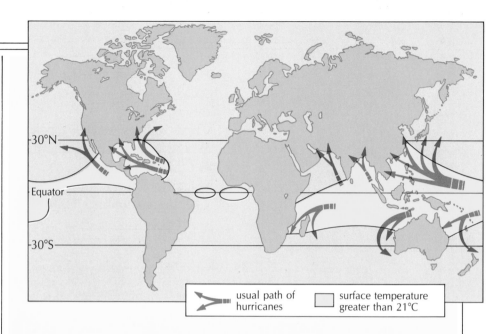

Fig. 19-6 The arrows on this map show the usual paths of the world's hurricanes, cyclones and typhoons. Where do these storms first develop?

usual path of hurricanes

surface temperature greater than 21°C

A **storm surge** is a large movement of water caused by the high winds of a typhoon or hurricane.

in a spiral, causing a hurricane. The larger the heated air mass is, the larger the hurricane. This process also causes tremendous winds within the hurricane itself. Hurricanes are like engines that run on heat. They convert heat energy into wind power. If this heat energy could be converted to electrical energy, there would be enough power to supply the entire North American continent for more than six months.

Hurricane season is generally from June to October; the peak months are September and October. This is because the sea is at its warmest and the rate of evaporation is highest at this time of year. However, hurricanes last for only a short time, a few days at most. The winds usually die quickly once they reach the land, because they lose their source of heat—the sea. Contact with the surface of the land also breaks the circular pattern of the winds.

Fierce winds are not the only characteristic of hurricanes. They are accompanied by heavy rain. This rain often lasts for several days and can total 15 cm. This heavy rainfall can cause severe flooding on land, such as that which occurred with Hurricane Hazel. Areas near ocean coasts are flooded by **storm surges**, sudden rises in the sea level caused by high winds pushing water toward land.

YEAR	DATE	EVENT	NAME	LOCATION	DEATHS
1969	16-17 Aug.	H	Camille	Massachusetts, Louisiana	256
1970	31 July-5 Aug.	H	Celia	Cuba, Florida, Texas	31
	20-21 Aug.	H	Dorothy	Martinique	42
	15 Sept.	T	Georgia	Philippines	300
	14 Oct.	T	Sening	Philippines	583
	15 Oct.	T	Titang	Philippines	526
	13 Nov.	C		Bangladesh	300 000
1971	1 Aug.	T	Rose	Hong Kong	130
1972	19-29 June	H	Agnes	Florida to New York	118
	3 Dec.	T	Theresa	Philippines	169
1974	11 June	S	Dinah	Luzon Island, Philippines	71
	11 July	T	Gilda	Japan, South Korea	108
	19-20 Sept.	H	Fifi	Honduras	2 000
	25 Dec.	C		Darwin, Australia	50
1975	13-27 Sept.	H	Eloise	Caribbean, Northeast U.S.A.	71
1976	20 May	T	Olga	Philippines	215
1977	25 July	T	Thelma	Taiwan	
	31 July	T	Vera	Taiwan	31
1978	27 Oct.	T	Rita	Philippines	400
1979	30 Aug.-7 Sept.	H	David	Caribbean, Eastern U.S.A.	1 100
1980	4-11 Aug.	H	Allen	Caribbean, Texas	272
1981	25 Nov.	T	Irma	Luzon Island, Philippines	176
1983	18 Aug.	H	Alicia	South Texas	17
1984	2 Sept.	T	Ike	South Philippines	1 363
1985	25 May	C		Bangladesh	10 000
1988	12-17 Sept.	H	Gilbert	Caribbean, Mexico	250

Fig. 19-7   The worst hurricanes, typhoons and cyclones of the years 1969-1988.

H-hurricane, T-typhoon, C-cyclone, S-storm

ACTIVITY TWO

1. Use an atlas and Fig. 19-6 to identify the countries most affected by these hurricanes. List them in your notebook.

2. Look at Fig. 19-3 and refer to the section in Chapter 11 on the Strange Stavanger climatic mystery.
   a) What effect might ocean currents have on the development and path of hurricanes?
   b) Where do hurricanes most often form?

c) What directions do hurricanes travel
   (i) in the Northern Hemisphere?
   (ii) in the Southern Hemisphere?

3. What causes hurricanes to form?

4. a) Using the information from Fig. 19-7, list the number of storms by month, from May to December.
   b) Which months have the greatest number of storms?

5. Using an atlas and an outline map of the world
   a) mark the directions that the storms travel.
   b) mark the locations, using dots, of the storms in Fig. 19-7.
   c) calculate the number of deaths in Fig. 19-7 for each of the following regions:
      • Caribbean/North America
      • India, Bangladesh and east to Vietnam
      • Philippines
      • China, Korea and Japan
      • Australia.
      (i) Which region had the greatest number of deaths?
      (ii) Speculate on the possible reasons for this.

6. a) In what year were both men's and women's names used to identify hurricanes?
   b) Why do you think only women's names were used before this time?

7. If there are many hurricanes in a certain location
   a) why do people stay there?
   b) what can they do to protect themselves?

Dealing with hurricanes

What can people do to protect themselves and their property from destruction by hurricanes? One answer is for people to move away to a hurricane-free area. Because they do not want to leave behind their homes, families, friends and jobs, most people do not find this a suitable solu-

Meteorological equipment refers to the instruments that can measure the characteristics of the weather, such as a rain gauge or an anemometer.

Fig. 19-8 Would you know what to do during a hurricane?

tion. A second solution is for people to build homes that are able to withstand the forces of the hurricane. However, these homes are very expensive to build and therefore impossible for the majority of people. The early detection of hurricanes as they form over the ocean can also save lives. Some people work to find, and then follow, these storms. Colonel Joseph B. Duckworth was an Army Air Forces flight instructor. On July 27, 1943, he was the first person to fly through the eye of a hurricane. Having completed this record-breaking flight, he did it again, taking the base weather officer with him. As a result of these flights, a group of "hurricane hunters" were organized. Hurricane hunters fly aircraft equipped with the most modern meterological equipment. Their purpose is to save lives through the early detection of hurricanes.

HURRICANE SAFETY RULES

1. Have extra canned food, tools and batteries ready for the hurricane season.

2. Listen to weather reports often.

3. a) Avoid last minute hurry when your area receives a hurricane warning.
   b) Keep calm.
   c) Leave low-lying areas.
   d) Leave mobile homes.
   e) Board up windows.
   f) Fasten down outdoor objects so they don't blow away.
   g) Store drinking water.
   h) Check battery-powered equipment to make sure the batteries work.
   i) Keep car fueled.
   j) Stay at home if it's sturdy and on high ground.
   k) Remain indoors.
   l) Monitor the position of the storm.
   m) Beware of the eye of the hurricane. Don't think the storm is over.

4. a) Stay out of disaster areas.
   b) Drive carefully.
   c) Avoid loose and dangling electrical wires.
   d) Prevent fires.

A **reservoir** is a large holding area for water built to prevent flooding during a storm.

A **control dam** is a small dam placed along a river or stream to control the flow of the water and possible flooding.

Conservation and flood control also help to protect people and property from the hurricane's destructive forces. After Hurricane Hazel in 1954, many areas of eastern North America, including the Humber Valley, began programmes. They built **reservoirs, control dams** and flood-control channels to help limit flooding. They no longer allowed people to build on flood plains, and they established flood-warning systems. There has not been a hurricane in Southern Ontario since 1954, but Southern Ontario is now better prepared to handle one.

Osaka, Japan has built a typhoon defense system. This helps to prevent flooding from rivers and storm surges during typhoons. A complex system of tidal gates was built to decrease the flow of storm surges. How does the arch tidal gate shown in Fig. 19-9 help to reduce damage?

ACTIVITY THREE

1. Why do hurricanes diminish and eventually die out? Can you think of a simple example to illustrate this process?

2. Speculate on why people continue to live in areas where these storms occur again and again.

3. Study the Hurricane Safety Rules in Fig. 19-8. How does

Fig. 19-9 This arch tidal gate is used in Osaka, Japan to prevent flooding due to storm surges.

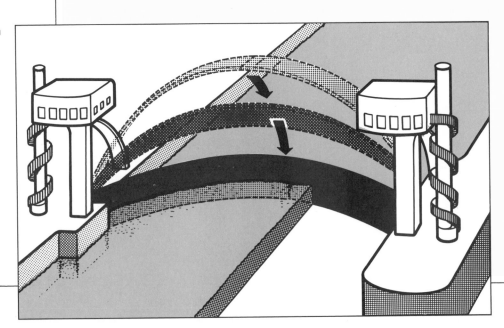

each rule help to prevent death and reduce the amount of destruction?

4. Why do you think that it takes a catastrophe such as Hurricane Hazel before steps are taken to prevent deaths from such natural disasters?

WHAT YOU HAVE LEARNED

Hurricanes are violent wind storms which rotate around a central core called the eye. They occur mainly in tropical regions, moving both north and south away from the Equator. They result from convectional heating at the surface of the ocean, and occur during the late summer and early fall.

In recent years, conservation authorities have built systems to control the flooding that results from hurricanes, and many lives are saved by the early warnings provided by modern meteorological technology.

LOOKING BACK

1. What is a hurricane?

2. Describe three patterns in the location and structure of hurricanes.

3. In what direction do the winds rotate around the eye of a hurricane in the Northern Hemisphere?

4. Describe the direction a hurricane travels as it moves away from the Equator in the Northern Hemisphere.

5. Explain some of the various means that people use to deal with hurricanes.

EXPANDING YOUR LEARNING 📝 🧭

6. a) What type of land use would be best suited for land in a river's flood plain?
   b) Visit a river in your area or look at a topographic map that includes a river. Determine the various types of land use along its flood plain.

CHAPTER 20

The Funnel of Death

Fig. 20-1 The location you will learn about in this chapter.

WHAT YOU WILL LEARN

Tornadoes are extremely severe storms that can destroy lives and property in moments. However, they cover a relatively small area. Therefore, the focus questions geographers ask concerning tornadoes, such as ''where?,'' ''why there?'' and ''what is the importance of it being there?'' are very important.

In this chapter we will look at the effect of a tornado through a story about a girl and her family to try to explain these important questions.

KEY WORDS

tornado	vortex	storm cellar
funnel		

Tornado: The unpredictable disaster

Stasia Lindsberg of Tulsa, Oklahoma had just returned home from school. It was a very hot and humid June day, so she immediately went to the refrigerator for a tall, cool drink. As she stood there, she glanced out the window. In the distance she saw dark billowing clouds. She had often seen such clouds and knew that they usually warned of an approaching thunderstorm.

During the playing of her favourite song, the radio announcer reported a severe weather warning for the next six hours. This

Fig. 20-2 A tornado approaches Edmonton homes in 1987. What would you do if you saw this storm coming?

was also very common before summer storms in the area. Minutes later, there was a second announcement. A tornado had just touched down 20 km from her home.

She looked out the window and saw a huge funnel-shaped mass of black, moving swiftly in her direction. She knew she should run to safety.

What Stasia saw coming was one of the most destructive and violent storms produced by nature—a **tornado**. Tornadoes do not last very long or travel very far. But while they last, the winds inside the **funnel** are very strong, moving in a counter-clockwise direction at speeds up to 650 kilometres per hour. The area in the funnel is called the **vortex**. The vortex is generally 300 to 400 m wide and up to seven kilometres in length. It moves along the ground at speeds up to 60 kilometres per hour. Heavy rain and hail often come before a tornado.

Tornadoes occur all over the world but most occur in the midwestern United States. Tornado season runs from March to September, but most tornadoes occur between March and June. The most common time of day for tornadoes is from 3 p.m. to 7 p.m., the hottest time of the day. The heat from the ground rises quickly, which causes currents of air to move upward. Cooler air is pulled toward the ground. The rising warm air begins to rotate around the cooler air, forming winds. These winds move faster and faster, causing the funnel of air, the vortex, to form. The birth of a tornado is shown in Fig. 20-3.

These storms first form hundreds of metres above the earth during warm, humid, changeable weather. They are usually part of severe thunderstorms. They occur when dry, cold air from the north collides with warm, moist air from the south. They begin at different places along the path of the thunderstorm, travel a short distance and then die out. Not all tornados even reach the ground, and some just touch down and spin directly back up, causing little or no damage.

ACTIVITY ONE

1. What is a tornado?

2. Describe the characteristics of a tornado.

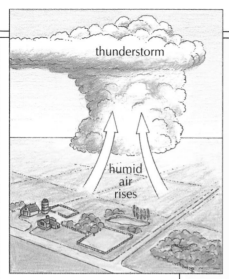

thunderstorm

humid air rises

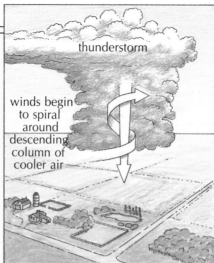

thunderstorm

winds begin to spiral around descending column of cooler air

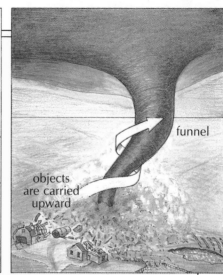

funnel

objects are carried upward

Fig. 20-3 How a tornado is formed.

A **storm cellar** is a shelter built under a house or in the side of a hill as protection from tornadoes.

3. How does a tornado differ from a hurricane?

4. a) What causes tornadoes to form?
   b) With what type of storm are tornadoes usually associated?

5. a) When is the tornado season in North America?
   b) Why do you think the season occurs when it does?
   c) Explain why tornadoes occur between 3 p.m. and 7 p.m.

Tornadoes: Lightning devastation

Once Stasia realized that she had only about a minute to get to the safety of the **storm cellar**, she ran. She remembered what she had been taught about taking shelter:

a) In an open area lie flat in a ditch.
b) In a house move to the basement wall closest to the oncoming storm.
c) Never stay in a car or trailer.
d) The safest place is an underground shelter.

Outside the house, Stasia could barely make any headway against the wind. Tree branches, leaves, garbage cans and papers were flying everywhere. She finally reached the doors of the storm cellar, pulled them open and went inside. No sooner had she done this than the intensity of the wind increased

Fig. 20-4 In areas where tornadoes are common, many homes have nearby shelters or underground storm cellars.

Fig. 20-5 An experiment that demonstrates the force created by low air pressure. Do not try this experiment without adult supervision.

dramatically. The sound was deafening. She imagined it was like standing beside a jet engine going at high speed. Over the roar of the wind she could hear the sound of shattering glass and cracking wood. She wondered anxiously about her parents who were both at work. Were they safe? Did they know what was happening?

Finally, the noise began to lessen until there was silence. She pushed open the door of her shelter and looked around. What she saw shook her badly. Where her home had been, there was only a hole in the ground. Trees were uprooted, power-lines were down and a neighbour's car was upside down in their front yard.

The winds of a tornado are the major source of power and destruction. They can act in three ways. First, the winds around the vortex are powerful enough to blow down trees, tear off roofs or flatten buildings completely. Second, the vortex can cause houses to explode. This happens because there is a difference in air pressure between the vortex and the objects over which it passes. The vortex has very low pressure. Air outside the vortex is drawn into the low pressure area in the vortex. Unless the air within a house can move quickly enough, it may be pulled rapidly into the vortex, and the house may simply explode. Third, there is a strong upward motion of the air in the vortex. These winds suck up trees, houses, cars, trailers and other heavy objects and drop them some distance away.

ACTIVITY TWO

1. Where are the safest places during a tornado?

2. How did Stasia describe the sound of the wind at the height of the storm?

3. Explain how a tornado's winds cause destruction.

4. a) In order to understand just how powerful air pressure is, ask your teacher to try the experiment in Fig. 20-5.
   (i) Hard boil an egg and remove the shell.

241

     (ii) Find a bottle or jar with a mouth slightly smaller than the width of the egg.

     (iii) Place a lit match or small candle into the bottom of the bottle.

     (iv) Immediately place the egg on the top of the bottle and observe what happens.

  b) Which of the three destructive forces of a tornado is illustrated by the experiment?

5. Why would a storm cellar be safer than the basement of a house?

Where do tornadoes occur?

Fig. 20-6 shows the 12 worst tornadoes since 1925. These are not the only ones, but they have caused the greatest number of deaths. The United States averages 655 tornadoes per year. They cause billions of dollars in damage to property and considerable loss of life. But Ontario has tornadoes as well, about 25 per year.

ACTIVITY THREE

1. Use a bar graph to illustrate the months when the worst tornadoes occur.

Fig. 20-6 Major tornadoes in North America since 1925. What patterns appear on this chart?

YEAR	DATE	LOCATION	NUMBER OF DEATHS
1925	18 Mar.	Missouri, Illinois, Indiana	689
1932	21 Mar.	Alabama (series)	268
1936	5 Apr.	Tupelo, Mississippi	216
	6 Apr.	Gainsville, Georgia	203
1944	23 June	Oklahoma, Pennsylvania, West Virginia, Maryland	150
1945	12 Apr.	Oklahoma, Arkansas	102
1947	9 Apr.	Texas, Oklahoma, Kansas	169
1952	21 Mar.	Arkansas, Missouri, Tennessee	208
1971	21 Feb.	Mississippi Delta	110
1974	3-4 Apr.	Alabama, Georgia, Tennessee, Kentucky, Oklahoma	350
1984	9 June	Western U.S.S.R.	400
1985	31 May	New York, Pennsylvania, Oklahoma, Ontario (series)	90
1987	31 July	Edmonton, Alberta	26

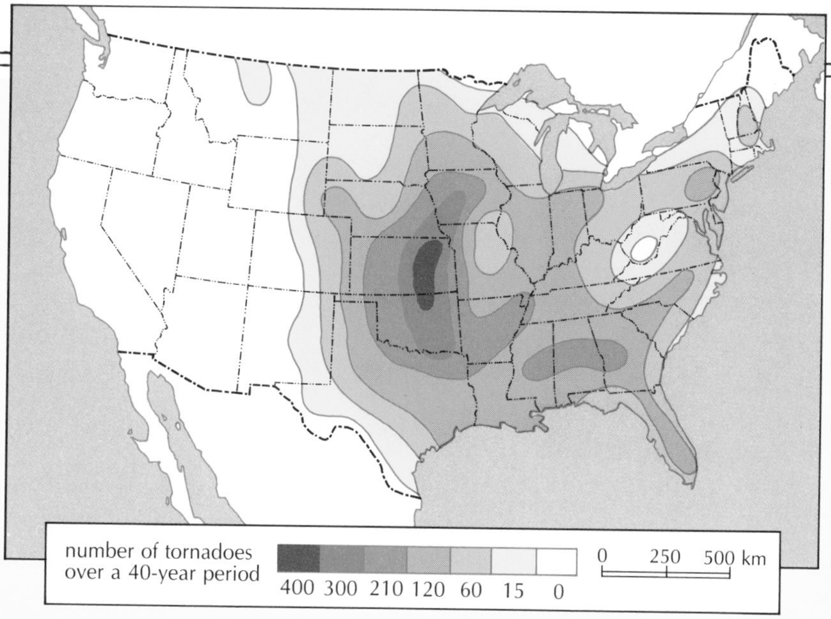

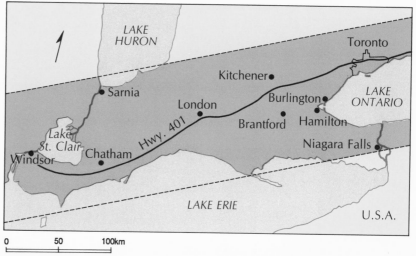

Fig. 20-7 The distribution of tornadoes in the United States over a forty-year period.

number of tornadoes over a 40-year period
400 300 210 120 60 15 0

0 250 500 km

Fig. 20-8 In Ontario, the area in which "twisters" are most likely to occur is known as "Tornado Alley." Why does it have this name?

LAKE HURON

Toronto

Kitchener

Sarnia

London

Burlington

LAKE ONTARIO

Brantford

Hamilton

Lake St. Clair

Chatham

Hwy. 401

Niagara Falls

Windsor

LAKE ERIE

U.S.A.

0 50 100km

2. Locate the places in Fig. 20-6 on an outline map of North America. Do they generally fit the patterns found in Figs. 20-7 and 20-8?

3. Look at Fig. 20-6 and speculate on why the tornado on Feb. 21, 1971 did not occur during the tornado season.

4. Discuss reasons why the midwestern U.S. has the greatest number of tornadoes.

Fig. 20-9 In 1985, Barrie, Ontario was struck by a tornado that damaged this school as well as many homes and businesses.

Defending against disaster

When Stasia's parents returned home, they found her sitting on an uprooted tree. She was very glad to see them, and wanted to know how the disaster could have been prevented. Her dad told her that there was really no way to prevent tornadoes themselves. However, he explained, people can do things to cut down on the amount of damage caused by tornadoes.

Buildings can be built to withstand the tornadoes' tremendous force. They must be constructed from heavier materials than usual. They also should be anchored to their foundations. These measures help to protect buildings against the winds and air pressure of tornadoes.

To protect people, weather services in most countries watch for tornadoes and collect data from radar, satellites, weather balloons and pilots. Because it is hard to predict the path of a tornado, warnings are given for large areas, usually 160 km to 400 km in size. People must watch for the signs of tornadoes, listen for weather information and prepare shelters to protect themselves if they live in places where tornadoes are frequent.

ACTIVITY FOUR

1. What methods do meteorologists use to track storms?

2. Why do meteorologists warn people that a tornado is coming, even when they do not know the exact location?

3. What can be done to decrease the death and destruction resulting from tornadoes?

4. Find out more about the relief operations that were carried out by the Mennonites following the Barrie, Ontario tornado in 1985. Write a short paper on how they helped people after this disaster.

5. Read some newspaper accounts and books that have been written about tornadoes or disaster preparations or relief in your area. Describe how people help one another.

WHAT YOU HAVE LEARNED

It is difficult for people to protect themselves against tornadoes. They do not last long and strike unexpectedly. Although tornadoes occur world-wide, most occur in the midwestern United States. People have found ways of protecting themselves. They try to build safer buildings and to have nearby shelters where they can hide. They listen for weather reports to help them find out when a tornado might strike.

LOOKING BACK

1. Why are tornadoes unpredictable and difficult to defend against?

2. Explain the three ways in which the winds of tornadoes cause destruction.

3. Examine Fig. 20-8. Speculate on why tornadoes occur here regularly.

EXPANDING YOUR LEARNING

4. Choose one severe tornado and research what happened.
   a) Decide what focus questions you will ask to begin your investigation, or ask your teacher for some ideas. Some topics to cover could include:
      • the time of year
      • the weather conditions
      • the effects of the storm
      • the assistance given to the victims
   b) Communicate your results to your classmates through an oral report (a presentation or news interview), or a written report (you could write in the style of a newspaper article), which could be handed out. Each student's finished report could be assembled to form a class "Book of Tornadoes."

5. Imagine you were in a storm cellar during a tornado. Write about what happened and how you felt.

From the Depths of the Earth

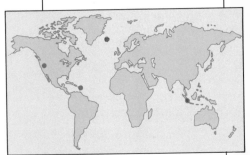

Fig. 21-1   The locations you will learn about in this chapter.

WHAT YOU WILL LEARN

You have already learned that volcanoes occur in fold mountains, ocean trenches and mid-ocean ridges. In many cases they cause destruction when they erupt near communities, but they are also responsible for building new land, such as the island of Surtsey.

In this chapter we will learn more about volcanoes; what they are and where they are found. Using newspaper articles, we will look at different types of volcanoes and their different types of eruptions.

KEY WORDS

dormant	fissures	nuée ardente
extinct	tsunami	eruption
lava		

Volcanoes: Why and where do they erupt?

If we could journey into the earth, we would find that the temperature increases towards the centre. The temperature at a depth of 600 m is about 60°C while at 100 km it is 1200°C. At this temperature rocks melt into a thick molten mass called magma.

Fissures are cracks or openings in the earth's crust through which lava can flow.

Lava is the liquid rock, or magma, that erupts from volcanoes.

An **eruption** is the sudden escape of molten rock, or lava, from a fissure or a volcano.

Where there are cracks, or **fissures**, in the earth's crust, magma is forced to the surface due to the tremendous pressures within the earth. When magma reaches the surface, it is known as **lava**. Once the lava is forced out into the air, it begins to cool and harden. If there are many eruptions over a long period of time, a mountain will be formed from the layers of cooled lava as they harden into rock.

There are three stages in the life of a volcano—active, **dormant** and **extinct**. Active volcanoes erupt quite often. Dormant volcanoes have not erupted for a long time but might again at some time in the future. Finally, the oldest volcano is an extinct volcano, which will not erupt again.

Volcanoes can erupt in different ways. Their **eruptions** can take the form of ash, hot gases, rocks and lava. Sometimes lava may slowly flow from the mountain, but at other times, the volcano erupts in a tremendous explosion.

There are also different kinds of volcanoes. The most common types of volcanoes are shield volcanoes, composite cone volcanoes, and ash or cinder volcanoes. Each of these three types has a distinctive shape and is formed in a certain way. Most of the world's volcanoes are of the composite cone type. Fig. 21-2 shows how these three types of volcano form.

The different types of volcanoes occur all over the earth. (See Fig. 21-3.) They are common in fold mountains and at the edges of plates of the earth's crust, where the plates are sliding together or pulling apart. However, as Fig. 21-4 shows, each type of volcano can cause a tremendous amount of damage and loss of life, wherever it is located on the earth.

Fig. 21-2   Shield volcanoes, ash or cinder volcanoes, and composite cone volcanoes. How does each type form?

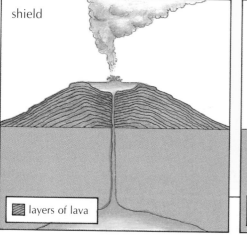

shield

layers of lava

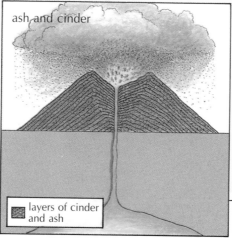

ash and cinder

layers of cinder and ash

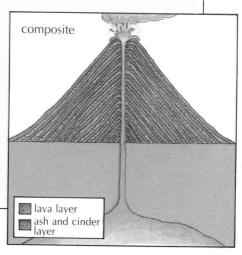

composite

lava layer
ash and cinder layer

Fig. 21-3 The world's active volcanoes.

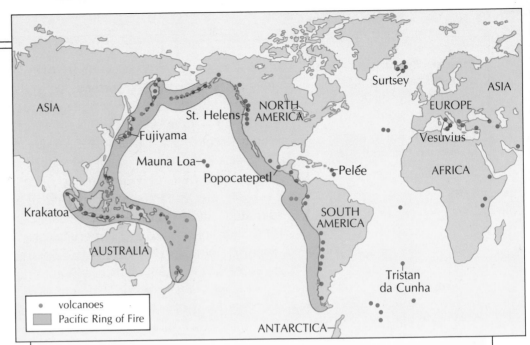

Fig. 21-4 The worst volcanic eruptions in history.

DATE	MOUNTAIN	LOCATION	NUMBER OF DEATHS
A.D. 79	Vesuvius	Italy	20 000
1631	Vesuvius	Italy	4 000
1669	Etna	Italy	20 000
1815	Tambora	Indonesia	12 000
1883	Krakatoa	Indonesia	36 000
1902	Pelée	West Indies	30 000
1963	Agung	Bali	1 600
1979	n.a.	Java	175
1980	St. Helens	United States	60
1985	Nevado del Ruiz	Armero, Colombia	23 000

ACTIVITY ONE

1. Use some reference books to find out the temperatures at which different types of rock melt.

2. Look at Fig. 21-3. What part of the world has the most volcanoes?

3. List the three types of volcanoes and summarize their characteristics.

4. a) Using an atlas and the data in Fig. 21-4, locate each of the places named on an outline map of the world.

   b) Identify the five worst volcanic eruptions in terms of the number of lives lost.

Eruptions in the news

Mr. Tanel's geography class decided to study volcanic eruptions by examining four major eruptions. The students worked in groups of four. Each group member selected one volcano to research, then returned to the group to report. The four volcanic eruptions were:

- Krakatoa   Java, 1883
- Mt. Pelée   Martinique, 1902
- Surtsey   Iceland, 1963
- Mt. St. Helens Washington, 1980

Each student used the following information to research one eruption.

Indonesian mountain vanishes, thousands killed following massive eruption

JAKARTA, JAVA—At 10:02 a.m. on August 27, 1883, the island of Krakatoa blew up. The tsunami that followed killed an estimated 36 000 inhabitants in the lowland regions of Sumatra and Java. The tsunami reached up to 30 m above normal sea level.

For several months the volcano on Krakatoa had been showing signs of erupting. On the day before the fateful blast, a series of increasingly intense explosions began. In one of these explosions, ash was blown 25 km into the sky. The sound of the explosion broke the eardrums of many crew members on a freighter about 40 km away.

With the blast on August 27, a cloud of ash was sent 80 km into the atmosphere. The blast was heard up to 5000 km away. About 20 cubic km of rock debris was rocketed 24 km into the atmosphere. The 800-metre-high mountain had disappeared from the face of the earth, leaving behind a huge hole. The sea burst into the hole and created a 30-metre-high tsunami that spread out over the surrounding areas, destroying 300 towns and villages. The cloud of ash released by the explosion eventually surrounded most of the earth.

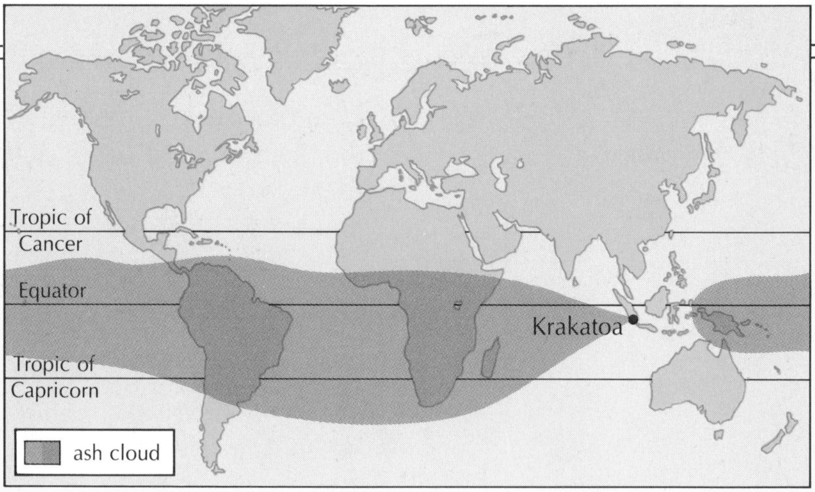

Fig. 21-5 A layer of ash from the eruption of Krakatoa in 1883 eventually surrounded the earth.

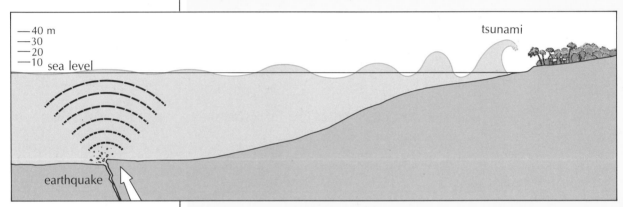

Fig. 21-6 The creation of a tsunami. Tsunamis can be caused by earthquakes, hurricanes or volcanoes.

Refer to Chapter 8 for the description of a tsunami.

ACTIVITY TWO

1. a) Explain the term "**tsunami**."
   b) What caused the tsunami that struck Sumatra in 1883?
   c) Explain what happened before, during and after the explosion on Krakatoa.

2. What caused the greatest loss of life in this natural disaster?

3. Why would the eardrums of the sailors have been broken at such a distance?

4. On your outline map of the world, locate Krakatoa. Draw a circle representing the area that heard the sound of the blast.

5. Write a newspaper article describing the tsunami as it approached your village on the coast of Java.

Mt. Pelée consumes city of 30 000—two survive

ST. PIERRE, MARTINIQUE—At 7:50 a.m. on May 8, 1902, Mt. Pelée blew up. The volcanic eruption totally destroyed the city of St. Pierre. A cloud of extremely hot gases with a temperature of about 1200°C, combined with ash and volcanic debris, shot straight up in a billowing cloud. This cloud of hot gases and dust is called a **nuée ardente**. At the same instant, some of the cloud blasted out sideways. It travelled at a speed of 33 metres per second down the side of the mountain, hitting St. Pierre with the force of a nuclear explosion.

The volcano had been issuing warning signs for some time. In February, the smell of sulphur gas was noticeable. Sulphur gas is a part of lava, and is released when the lava is under increased pressure. At the be-

ginning of April, steam was seen coming from vents at the top of the mountain, and by the end of April the mountain was spewing out clouds of ash. During the first week of May, the ash had reached a depth of several centimetres around the city. Thousands of insects and reptiles were invading the city to escape the mountain. By May 6, there had been several small explosions and eruptions.

In only an instant, on the morning of May 8, total destruction was everywhere. In St. Pierre nothing was left standing.

There were only two survivors in St. Pierre: a shoemaker and a prison inmate. Both escaped by sheer luck to tell their stories. Why did so many people remain?

Fig. 21-7   These before and after photos show Mt. Pelée's destruction of St. Pierre.

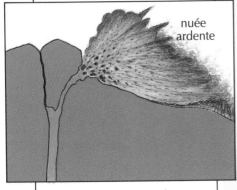

Fig. 21-8   The eruption of Mt. Pelée in 1902 sent a nuée ardente, a cloud of hot gases and debris, down on the city of St. Pierre.

nuée ardente

ACTIVITY THREE

1. Locate Mt. Pelée on the outline map of the world you used in Activity One.

2. What were some of the warning signs that there was going to be an eruption?

3. a) What actually killed the 30 000 residents of St. Pierre?
   b) Name this type of eruption.

4. What could have been done to prevent this tragedy? Why do you think the residents stayed despite all the warning signs? Discuss.

5. Use the photographs in Fig. 21-7 to write a diary entry as if you were one of the two survivors describing what you saw and felt.

Sea gives birth to new volcanic island

REYKJAVIK, ICELAND—On November 14, 1963, the crew of a fishing boat sighted what they thought was a ship on fire. As they approached the columns of smoke, they realized that what they saw was volcanic ash and steam. They later found out that they had seen the signs of a volcanic eruption occurring beneath the sea. Within several hours the clouds of steam and ash had spread several thousand metres. As the eruption continued, it became apparent that a new island was being formed. This island was named Surtsey.

There were several clues that this was about to happen. First, the temperature of the sea around the area increased. Second, the odour of sulphur was very strong in the air. Third, there were several weak tremors in the days before the event.

Over a four-year period, Surtsey grew from a fissure on the sea floor to a land-mass with an area of 2.5 square kilometres and 174 metres above sea level. During these years, there was a constant series of explosions, which shot rock fragments, lava and ash high into the air.

The growth of Surtsey took place in three stages. First, lava built up from the sea floor to just below the surface of the water, a height of 120 m. Then a series of explosive eruptions built an island of loose volcanic debris. Finally, the explosions stopped, and the lava flowed gently from the volcano hardening in layers over the volcanic rock debris.

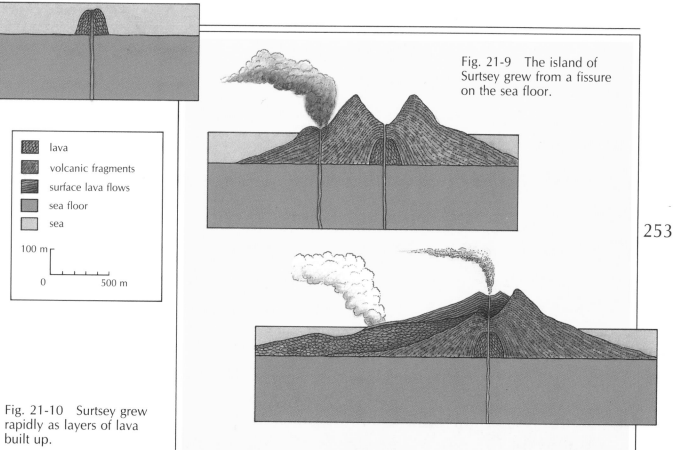

lava

volcanic fragments

surface lava flows

sea floor

sea

100 m

0   500 m

Fig. 21-9 The island of Surtsey grew from a fissure on the sea floor.

253

Fig. 21-10 Surtsey grew rapidly as layers of lava built up.

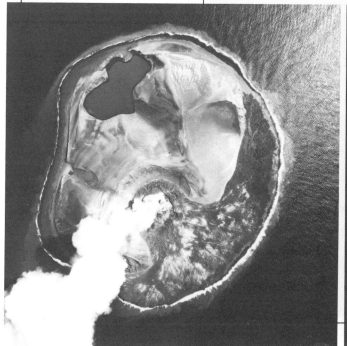

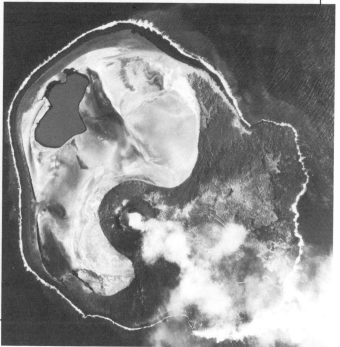

ACTIVITY FOUR 🌐 📷 ✍

1. Locate Iceland and the island of Surtsey on the world map you used in Activity One.

2. Using Figs. 21-9 and 21-10, explain the three stages in the development of the island.

3. Identify the clues that allowed people to understand what was happening under the sea before the island appeared.

4. The captain of each ship keeps a log, or record, of where the ship goes and any events that occur. Write the log entry as it might have been written by the captain of the ship that first saw signs of the birth of Surtsey.

Rain of ash shrouds Pacific Northwest in wake of blast

VANCOUVER, B.C. AND SEATTLE, WASHINGTON—On May 18, 1980, at 8:32 a.m., an event many scientists had predicted suddenly happened—one whole side of Mt. St. Helens in Washington blew apart. A huge cloud of ash spewed forth and rose thousands of metres into the atmosphere. The mountain was now almost 400 m shorter. An area of 600 square kilometres was completely devastated and covered with a thick layer of grey ash.

Scientists had been watching the volcano for years, measuring changes with instruments such as the seismograph. They said that pressure from within the volcano had increased drastically and a bulge of magma was rising inside. A small earthquake opened up part of the mountain, allowing tonnes of rock, ice and soil to flow down the sides. Hot gases and steam, travelling at speeds up to 500 kilometres per hour, were expelled straight up as well as out the side. Several quick explosions propelled some 300 million tonnes of volcanic debris, mostly ash, into the air.

The results were the deaths of 61 people and millions of fish and birds, and the destruction of millions of hectares of forest and crops. The humans, animals and plants were smothered, choked by the hot gases and ash. Many homes were buried beneath hundreds of tonnes of mud and ash.

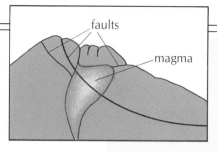

faults

magma

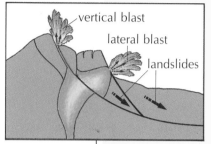

vertical blast

lateral blast

landslides

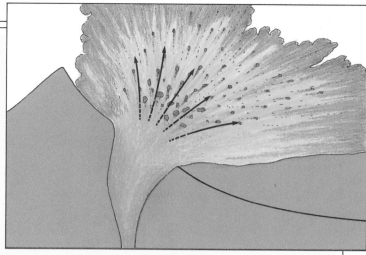

Fig. 21-11   Mt. St. Helens' eruption occurred in three stages.

Fig. 21-12   The eruption blasted away 300 million tonnes of the mountain.

ACTIVITY FIVE

1. Locate Mt. St. Helens on a map of the world. What type of volcanic eruption was this?

2. What was the final event that caused the mountain to blow apart?

3. What two factors do you think caused the greatest amount of destruction?

4. How would the location of this eruption and modern technology help volcanologists (scientists who investigate volcanes) to learn much more from Mt. St. Helens than they could from Mt. Pelée?

5. Why do you think that some people did not leave the area when they received warnings about the volcano?

6. Look at the diagrams and photographs in Figs. 21-11 and 21-12 and use your own words to describe the events that occurred. You might do this in the form of a newspaper article, a television news report, an interview with a witness or a first-hand account.

WHAT YOU HAVE LEARNED

Volcanoes occur when molten rock is forced up through cracks in the plates of the crust until it comes to the surface. Depending on the type of lava that is forced out and the type of eruption that occurs, the volcano can assume various shapes and sizes. The most common types are shield volcanoes, ash or cinder volcanoes, and composite cone volcanoes.

LOOKING BACK

1. Prepare and make a presentation on one or more of the newspaper articles. Communicate your findings by using a television interview or newspaper article format.

2. In what ways were each of the disasters similar? In what ways were they different? Locate information describing the type of eruption, the warning signs, the destructive forces that were present, the events immediately before and after the eruption, and the number of deaths. Record your results in a chart.

EXPANDING YOUR LEARNING

3. Speculate on the effect the cloud of ash released by Krakatoa would have had on the parts of the earth it covered.

4. Suggest ways to prevent the tremendous number of deaths from this type of natural disaster.

5. Compose a poem or a short story illustrating the awesome power of the volcano.

UNIT REVIEW 🔍 📓 📝

1. Name two patterns which describe one of the three types of natural disaster discussed in this unit.

2. a) Name the type of disaster that occurs most often according to the information in this unit.
   b) Name the type of disaster that has killed the most people.
   c) Which of these disasters is the easiest to do something about?
   d) What can scientists do to help prevent death and destruction caused by natural disasters?

3. You are in charge of an agency that is sending supplies to an area hit by a natural disaster. Consider a disaster
   (i) in your own country
   (ii) in a distant part of the world
   a) Make a list of emergency supplies that you would send.
   b) What problems might you have getting these supplies to the people who need them?

4. You are a newspaper reporter at the scene of a volcanic eruption. Write a story of the events leading up to the disaster as well as what happened during and after. In your report, think about the people and their feelings. (It might be useful to interview some of them.)

5. Research another natural disaster not discussed in this unit. Examine
   a) location
   b) causes
   c) effects
   d) patterns of movement
   e) damage and loss of life
   f) methods of control and prevention
   g) emergency aid

UNIT VI
River Systems

CHAPTER 22

What Makes a River Run?

Fig. 22-1   The location you will learn about in this chapter.

WHAT YOU WILL LEARN

Rivers are part of a huge system called the water cycle. In this chapter you will learn how the water cycle works and why a river continuously runs to the ocean, even during dry periods. You will discover that a river contains many sources that contribute to its flow.

KEY WORDS

water cycle	**mouth**	**tributaries**
intermittent stream	**ground water**	**source**

Where does the water come from?

> "For men may come and men may go,
>   But I go on forever."
>
> from "The Brook"
> by Alfred, Lord Tennyson

Rivers have always fascinated people. Poets have tried to capture the unique quality of a river, and painters have used rivers as the focal point of their art. Explorers have endured hardships in order to discover the mysteries of unmapped rivers. River valleys have always attracted large numbers of people and cities have grown up along their banks.

What is the attraction of rivers? Rivers contain water, and water is an essential requirement for life. Although 70 percent of the earth's surface is covered with water, most of it is salt water, which humans cannot drink. Rivers are our main source of fresh water, which we use to drink, to keep ourselves clean and to grow our crops.

Rivers are passageways for excess water to travel from higher land down to the sea. Since rivers are always flowing or "running," they are continually bringing a new supply of water. If we use the water or make it dirty, it seems as though there is always a new supply of clean water to take its place. Where does this regular supply of fresh water come from?

When it rains, the water finds its way into the rivers. Some rain falls directly into the rivers, but some water may take a day or so to reach the rivers because it is absorbed into the ground or runs into storm sewers. However, the water eventually reaches the rivers, and once it does, the amount of water in each river increases and so does its speed. Readings are taken at points along the river in order to find out the speed, or rate, of flow of the water.

Fig. 22-2 Twenty Mile Creek and Balls Falls.

Fig. 22-3 The daily average rate of flow and amount of precipitation was measured at Balls Falls during the month of September, 1984.

DATE	AVERAGE RATE OF FLOW (in cubic metres per second)	PRECIPITATION (in millimetres)	DATE	AVERAGE RATE OF FLOW (in cubic metres per second)	PRECIPITATION (in millimetres)
Sept 1	.02	—	Sept 16	20.60	—
2	.02	6.8	17	12.40	—
3	.05	5.6	18	6.17	—
4	.06	.2	19	3.36	—
5	.05	—	20	2.04	—
6	.04	—	21	1.38	—
7	.03	—	22	1.00	—
8	.02	—	23	.66	.6
9	.01	—	24	.45	2.9
10	.04	21.0	25	.40	—
11	1.98	40.6	26	.62	18.0
12	6.46	1.3	27	1.09	—
13	4.82	25.0	28	1.68	—
14	8.80	9.6	29	1.97	—
15	18.10	17.6	30	1.80	—

ACTIVITY ONE

1. Use Fig. 22-3 to examine the rate of flow in Twenty Mile Creek for one month.
   a) Round off each number in the rate of flow column to the nearest tenth.
   b) Round off the amounts of precipitation to the nearest millimetre.
   c) Use the rounded-off figures to construct two bar graphs, one for the rate of flow, the other for the amount of precipitation.

2. Examine your graphs carefully.
   a) When did the rate of flow in Twenty Mile Creek increase?
   b) Which increase was the greatest? Which was the smallest?
   c) When did the most rain fall during the month of September? What happened to the flow in Twenty Mile Creek during this period?

To round off to the nearest tenth, examine the number in the hundredths position. If it is five or greater, round up to the next tenth. If it is four or lower, round down to the next lowest tenth. For example, 6.46 is rounded up to become 6.5, and .44 becomes .4 when it is rounded down.

3. What can you conclude about the relationship between stream flow and precipitation?

4. Explain why the greatest stream flow always occurred a day or two after the precipitation peak.

The water cycle

Precipitation is the major source of the water flowing in a river. Precipitation and rivers are two important stages in the **water cycle**.

The first step in the water cycle is precipitation, which falls as rain, hail or snow. When the precipitation falls on land, some of it runs directly into rivers, lakes and oceans. Some of it trickles down through the soil to become part of the **ground water**, the supply of water underground, within the rocks and soil. Some of it is absorbed by plants while some remains on the surface of the land.

In the second stage of the water cycle, the heat from the sun causes water in the oceans or on the surface of the land to evaporate. Plants and animals also release water vapour into the air. The water vapour rises and cools. As it cools, it condenses into tiny droplets of water that we see as clouds. This condensation is the third stage of the water cycle. When the weather conditions are right, this moisture will again fall to earth as precipitation. The water cycle repeats itself again and again, supplying the earth with water. Rivers are one stage in this continuous water cycle.

Fig. 22-4 How does the water cycle help to keep rivers flowing?

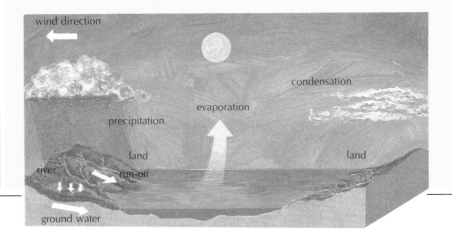

ACTIVITY TWO

1. a) List the three stages of the water cycle.
   b) Explain each of the stages.

2. Obtain a potted plant such as a geranium. Place a clear plastic bag over the plant and tie the bag around its stem. Put the plant in a sunny spot for a few hours. What happens to the inside of the plastic bag? What role do plants play in the water cycle?

3. Fill two dishes with an equal amount of water. Place one dish in a sunny spot and the other in shade. In which dish does the water disappear more quickly? What does this suggest about the role of the sun in the water cycle?

What keeps rivers flowing?

I f precipitation is the major source of water flowing in a river, why do rivers continue to flow when there has been no rain? In fact, some streams do dry up each summer. These streams are known as intermittent streams, and are shown on maps as dotted blue lines.

When something is intermittent, it means it is not constant, but stops and starts or pauses from time to time.

Fig. 22-5 A block diagram of a river system.

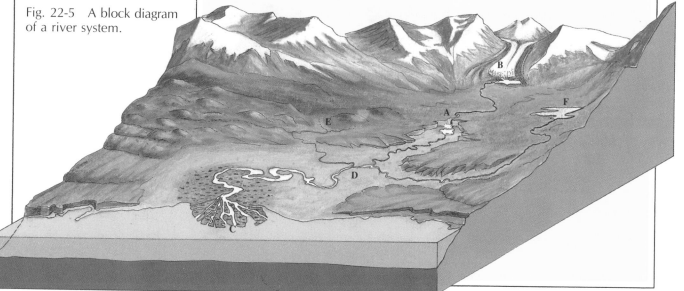

A **drainage basin** is an area of the earth's surface that is drained by a river system.

The **mouth** is the point where a river or stream empties into another stream, river, lake or sea.

The **source** is the place where a river or stream begins.

Larger rivers keep flowing because they have a system of **tributaries**, smaller rivers or creeks that drain water from the surrounding land and supply it to the main river. Gravity helps the water flow from higher land down to lower land, where it forms rivers. These, in turn, flow into the oceans. The entire area drained by one river system is known as the river's **drainage basin**.

If you examine a river on a map, you will see that one end empties into a larger body of water—an ocean, a lake or a larger river. This is called the **mouth** of the river. If you follow the river upstream, you will see that it becomes smaller and narrower, and then it ends suddenly. This end is the **source** of the river. The source may be a small pond, a lake or a swamp.

Fig. 22-6   Can you identify these parts of a river system?

It may be a glacier that is melting slowly or a spring flowing from deep within the ground. Each of these sources stores water and provides the river with water during dry periods.

Human beings also affect the flow of rivers. Dams are sometimes built to store water. The stored water can be used to increase the flow during dry periods. In this way, humans can control a river's flow.

Humans can also cause the river's flow to be unpredictable. In the natural environment, trees and other forms of vegetation slow down the rain and give the ground a chance to absorb it. Cutting down forests and clearing vegetation can decrease the amount of water the ground can absorb and can cause erosion. Paved roads and parking lots also prevent water from entering the ground. The water runs into storm sewers that carry it directly into rivers. This can cause the rivers to flood, because the ground has no chance to absorb any of this water.

Natural sources that provide the river with water, such as marshes or springs, may be drained or filled in to allow construction on the land. It is important that we understand what makes rivers run and how humans can affect this process, so our rivers will continue to provide us with fresh water.

ACTIVITY THREE 📷 ✏️

1. Examine Figure 22-5. Give the letter that shows each of the following:
   • a river's source in the form of a lake
   • a river's source in the form of a glacier
   • an intermittent stream
   • a waterfall or rapids
   • the mouth of a tributary river
   • the mouth of the main river

2. Examine the photographs in Fig. 22-6. Locate the scene shown in each photograph on the river system in Fig. 22-5.

3. What role does gravity play in the flow of rivers and the water cycle?

4. How have humans affected the flow of the river in Fig. 22-7?

Fig. 22-7 Humans can also affect a river's flow.

WHAT YOU HAVE LEARNED

In this chapter you looked at one particular pattern—the movement of water. You investigated one river and saw how precipitation affected its volume and rate of flow, and that there is a delay of a day or two before rainwater reaches the river. Secondly, you saw how the water cycle works and how it helps to keep the rivers flowing. Finally, by looking at an imaginary river system, you should be familiar with its parts and how each contributes to the system as a whole.

LOOKING BACK

1. Define the following terms:
   - ground water
   - tributary
   - intermittent stream
   - a river's mouth

2. a) Explain the relationship between precipitation and the flow of rivers.
   b) Develop a simple experiment to show this relationship.

Fig. 22-8 This is one method of measuring the rate of flow in a river or stream.

3. Construct a model of the water cycle. Place a pan of water on a hot plate. Bring the water to a boil. Once it boils, hold a second pan containing ice cubes above the boiling water. What happens to the bottom of the pan of ice cubes? If a warm pan is held above the boiling water, does the same thing happen? Write a short report describing your model and how it represents the water cycle.

EXPANDING YOUR LEARNING

4. a) Examine a map of a river system in your local area. Locate its mouth, its source or sources, and its various tributaries. Why does it flow in the direction that it does?
   b) Organize a field trip to a local river or stream and identify some of the features of a river system.
   c) Measure the rate of flow at various locations on the river using a stop watch, a ping-pong ball and a measuring tape, as shown in Fig. 22-8.

Careers in geography: Water Resources Technician

Water resources technicians work to maintain and improve river valley systems. They are interested in storm damage and flood control in water quality, and in protecting valley resources. Water resources technicians study Water Resources Engineering at community college or university. They need skills in math, science, computers and communication. They study reports for technical accuracy and suitability, visit river valleys and work with consultants and developers interested in river valleys. They write letters and reports to help people understand our valley systems and to manage them well.

Christine Doody-Hamilton is a Water Resources Technician for the Metro Toronto Region Conservation Authority. She enjoys her job because she feels that protecting our water and valley resources is an important task. "Engineering is not just hard hats and work boots. There are many creative elements to design and planning."

Fig. 22-9 People who work in the field of water resource management use maps and reports to find the best uses for our rivers.

CHAPTER 23

Where Does a River Run?

Fig. 23-1 The location you will learn about in this chapter.

WHAT YOU WILL LEARN

In this chapter, you will look at some of the physical patterns of a river system, as seen through the eyes of a famous explorer—Alexander Mackenzie. You will discover how physical features affect a river system. Finally, you will look at the changes in the level of water caused by a dam in a river system.

KEY WORDS

continental divide	meltwater	contour

Alexander Mackenzie: River explorer

One of Canada's greatest geographers was an explorer named Alexander Mackenzie. During the late eighteenth century he was searching for an easy route across Canada to the Pacific. At that time, the fur trade was important to Canada's economy and Mackenzie wanted to make it easier to move the furs from the areas where they were caught or traded to areas where they could be sold. In 1789, he travelled from Fort Chipewyan down the river that now bears his name. He hoped that it would bring him to the Pacific Ocean. However, after flowing west for many kilometres, the river began to turn to the north and he eventually found himself at the Arctic Ocean.

In 1792 he decided to try again. This time he travelled up a tributary of the Mackenzie called the Peace River. This journey

Fig. 23-2 Mackenzie explored several major river basins, including the Mackenzie, the Peace and the Fraser.

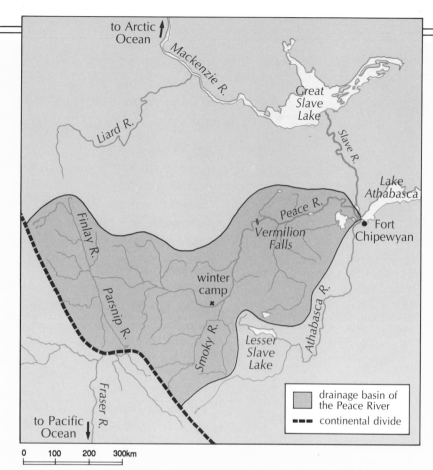

The **continental divide** is the line of high land that separates the drainage basins of all the rivers on a continent that drain into one ocean from the drainage basins of all the rivers draining into another.

brought him to the southernmost source of the Mackenzie River system. He crossed the **continental divide** and successfully reached the Pacific Ocean. His journal of this trip is a fascinating account of his travels. The following account is loosely based on this journal. As you read the account, follow Mackenzie's route on the map in Fig. 23-2.

An Explorer's Journal

October 10, 1792
We set out in the canoe from Fort Chipewyan across Lake Athabasca. The land here, from the Athabasca River to the Peace River, is very flat and low. Many small rivers and lakes connect Lake Athabasca, the Peace River and the Athabasca River.

Fig. 23-3 Explorer Alexander Mackenzie set out to find a route across Canada to the Pacific Ocean.

Fig. 23-4 As Mackenzie began his journey on the Peace River, he found it wide and easy to navigate.

October 12, 1792
We entered the Peace River which flows into Lake Athabasca from the west. The current, which is flowing east, is not strong so we travel quickly.

October 17, 1792
At three this afternoon, still heading west, we reached a spectacular falls. The river here is about 350 metres wide with the falls about six metres high. We portaged for approximately two kilometres uphill until we were able to travel on the water once again.

October 25, 1792
As we continue to travel up the Peace, the weather is getting colder and snow is beginning to fall. During the last few days we have passed several tributaries flowing into the river from both the north and the south.

November 1, 1792
We finally reach a good place to camp for the winter, just upstream from where a large tributary enters the river. Here the river banks are steeper than downstream. Looking west we can see in the distance a ridge of high land. We hope that once we cross it, the land will begin to slope down towards the Pacific.

May 9, 1793
After a long, hard winter we finally set out on our journey once again. As we near its source, the river quickly becomes narrower. High cliffs rise up on both sides. In many places the strong current undercuts the banks.

May 16, 1793
The current continues to grow stronger. There are many rapids and waterfalls around which we are forced to portage.

May 23, 1793
The river here is not more than 50 metres wide. It

Meltwater is water coming from a melting glacier or melting snow.

Fig. 23-5 When Mackenzie neared the source of the Peace, he found it had narrowed to a channel of rapids between tall cliffs. Why did the river change?

flows between towering cliffs of rock. From great heights, large chunks of these rocks often fall, causing concern for our safety. We pass many small creeks overflowing with meltwater from mountain snow. The mountains are bare without any trees to decorate them.

May 31, 1793
Today we reached a point where the Peace River divides, forming two branches. We must decide which branch to follow, the one to the north or the one to the south. Our guides warn us that the northern branch will soon be lost in many mountain streams. Thus we will follow the southern route hoping that it will take us to the Pacific, or at least to another river that will.

June 10, 1793
It looks as though this river will not lead us to the Pacific after all. However, we are cheered when we meet a man who claims to know the source of a river that flows west. He says it begins in a small lake just south of here. Our hopes are renewed as our new guide leads us up tributaries that are only three metres wide.

June 11, 1793
After a day of excitement and hard work we reach the lake that is the source of the tributary that we have been following.

June 12, 1793
We cross over a ridge of land to another small lake. A river flows out of this lake, running west. We are certain that this is the river that will lead us to the Pacific.

ACTIVITY ONE 🌐 📓

1. a) In what direction does the Peace River flow?
   b) How did this influence Mackenzie's voyage?

c) Describe the Peace River at
   (i) Vermilion Falls
   (ii) between the location of the winter camp and the place where the river divides.

2. On an outline map of Fig. 23-2 trace Mackenzie's first voyage in blue and his second in red.

3. What is the Peace River called as it flows north from Lake Athabasca?

4. What is the name of the river that flows out of Great Slave Lake?

5. Into what ocean do the waters of the Peace River eventually flow?

6. Use an atlas to find which mountains form the continental divide between the drainage basins of the Pacific and Arctic oceans.

The effect of landscape on flow

Mackenzie had found a river that ran west into the Pacific Ocean, the Fraser River. He soon discovered that it was too fast-flowing for easy navigation. In fact, he had to walk beside it for most of the way! Even this was not easy because of the landscape through which the river flowed.

Rivers follow the slope and **contour** of the land through which they pass. By looking at the surrounding landscape, Mackenzie might have guessed what the Fraser River would be like. Because the Fraser River flows through the Rocky Mountains, the water must follow a steep slope, causing it to flow very quickly and therefore be very dangerous to try to navigate.

On the other hand, some rivers run through flat land and therefore they move slowly and are generally easy to navigate.

If Mackenzie were to examine a modern map of the Peace River, he might not recognize it as the river he explored. In 1968,

Navigation is the act of steering or guiding a ship or plane.

The **contour** of a landscape refers to the outline or general shape of the land.

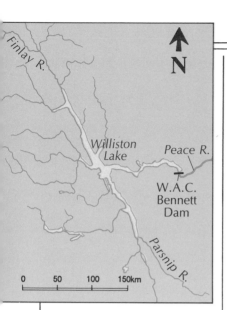

Fig. 23-6 The upper Peace River area. How has the W.A.C. Bennett Dam changed the landscape Mackenzie saw?

Fig. 23-7 The W.A.C. Bennett Dam and Williston Lake.

the W.A.C. Bennett Dam was built on the Peace River downstream from the point at which the river divides. The dam produced British Columbia's largest freshwater body, Williston Lake (see Figs. 23-6 and 23-7). It flooded some of the most spectacular canyons of the Peace River as well as flooding the Finlay and Parsnip rivers. The new lake has an unusual shape, reaching out in many directions with long narrow arms. In fact, Williston Lake has a very predictable shape. It simply follows the contours of the old river valleys. If the water in the lake rose ten metres, all of the land along the narrow arms would flood to the same depth of ten metres.

How geographers work: Contour lines

The lines on the map in Fig. 23-8 are contour lines. Contour lines can be used to indicate the contour of an area by joining points of equal elevation together. Each contour line is ten metres higher in elevation than the one below it. A river runs through the valley below the lowest contour line. When these lines are close together, they indicate that the slope of the land is steep. Therefore, when the lines are farther apart, they indicate a gentler slope. What do the contour lines on Fig. 23-8 indicate about the contour of this area?

274

Fig. 23-8   A contour map showing an area similar to the Peace River. What physical features are indicated by the contour lines?

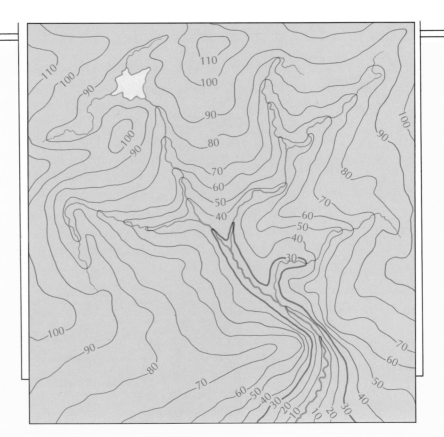

ACTIVITY TWO

1. Examine Fig. 23-6. From which direction is the river flowing? How can you tell?

2. Examine Fig. 23-8, which shows the contour of the area surrounding a river.
   a) What direction does the river run?
   b) What direction do the contour lines always seem to bend when they cross the river or its tributaries? Explain this pattern.

3. a) In one location on Fig. 23-8, the main river flows through a narrow valley. This is the location at which the 60 m contour lines come the closest together on either side of the river. Locate this spot.
   b) Imagine that a dam was built across the river at this point. If the water rose behind the dam to a height of 30 metres, all the land below the 30-metre contour line would be

flooded. If the water rose to the 40-metre line, where would the shoreline of the new lake be?

c) On a copy of Fig. 23-8, mark the location of the dam, and label it with a name you have chosen. Use blue to outline the shape of the lake that would form behind the dam if the water rose to 60 m.

4. Predict the effects dam construction would have on
   a) natural vegetation in the area
   b) wildlife
   c) hydro-electric production
   d) water supplies for the surrounding urban areas
   e) local employment

Rivers of North America

In the previous section you looked at one particular river system. Now you will use Fig. 23-9 to identify the ten major river systems on the North American continent and their drainage basins. You will see that each river system is separated from the others by a divide—a height of land or mountain range that keeps them apart.

ACTIVITY THREE 🌐 📊 ✍️

1. The Peace River drainage basin is part of the larger Mackenzie River drainage basin. Use a heavy black line to draw the Mackenzie River drainage basin on an outline map of Fig. 23-9.

2. Use an atlas to identify the nine other river systems shown on Fig. 23-9.

3. Draw a solid black line around the drainage basin for each of these river systems on the map you used in question 1.

4. Colour your map using five colours. Choose one colour to show the areas draining into each of the following:
   • the Pacific Ocean   • the Gulf of Mexico
   • the Arctic Ocean   • the Gulf of St. Lawrence
   • the Atlantic Ocean

5. Where does most of Canada's land area drain?

6. Where do the waters of Southern Ontario drain?

7. Using the bar graphs on Fig. 23-9,
   a) estimate the total annual volume of flow for each of the
   rivers included.

Fig. 23-9 North America's ten major river systems and their drainage basins. The bar graphs show the volume of flow by month in billions of cubic metres.

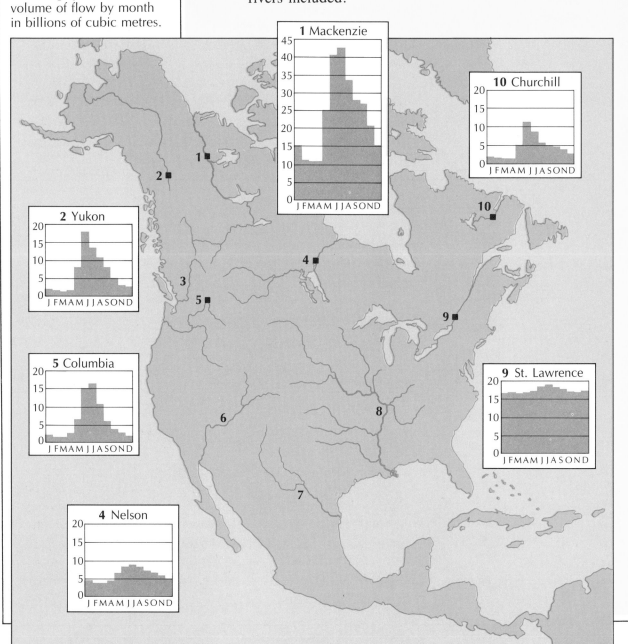

b) indicate the months of the greatest volume of flow for each river.

c) speculate on why the months of greatest flow vary from river to river.

WHAT YOU HAVE LEARNED

In this chapter, you journeyed with Mackenzie as he explored his route to the Pacific. During his exploration, he saw how the physical features of the surrounding landscape affected the river system. He also saw that the rate of flow depended on the slope and contour of the land and that the direction of the flow was influenced by the various heights of land, or divides. You learned what contour lines are on a map and what they represent in the real world. Finally, you know what the ten major river systems in North America are and you should be able to locate them on a map.

LOOKING BACK

1. Using Fig. 23-9 and an atlas, identify the major physical feature that creates the divide between each of the five major drainage areas in North America.

2. Explain why Mackenzie was unable to navigate on the Fraser River through the Rocky Mountains and was therefore forced to travel overland to the Pacific.

3. Explain the present shape of Williston Lake. What features of the landscape make it long and narrow rather than round?

EXPANDING YOUR LEARNING

4. Some people feel that dams are a good idea, while others oppose them. In order to learn about the positive and negative effects of dams, locate articles in newspapers and magazines that describe the feelings and positions of people on both sides of the question. Form small groups, divide and read the articles, then judge the reasons given for and against building dams. Present your group's findings to the other groups in the class.

CHAPTER 24

The Gift of the Nile

Fig. 24-1   The location you will learn about in this chapter.

WHAT YOU WILL LEARN

Our natural environment is made up of everything around, on and within the earth. We all live within this environment, and we affect and are affected by it.

Here you will study the Nile River, the world's longest, and look specifically at how it has affected the lives of those who live near it and depend on it. In addition, you will see how we have changed this environment by interfering with the natural flow of the river in order to increase agricultural production.

KEY WORDS

cataract	delta	pyramids

The gift of the Nile

How many months will it be until your summer holidays begin? To answer, you need a calendar to divide the year into segments of time. Every society has some way to measure time. Today, most of the world uses a calendar based on the orbit of the earth around the sun. In the past however, some based their calendar on the changing position of the stars. Others used the phases of the moon. In ancient Egypt, the calendar was based on the water level of the Nile River.

From 3200 B.C., the people of ancient Egypt lived in the

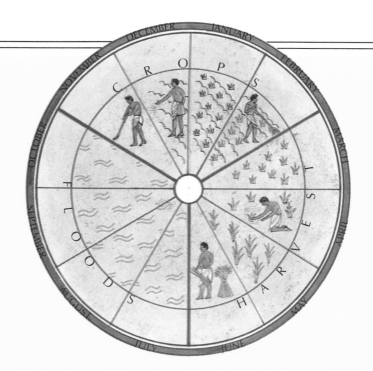

Fig. 24-2 The ancient Egyptian calendar was based on the Nile's yearly cycle of high and low water levels.

Nile Valley, which remained one kingdom for three thousand years. The Egyptians of that time depended so much on the Nile that they called Egypt ''The Gift of the Nile.'' The Nile provided the water needed to grow crops in a hot climate and to move goods from place to place along its length. It fed the cities that clustered along its banks.

The Nile River had a sequence of periods of high and low water every year. The ancient Egyptian calendar was based on this annual sequence of floods, growth and harvest. The Nile flooded from the end of June till late October, depositing rich silt from the upper areas of the river. Crops were then planted in this improved soil. They grew from late October to late February, irrigated by the waters of the Nile. By the time the waters had receded, the crops were ready for harvest. They were then harvested from late February until the end of June.

The Nile was very important to the Egyptians. It brought prosperity in two forms—fertile soil during flood season and irrigation water in crop season. Much of Egypt and Sudan to the south are made up of deserts, so that fertile soil and plentiful water are like gifts. Today, as in the past, the Nile provides water for a dry land.

ACTIVITY ONE

1. a) What is the basis of the most common modern calendar?
   b) What is the basis of the ancient Egyptian calendar?

2. What two requirements for successful farming are provided by the Nile?

3. During which months on the calendar of the Nile are the
   a) floods?   b) crops?   c) harvest?

4. Write a brief story describing farm life along the Nile in ancient Egypt.

A journey down the Nile

Imagine yourself travelling down the longest river in the world, from the Equator to the Mediterranean Sea. You would see many changes in the river itself, as well as in the climate and lands through which it passes. All along the Nile you would see how vital it is to the life of northeast Africa and how the people who live along its banks depend on it for their survival. (Refer to Fig. 24-4 as you read the rest of this chapter to help you to follow your course down the river.)

There are actually two Niles; the White Nile and the Blue Nile. The source of the White Nile is Lake Victoria, high in the mountains of Uganda. A dam at Owen Falls controls the level of Lake Victoria and provides hydroelectricity for the surrounding areas. The White Nile drops a second time at Victoria Falls. Below Victoria Falls, the river winds through wooded grasslands towards Sudan. Although the area is right on the Equator, the climate is quite moderate because of its elevation. It is about 20°C all year in Kampala, Uganda's capital.

In Sudan, the White Nile enters a huge marshy area known as the Sûdd. This swamp is covered by tangled tropical vegetation. It is so big that you could fit the whole province of New Brunswick into it!

Beyond the Sûdd, near Khartoum, the White and the Blue Nile come together. The Blue Nile begins in Lake Tana in the Ethiopian highlands. North of Khartoum, the dry lands farther

Fig. 24-3   The Nile serves as a busy highway for both Egyptians and visitors.

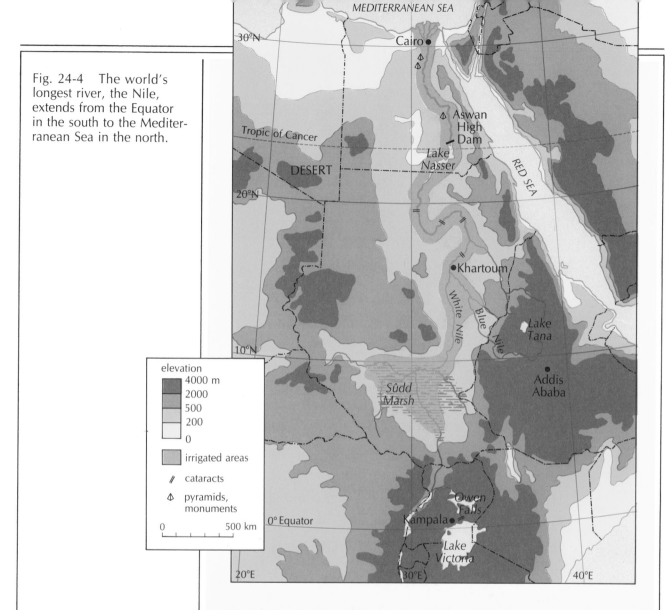

Fig. 24-4 The world's longest river, the Nile, extends from the Equator in the south to the Mediterranean Sea in the north.

Cataracts are a series of rapids or waterfalls in a river.

from the river cannot support crops; only a small amount of sheep and cattle herding is possible. Yet Khartoum and the area to the north along the river form the most populated areas in Sudan, largely because irrigation makes it possible to grow citrus fruit, bananas, sugar cane and cotton in the Nile Valley. Farther north, the Nile moves through a series of rapids, or **cataracts**. This is a region of hot, dry desert. Few people live away from the river, but crops of citrus, cotton and dates thrive in the river valley.

Fig. 24-5 The longest rivers of each continent. Where is the longest North American river located?

RIVER	LENGTH *(in kilometres)*	CONTINENT
Amazon	6400	South America
Mackenzie	4216	North America
Murray-Darling	3696	Australia
Nile	6656	Africa
Volga	3510	Europe
Chang Jiang (Yangtze)	6342	Asia

ACTIVITY TWO

1. Which river is the longest in the world?

2. Rank the rivers in Fig. 24-5 from longest to shortest.

3. a) In what direction does the Nile River run?
   b) Look at the elevation legend in Fig. 24-4 and explain what happens to the land from Lake Victoria to Cairo.

4. Use Fig. 24-4 to find the following parts of the Nile:
   a) the source of the Blue Nile   c) a tributary
   b) the source of the White Nile   d) a marsh

5. a) Through how many degrees of latitude does the Nile flow?
   b) Through how many degrees of latitude is there irrigated land along the Nile?

6. Using an atlas, identify the four countries and their capital cities through which the Nile flows.

From Aswan to Cairo

As we proceed down the river we come to the Aswan High Dam on the Egypt-Sudan border. The dam has backed up the Nile River to form Lake Nasser, one of the four largest reservoirs in the world. Lake Nasser provides enough water to irrigate nearly half a million hectares of land. Because of this, Egyptian wheat production increased by 50 percent soon after the dam was built in 1971. Before the Aswan High Dam was built, most Egyptian farmers planted one crop a year. Now there is water all year, allowing two, and in some areas, even three crops a year to be grown.

Fig. 24-6 Modern Cairo, Africa's largest city, is situated on the Nile below the Nile Delta.

A **delta** is an area of soil or silt deposits built up at the mouth of the river. Often the river separates into a number of channels in its delta.

The Pharaohs, or kings, of ancient Egypt built huge tombs for themselves called **pyramids**, many of which are still standing.

The Aswan High Dam project took eleven years to build. Special steps were taken so that Lake Nasser would not cause any damage. For example, ancient Egyptian temples were moved to higher land and an entire Sudanese town was relocated. The dam includes a hydroelectric plant which supplies enough electricity for all of Egypt and much of Sudan. The Aswan High Dam also prevents raging floodwaters from damaging parts of Egypt.

The Aswan High Dam has also had some negative effects. Instead of flooding onto the fields beside the river, as it had for thousands of years, fertile soil is now piling up behind the dam. As a result, Egyptian farmers now must rely on heavy amounts of fertilizer to improve their soil. The dam also affects the **delta** of the Nile, the area at the river's mouth where silt in the river water is deposited. The Nile Delta is no longer receiving as much soil as before. This allows salty sea water into the river channels of the delta. The sea water erodes the land and ruins the farming. Changing a river system with major dam or canal projects often brings about serious problems with the natural environment and for the people living along the river's banks.

From Aswan to Cairo the Nile is alive with river traffic. The **pyramids** and monuments of the ancient Pharaohs along the river attract tourists, and barges carry the products of the region. Cairo is more than double the size of any other African city.

Fig. 24-7 How does Cairo's climate affect farming in this area?

In a region of almost no precipitation, the irrigated farms of the Nile and its delta support the highest population density in all of Africa. Today, as much as in ancient times, Egypt truly is "the gift of the Nile."

CAIRO, EGYPT Elevation 116 m

	J	F	M	A	M	J	J	A	S	O	N	D
mm	5	5	5	3	3	2	0	0	2	2	3	5
°C	13	15	17	21	25	27	28	28	26	24	20	15

ACTIVITY THREE

1. a) Lake Victoria is the world's third largest lake. Which are the first and second largest?
   b) Use an atlas and Fig. 24-4 to find the elevation of Lake Victoria.

2. Describe a journey down the Nile during which you pass through the Kampala area, the Sûdd Marsh area, and the area of the cataracts.

3. Using your atlas, find the name of the highland in which the Blue Nile begins.

4. Should the Aswan High Dam have been built? Answer this question from the point of view of
   a) a farmer living below the dam.
   b) a farmer living in the Nile Delta.
   c) someone living in the city of Cairo.

5. Look at the climatic data for Cairo, Egypt in Fig. 24-7. Approximately how much precipitation falls in this city each year? (For comparison, Toronto receives approximately 800 mm annually.) How will this amount of precipitation affect farming in the Cairo area?

6. Draw and label a climate graph for Cairo.

7. Vegetation requires temperatures of at least 6°C to grow.
   a) Draw the 6°C growing temperature line across the graph.
   b) How many months long is the growing season at Cairo?

c) Compare this with the growing season in ancient times as shown in Fig. 24-2.

WHAT YOU HAVE LEARNED

For centuries, the changes in the Nile have been used to divide the calendar into agricultural seasons of floods, crops and harvest. With the flooding of the Nile came water for irrigation and the new soil necessary for crops. By constructing the Aswan High Dam, the natural flow of the Nile has been interrupted. The annual flooding has been halted and along with it the natural fertilization of the land. In addition, a large area above the dam was flooded, requiring the relocation of many homes and ancient structures. The Nile continues to have a strong impact on the many different environmental and cultural regions through which it passes.

285

LOOKING BACK

1. Of the four countries through which the Nile River flows, which do you think depends the most on the Nile? Why?

2. How have the lives of Egyptian farmers been changed by the Aswan High Dam?

3. Identify the country in which each of the following is located:
   a) the Nile Delta
   b) the Aswan High Dam
   c) the Sûdd Marsh
   d) the source of the Blue Nile
   e) the source of the White Nile

EXPANDING YOUR LEARNING

4. a) If Lake Nasser is the fourth largest reservoir in the world, which are the three largest?
   b) On which rivers are these reservoirs built?
   c) Why were they built?
   d) Have there been any negative effects caused by these projects?

5. The Nile River has a delta at its mouth. Why do some rivers form deltas while others do not? Locate three other rivers that have formed deltas.

Rivers: A Resource for Everyone

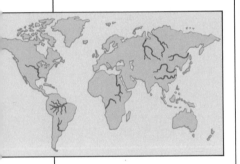

Fig. 25-1 The locations you will learn about in this chapter.

WHAT YOU WILL LEARN

We expect a great deal of our rivers. We play and bathe in them and drink from them. We use them to cool the machines in our industries. Often, however, we do more than use our rivers, we also abuse them, and yet we expect them to continue to serve us.

In this chapter, you will look at the importance of rivers and how people use them. You will have the opportunity to participate in a role-playing situation. This will emphasize some of the difficulties in using and conserving our rivers.

KEY WORDS

consumer	**pesticides**	**sewage**
waste materials		

How important are our rivers?

In this unit, we have seen several uses for rivers; as sources for our water supply and reservoirs for rainfall, as transportation routes, and as sources of hydroelectric power and crop irrigation. Now we will examine recreational and industrial uses of rivers.

As recreational areas, rivers serve a very useful function in our modern society. Many people go to campsites along our rivers, or travel the waterways in boats of all sizes. Fishing on rivers is another popular recreation.

Fig. 25-2 Our rivers provide areas for recreation.

Fig. 25-3 The pulp and paper industry is one of the largest water consumers today. How do they use the water?

For centuries, people have used rivers to mark political boundaries between countries, states, or other regions. Cities were often founded on rivers to take advantage of the river's function as a transportation and trade route.

Today, industries are probably the single largest **consumer** of water both in an indirect and a direct sense. Indirectly they consume vast amounts of hydroelectric power, while directly they use water in processing their products. Two of the largest water-consuming industries are the pulp and paper industry and the iron and steel industry. Paper factories use water to wash the wood, and later to mix with wood pulp to form paper. In the iron and steel industry, water is used both to cool and to wash their products.

ACTIVITY ONE

1. a) List three different ways that people have used rivers in the past.
   b) List five ways that people use rivers today.
   c) Do any of the modern uses of rivers conflict with one another? How?

2. a) Use your atlas to locate the following rivers:
   - the St. Lawrence
   - the Amur
   - the Rio Grande
   - the Oder
   - the Yalu
   - the Rhine
   - the Donau (Danube)
   - the Uruguay

   b) Which countries are separated by each river?

Are we killing our rivers?

Many industries dump most of their **waste materials** into rivers, and municipalities often send untreated or partially-treated **sewage** back into the rivers. Fertilizer and **pesticides** from agricultural areas also end up back in the rivers by entering the soil and, therefore, the ground water.

Once dumped, these wastes are only seen by those people who live downstream and who also must use the waters of the river. As a result, many rivers, which begin at their source with sparkling clear, clean water become slow, dirty and full of pollution.

Pollution kills the life in the rivers. It prevents people from using rivers for recreation because many of the polluting substances can make humans ill. Pollution also presents a health hazard to those living near a river or those using its water as a source of drinking water. Most water from rivers near large cities must first be purified with chemicals in water-treatment plants near the rivers. This is a very costly process and as new and more dangerous substances are being discovered in the rivers the cost will continue to rise. In many areas of the world, water is not treated before use because of this cost factor.

Rivers are important not only as sources of recreation, irrigation and industry, but also as a primary source of one of our major requirements—drinking water.

The world's largest cities are located along rivers. Billions of people depend on rivers to provide their drinking water. Yet rivers in many parts of the world are now extremely polluted, to the point where they cannot be saved. Many rivers are not yet hopeless, but only quick action will save them.

Waste materials are what is left over after industrial processes and manufacturing.

Sewage is the waste material of homes and industries which is removed in urban areas by underground pipes.

Pesticides are strong chemicals used to kill insects.

Fig. 25-4 A river choked by pollution cannot always be saved. What can be done to prevent this from happening?

ACTIVITY TWO

1. List the problems that we are confronting concerning our rivers.

2. a) What kinds of contaminants pollute our rivers?
   b) Which kind do you feel are the most serious? Why?

3. a) Use your atlas to locate the following rivers:
   - the Hudson
   - the South Saskatchewan
   - the Chang Jiang (Yangtze)
   - the Dijlah (Tigris)
   - the Nile
   - the Irrawaddy
   - the Donau (Danube)
   - the Fraser
   - the Thames
   - the Seine

   b) For each river, identify the largest city found along its banks. (In order to determine the size of each city, use your atlas guide.)

   c) Is there a pattern to the positions of the largest city along each river?

WHAT YOU HAVE LEARNED

In this chapter you have learned of the many uses of our rivers. People have depended on rivers for recreation and hydroelectric power, and for transportation and manufacturing. But these uses of our rivers can conflict, especially when rivers become polluted by chemicals and other wastes. We need to act quickly to prevent the loss of more of the world's rivers, on which so many depend.

LOOKING BACK

1. For what purposes do industries use water?

2. a) Why do rivers become polluted?
   b) What effect does pollution have on the rivers?
   c) What effect does pollution have on those who live near and use rivers?

3. We have the technology to clean up our rivers. Why don't we do it?

EXPANDING YOUR LEARNING 🔲 🔲

The following role play will help you understand some of the issues relating to river use. The various people involved in the role play each will express one aspect or viewpoint concerning the topic.

Uses of a river: The waters of Widgetville

THE SCENE

Widgetville is a small community which depends on the town's major industry—The International Widget Company. Approximately 75 percent of the townspeople work for this company. Most of the remaining people are employed in businesses that depend on the company in some way.

During the last year, the International Widget Company found a cheaper and easier method of processing widgets. However, the new method uses far more water than the old one did. The company gets its clean water from the One Horse River. The manufacturing process makes the water dirty, so the company puts it through a waste treatment facility after it is used. The water is then returned to the river. The waste treatment process costs the company up to one million dollars a year. The water that is dumped back into the river smells and tastes like rotten eggs even though there are no harmful chemicals in it. Because the new process uses more water, the bad taste and smell are more obvious than they were before.

The people in the town of Candleton, 35 km downstream, have asked the company to improve the quality of the water. The odour and taste of the treated river water makes them sick, so many have to buy water. When the company refused to do anything about the water, the mayor of Candleton asked the Ministry of the Environment to investigate the situation.

The International Widget Company claimed that the water was clean and safe. It also said that it would be too expensive to improve their treatment facility. A new facility would cost five million dollars to install, plus an additional five million to operate every year. The company threatened to close its plant rather than agree to this added expense. This would cause 1500 people to lose their jobs. The result would be the death of the town of Widgetville because it would not be able to survive without its major industry.

What should the people do? Should the plant be forced to close at the expense of the town and its people? Should the environment be forced to suffer? Should the people of Candleton be forced to suffer? These are some of the problems that will be discussed at a public meeting in Widgetville. It is your responsibility to attempt to come to a fair solution.

THE PEOPLE

ROLE #1

You are the owner of the International Widget Company. Your company is the largest producer of widgets in the world and has plants in seven countries. If the plant in Widgetville becomes too costly to operate you will shut it down. You are a business person, and you are in this business to make money, though personally, you regret this situation.

ROLE #2

You have been the floor supervisor in the International Widget plant for the past seven years. You, your wife and three school-age children used your life savings to move permanently to Widgetville from the city, leaving behind all your friends and family. If the plant closes you will have lost everything, your job, your home and your future.

ROLE #3

You are an employee at the plant who is only four years from retirement. You have been with the company since it came to Widgetville 35 years ago. You have spent your adult life here, raised a family and have been looking forward to your retirement.

If the plant closes you will lose a portion of your pension unless you are willing to move to a plant in another country

Fig. 25-5 The towns of Widgetville and Candleton
are struggling with many of the complicated issues of
river use. What is your role and your concern in the
Widgetville meeting?

600 km away, at a reduced salary. If you do not move away, you will need to get another job to make up for the lost pension money.

ROLE #4

You are president of the Widgetville Chamber of Commerce, and you must try to convince the plant to remain in the town. If the plant is moved, most of the local businesses will close because they depend on the business from the plant and its employees. You are also hoping to find a compromise solution between the plant and the people who wish to see it improve its waste-water treatment or close entirely.

ROLE #5

Your responsibility as an official with the Ministry of the Environment is to ensure that the plant's waste-water treatment meets the government's strict standards for protection of the environment. You do not live in Widgetville but in a large city 500 km away.

ROLE #6

You are the mayor of Candleton, the town that is 35 km downstream from the plant in Widgetville. You are also a lawyer and are representing your townspeople in their fight to have their water clean and safe to drink again. You are running for mayor again in the next election, so it is an important battle for you to win in your town.

ROLE #7

You are a parent from Candleton whose child has developed serious allergies after drinking the tainted water. You must try to convince the company to properly treat its waste water or the Ministry of the Environment to shut the company down. You feel sorry for the people in Widgetville but the health of your child and the other children of Candleton is more important.

ROLE #8

You are a naturalist with a group that is trying to save the environment from destruction. You have spent the last two months studying the water in the One Horse River, and you have concluded that unless the waste water is treated properly, the wildlife and plant life of the river will be in danger. The only answer seems to be to demand that the company install the new waste-treatment system immediately. You must stress the urgency of this solution.

ROLE #9

You live on your family's 105-year-old farm ten kilometres downstream from the Widget plant, and you use the water from the river to irrigate your crops. As the result of the tainted water, you are having trouble selling your crops because they now have an unpleasant taste. You and your family depend on the money from selling your crops. You want the plant to clean up the water but you do not want the plant to close, because most of your business is with the people from Widgetville. If the plant closes and many people move away, you will have to spend more money in order to travel farther to sell your crops. This would reduce your sales profits even further.

UNIT REVIEW

1. As a summary of the preceding chapters, create a chart to compare these three rivers:
   a) the Mackenzie
   b) the Nile
   c) a local river
   For each river, include the following information: source, major lakes, tributaries, deltas, outlets, length, drainage area, port city, any special features, particular problems and the types of environments through which it passes.

2. Use the following chart to make a list of the world's ten longest rivers, including their lengths. Graph this information in order from the longest to the shortest:

RIVER	LENGTH (in km)	RIVER	LENGTH (in km)
Chang Jiang (Yangtze) (Asia)	6342	Irtysh (Asia)	4250
Paraná (South America)	4880	Huang He (Asia)	5464
Ob (Asia)	5409	Amur (Asia)	4444
Nile (Africa)	6656	Amazon (South America)	6400
Zaire (Africa)	4700	Mekong (Asia)	4000
Missouri (North America)	3726	Volga (Europe)	3510
Rio Grande (North America)	3040	Niger (Africa)	4200
Madeira (South America)	3400	Purus (South America)	3100
Yenisey (Asia)	4140	St. Lawrence/ Great Lakes (North America)	4000
Mississippi (North America)	3779	Mackenzie (North America)	4216
Lena (Asia)	4260	Murray-Darling (Australia)	3696

3. Choose one of the modern uses of rivers and study it in greater depth. (Look for such things as its effect on the environment and people and its benefits to people.)

4. Choose one or more of the following topics and do a research paper. Use various sources for your information.
   a) causes of river pollution
   b) effects of river pollution
   c) types of water purification used by various municipalities

5. Select one of the following major rivers from other parts of the world and research it, using the chart you created in question 1 as a guide. Select from
   • the Amazon
   • the Zaire
   • the Mekong
   • the Ob
   • the Yukon
   • the Lena

UNIT VII
Fragile Environments

What Is a Fragile Environment?

Fig. 26-1   The location you will learn about in this chapter.

WHAT YOU WILL LEARN

In Unit Two, environment was defined as "the characteristics of the surrounding region that affect a community." Unit One concentrated on the human community, whereas in this unit humans are seen as part of a larger natural community. The environment and natural community together make up an "ecosystem." Some of the physical characteristics of a region affect the type of ecosystem that develops there. If these important characteristics change, the ecosystem may be threatened. When this happens, the result is a fragile environment.

In this chapter, you will learn about the important characteristics of the environment that affect ecosystems. You will examine many changes that can occur in an environment, and how those changes can create a fragile environment.

KEY WORDS

photosynthesis	food web	producers
food chain	ecosystem	decomposers
fragile environment	carnivores	acid rain
herbivores	distribution range	

Why are the dinosaurs extinct?

Michael's class had just returned from a trip to the Royal Ontario Museum in Toronto. Michael had especially enjoyed the tour of the dinosaur gallery. Although he had seen pictures of dinosaurs in books before, they had not seemed real to him until he stood beneath their bones.

He asked the museum guide why there were no dinosaurs today. The museum guide answered, "Dinosaurs became extinct 70 million years ago. No one knows why this happened. Scientists think it was due to changes in the climate. Dinosaurs lived in warm, wet environments. However, as the climate slowly changed and the earth became colder and drier, the dinosaurs died."

Michael was fascinated by the museum guide's words. He knew that the earth is still changing. Deserts are growing in Africa, and many wild plants and animals are becoming extinct.

He could not help wondering whether humans, like the dinosaurs, might become extinct someday, too. He decided to find out more about the earth's environments, and how living things depend on them.

Environment refers to the conditions that surround living things. All living things have certain needs which must be met if they are to survive. Some of the conditions necessary for survival are:

1) the availability of food
2) the appropriate climate conditions, especially enough moisture and warmth
3) a clean environment

Fig. 26-2 How did a change to the conditions of its environment affect this species?

A **fragile environment** is an environment in which one or more of the conditions for survival are not met. Dinosaurs probably became extinct because their environment had become fragile. These may have been changes in the climate that reduced the temperatures and the availability of moisture. The food supply also may have been affected by the changes in climate. Volcanic eruptions may have polluted the atmosphere with poisonous gases. Whatever the specific causes were, the environment became so fragile that the dinosaurs and many other animals became extinct at the same time.

ACTIVITY ONE

1. In addition to the conditions for survival listed, what other conditions are critical for life?

2. Which environmental conditions would be responsible for the following situations?
   a) Earthworms are sometimes found on sidewalks after a rainstorm.
   b) Lawns turn yellow in summer.
   c) Many types of fruit, such as oranges and pineapples, are not grown in Canada.
   d) Birds such as robins and swallows fly south in winter.
   e) Many freshwater fish do not live in the ocean.
   f) Sugar maple trees in Ontario and Québec are dying in large numbers.
   g) A human being on the moon requires the protection of a space suit.

3. What environmental conditions make the following environments fragile?
   a) the Sahara Desert in Africa
   b) the northern part of Canada, above the Arctic Circle
   c) the top of a mountain
   d) a frozen pond

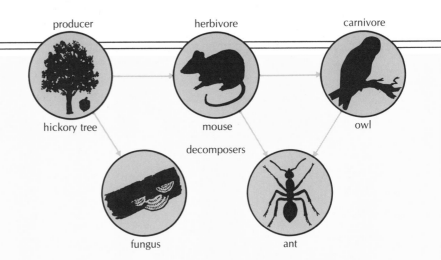

producer   herbivore   carnivore

hickory tree   mouse   owl

decomposers

fungus   ant

Fig. 26-3 Each link in the food chain is important to all the others.

The importance of food

All living things need food. Food provides the energy needed to move, to grow and to do all the other things that living things do. There are many types of food in the environment. Instead of competing for the same food, the plants and animals form a community in which each species requires a different kind of food. As a result, many different species of living things can live in the same environment.

An **ecosystem** is a community of plants and animals together with the community's physical environment. Humans are also part of an ecosystem. The living things in an ecosystem can be put into categories based on the type of food that they eat. Green plants are known as **producers**. This means that they make their own food, by a process called **photosynthesis**. Green plants use the energy of the sun to turn minerals into food. Animals that eat green plants are known as **herbivores**. Animals that eat other animals are known as **carnivores**. **Decomposers** are plants and animals that get their food from things that have died. As the decomposers use this food, they help the process of decay, which returns minerals to the environment.

Fig. 26-3 shows examples of each of these categories. You will notice that each category is linked to the previous one by an arrow. This type of diagram represents a **food chain**. It shows how a group of living things depend on one another for food. An ecosystem contains many food chains. These

Fig. 26-4 Which members of this food web are the producers?

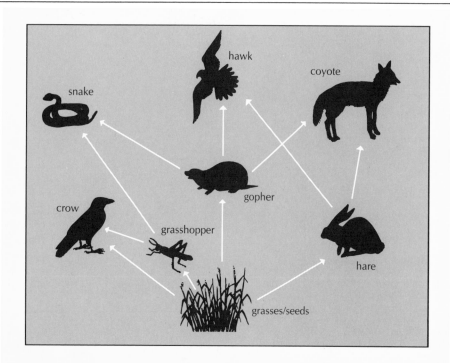

food chains can be linked together to form a **food web**. Fig. 26-4 shows an example of a food web.

The most important members of any food chain or food web are the producers. They are the original source for the foods eaten by each animal in the ecosystem. If these producers were to die, all the food webs and food chains within the ecosystem would collapse. As a result, ecosystems are usually named after the dominant green plants that live in them. For example, the food web in Fig. 26-4 would exist in a grassland ecosystem. The food chain in Fig. 26-3 would exist in a forest ecosystem.

ACTIVITY TWO

1. Look at the map of Canada's natural vegetation in Fig. 26-5. Each type of natural vegetation represents a different ecosystem. Choose one of Canada's natural vegetation regions and use reference books to research the following questions:
   a) What are the most important green plants in this region?

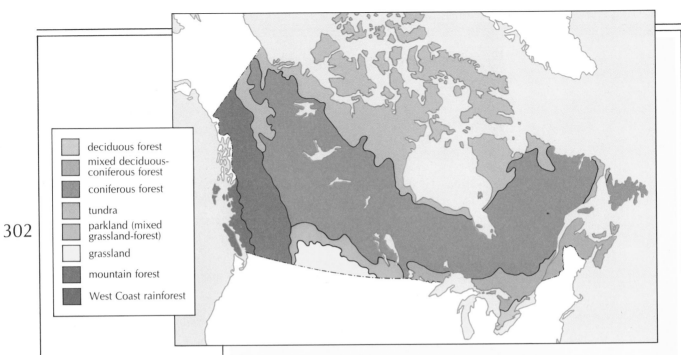

Fig. 26-5 Canada's vegetation regions. In which vegetation region is your community?

Legend:
- deciduous forest
- mixed deciduous-coniferous forest
- coniferous forest
- tundra
- parkland (mixed grassland-forest)
- grassland
- mountain forest
- West Coast rainforest

b) Give an example of a food chain that you might find in this ecosystem.

c) Describe some of the climate conditions in this region, especially precipitation and temperature ranges.

2. Examine Fig. 26-4, the diagram of a food web.
   a) Some animals eat both plants and animals. Find an example of one of these animals in the food web.
   b) Classify the remaining members of the food web as producers, herbivores, carnivores, or decomposers.
   c) What would happen to a food web within this ecosystem if all the grass died?
   d) What would happen to a food web within this ecosystem if all the hawks died?

3. A knowledge of food chains can be very useful to humans. Explain how humans might use knowledge of food chains in the following examples?
   a) roses ⟶ aphids ⟶ ladybugs
   b) tomato ⟶ tomato worm ⟶ robin
   c) wheat ⟶ grasshopper ⟶ praying mantis

The importance of climate

Climate is perhaps the most important element in the environment. Climate is especially important to plants. Unlike animals, plants cannot move or take shelter when the seasons or conditions change. Therefore plants are usually found only in places where the temperature and moisture conditions are ideal for their growth. The geographical area where a particular type of plant or animal lives is called its **distribution range**. Fig. 26-6 shows how closely temperature and moisture conditions can control the distribution range of a plant. If there are permanent changes to the climate of an area, then the plant will probably die out in that area. If the plant is an important part of a food web, then many animals may die, too.

ACTIVITY THREE 🌐 🔍

1. Examine Fig. 26-6.
   a) What climate condition seems to limit the western distribution of the sassafras tree?
   b) What climate condition seems to limit the northern distribution of the sassafras tree?

Fig. 26-6 The distribution of the sassafras tree in North America. What limits this range?

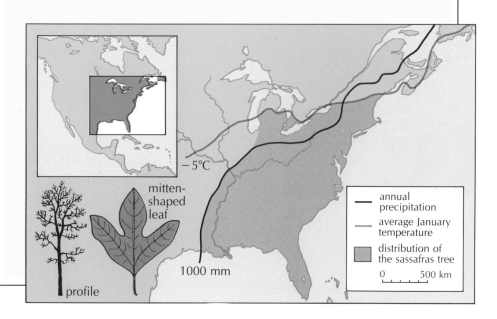

2. Human beings are unique because they live in nearly every environment on earth. Why are humans able to have such a large distribution range?

3. a) Examine a map of the world's population. In parts of the world where there are few people, conditions for human life are probably fragile. Describe the locations on earth where there are few people.
   b) Examine a map of the world's climates. Which climate regions have few people?
   c) What climate conditions seem to limit the distribution of people?

The importance of a clean environment

In many of the forests of Ontario and Québec, the sugar maple trees are dying. Forestry experts have studied the problem and most of them believe that the problem is caused by **acid rain**. Acid rain is formed when sulphur oxide, which comes from air pollution, mixes with the rain to form a weak sulphuric acid. Though the acid is weak, it can be strong enough to burn the leaves of trees (see Fig. 26-7), and even a weak acid gradually changes the conditions in the soil. Once there is acid in the soil the environment becomes fragile and the trees die.

Since the maple leaf is our national symbol, most Canadians have become aware of the problems of acid rain damage to maple trees and other plant and animal life. We need to keep our environment free from many other pollutants as well. Each time we add a new chemical to the environment, the environment changes. We make that environment fragile for the life that exists there.

Humans are the major cause of the pollutants that make environments fragile. However, there are natural types of pollution too. A vegetable garden grown near walnut trees will probably fail. The roots of the walnut trees produce a chemical that makes it difficult for other plants to grow. By "polluting" the soil so that other plants can't grow, the walnut trees can grow without any competition.

Fig. 26-7 These trees have been damaged by acid rain. Is there a way to prevent this damage?

ACTIVITY FOUR

1. Suggest why an aquarium needs to have clean water added at regular intervals.

2. How do decomposers help to keep the environment clean?

3. Acid rain is just one pollutant created by humans. What other pollutants do you see in your environment? What effect do these pollutants have on the environment?

WHAT YOU HAVE LEARNED

In this chapter, you learned that environments are fragile when certain conditions in the environment are not met. Food chains explain how each of the members of an ecosystem depends on other members for food. An ecosystem can become fragile when the food chains are disturbed. Precipitation and temperature are important climate conditions that affect ecosystems. Changes in the climate can cause fragile environments. Poisonous chemicals or pollutants are another condition that can make an environment fragile. As a member of many ecosystems, humans need to be concerned about fragile environments.

LOOKING BACK

1. Define the following terms:
   photosynthesis   ecosystem
   food chain   fragile environment
   food web

2. Why are plants essential to any ecosystem?

3. Draw a food web that includes human beings.

EXPANDING YOUR LEARNING

4. Select one type of plant. Use an encyclopedia or other reference books to answer the following questions:
   a) What is the distribution range of this plant?
   b) What climate conditions limit the distribution of this plant?

5. As a class, make a bulletin board on fragile environments. Display a map of the world and collect newspaper articles dealing with fragile environments. Pinpoint the location of each fragile environment on the map. If you have a current events period, report on one of these articles to your class. Some focus questions to find information about in the article include:

a) What plants or animals are threatened in this environment?

b) Are human beings threatened in this environment?

c) What conditions are causing this environment to be fragile?

d) To what extent are humans responsible for causing the fragile conditions?

Careers in Geography: Conservation Education Instructor

Conservation Education uses the outdoors as a classroom. Most Conservation Education Instructors work at outdoor education centres, which offer a variety of interesting outdoor programs, including Animal Ecology and Map-making. Some centres operate day programs and others have residential (live-in) programs.

Teaching Outdoor Education requires a degree in Geography, Biology, or Environmental Science, as well as a teaching degree. There are also technical positions and teaching assistant jobs at some education centres. These positions require a diploma in Outdoor Education or Recreation from a Community College.

Susan Leach has worked at the Boyd Conservation Field Centre as a Conservation Education instructor for seven years. She teaches students of all ages (seven years to senior citizens) in wildlife, water resources and forest management subjects.

Fig. 26-8   Susan Leach helps students investigate and appreciate the environment.

"My job gives me the opportunity to work with people in the outdoors, and I enjoy helping my students develop an awareness of the environment and of the need for conservation management of our natural resources."

The Shrinking Rainforest

Fig. 27-1 The location you will learn about in this chapter.

WHAT YOU WILL LEARN

Along the Equator, constant heat and humidity have helped to form one of the earth's richest ecosystems. The world's rainforests are a potential source of great wealth, but this wealth has not been exploited until recently. However, ecologists warn that the rainforests are fragile environments. If the rainforests are used carelessly, they may disappear.

In this chapter, you will learn why this rich ecosystem is a fragile environment. You will learn about the importance of the rainforest and the pressures that exist to develop it.

KEY WORDS

emergents	canopy	transpiration
leaching	Amazonia	Gross National Product
population doubling time	population density	

Into the rainforest

What is a rainforest like? The following account by a Canadian visitor to the Amazon region of South America describes a rainforest:

I awoke from a restless sleep, the heat and humidity weighing heavily on my chest. The total blackness seemed unnatural

Fig. 27-2 The lush vegetation in the rainforest is the result of plentiful heat and moisture.

to a person used to well-lit city streets. I could hear the sounds of strange creatures as they slithered through the brush. In the distance, I heard what sounded like a lion's roar. I sat up, wondering what it was, because I knew there were no lions in the Amazon.

I dressed quickly and went outside. I was told that the noise I heard was made by the howling monkeys who lived high above us in the forest treetops. As dawn arrived and it became lighter, we tried to see them with our binoculars. It was not easy. Three distinct layers of leaves separated us from the monkeys. They were in the tallest trees, which are known as **emergents**. Below these trees, a second layer, called the **canopy**, formed a solid mass of leaves. A third layer was made up of smaller trees that were scattered here and there, wherever there were openings in the canopy. (See Fig. 27-3.) Very little light filtered down to us from above, although the sun had now risen.

The monkeys awakened the entire forest. Birds chattered in the nearby shrubs. Lizards crawled through the herbs on the forest floor. Bees and other insects could be heard buzzing as they travelled from flower to flower. We had breakfast and broke camp. We walked a short distance through open forest until we were within 100 m of the river. Here there were fewer trees, allowing the sunlight to reach the forest floor. Many thick bushes and vines grew here. The undergrowth made it difficult to travel to the river where the canoes were tied up.

The sun was overhead as we began our journey downstream. As the heat increased, sweat poured from my forehead and stung my eyes. At about three o'clock in the afternoon, the sky grew hazy and storm clouds formed above us. Suddenly thunder crashed and rain began pouring down. At first the rain was a welcome change from the sun and heat, but it seemed to go on forever. Finally it stopped and the sun came out again. However, after the rain the increased humidity was unbearable. We went ashore where the shade of the trees sheltered us from the sun, but under the trees the humidity was even worse.

Fig. 27-3 Vegetation layers in the equatorial rainforest.

tall emergents

canopy

vines and aerial plants

small trees

shrubs

river

ACTIVITY ONE

1. What environmental conditions made the visitor feel uncomfortable in the rainforest?

2. What aspects of the rainforest were unfamiliar to the visitor?

3. How many layers of trees are there in a rainforest?

4. Define the following words:
   a) emergent
   b) humidity
   c) canopy

5. Why were the bushes and vines thicker near the river?

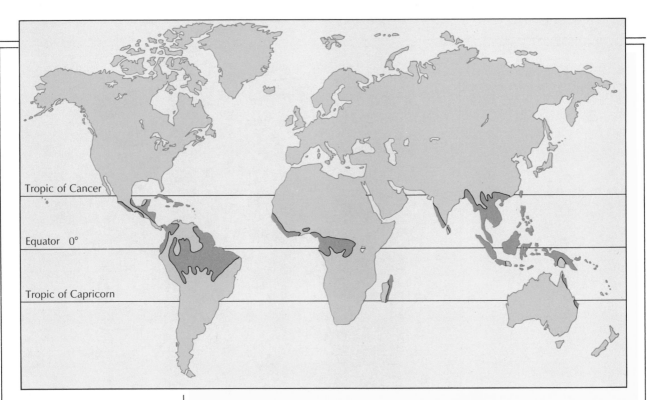

Fig. 27-4   Locations of the world's rainforests.

Refer to Chapter 11 to review convectional precipitation.

How do rainforests develop?

Fig. 27-4 shows the pattern of the earth's rainforests. Why are they all found along the Equator? Because this part of the earth gets the direct rays of the sun, the temperatures are very high all year long. This means that there is a twelve-month growing season. Compare that to the length of the growing season where you live!

This region also gets rainfall all year long. Because the sun also warms the air, a cycle of convectional precipitation results.

ACTIVITY TWO 🌐 📊 ✍️

1. Examine Fig. 27-4.
   a) In what three parts of the earth are rainforests located?
   b) Along which line of latitude are all of these rainforests located? Is there a pattern in the location of rainforests? Explain.

Fig. 27-5   What are the main differences between the climate patterns of Ottawa, Ontario and Taraquá, Brazil?

OTTAWA, ONTARIO
Elevation 79 m

	J	F	M	A	M	J	J	A	S	O	N	D
mm	55	55	59	65	68	80	85	85	80	68	74	73
°C	−11	−10	−3	6	13	18	21	19	15	9	2	−8

TARAQUÁ, BRAZIL

	J	F	M	A	M	J	J	A	S	O	N	D
mm	320	270	325	420	440	350	315	250	235	215	250	275
°C	26	26	26	26	25	24	24	25	26	26	26	26

Fig. 27-6   The daily pattern of rainfall at Kuala Lumpur, Malaysia. What causes this pattern?

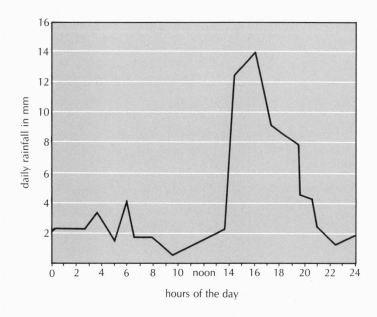

hours of the day

2. a) Why does air rise at the Equator?
   b) What happens to the moisture in the air as it cools?

3. Fig. 27-5 shows climate information for Taraquá, Brazil and Ottawa, Ontario.
   a) Draw a climate graph for both locations.
   b) Compare your two graphs.
   c) What do you notice about the temperature at these two locations over the course of the year?

d) What accounts for this difference?

e) What do you notice about the precipitation throughout the year?

4. Examine Fig. 27-6, the daily precipitation pattern at Kuala Lumpur, Malaysia.

a) At what time of the day does most of the rainfall occur?

b) Why would the rain tend to fall at that time of day?

Why are rainforests fragile?

Rainforests are one of the earth's richest ecosystems. The high temperatures and continuous rainfall allow plants to grow rapidly. There is a tremendous variety of plant and animal species. The rainforest plants produce plenty of food to support a large population of animals and human beings. How can such a rich ecosystem have a fragile environment?

The main reason is that rainforest soils are not fertile. The constant rain dissolves the nutrients in the soil. As the rainwater soaks into the ground, it washes the nutrients out of the top layer of soil and into the deeper soil layers, where they are beyond the roots of plants. This process, called **leaching**, is shown in Fig. 27-7. However, the rainforest plants have another source of nutrients.

The high heat and humidity of the rainforest cause dead plants and animals to decay quickly. As they decay, the minerals that they contain become part of the soil. The roots of rainforest trees are able to absorb these mineral nutrients before they are leached away. Most of the nutrients that plants need to grow are found in the rainforest plants themselves rather than in the soil. This creates an unusual situation. Many plants, such as orchids, take root in the branches of trees, rather than in the soil, because the trees are the best source of nutrients.

If the trees are cut down to make room for farming, most of the nutrients are removed with them. Crops can only be grown for a few years in the poor soils. Without the trees to protect the soil, the heavy rainfall causes continuous leaching, removing all of the remaining soil nutrients. The soil may become so poor that the forest will not grow back.

Fig. 27-7 The heavy rains in the rainforest climate cause leaching of mineral nutrients from the soil. How does clearing the land affect this process?

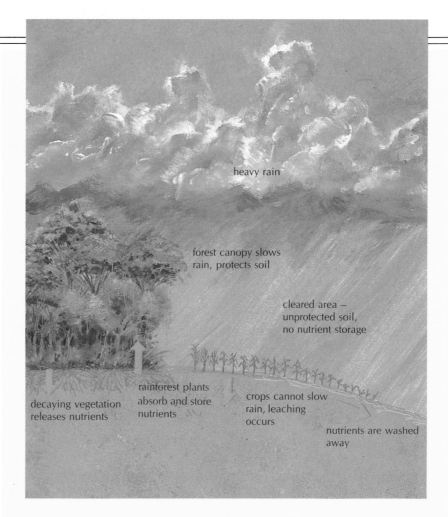

heavy rain

forest canopy slows rain, protects soil

cleared area – unprotected soil, no nutrient storage

decaying vegetation releases nutrients

rainforest plants absorb and store nutrients

crops cannot slow rain, leaching occurs

nutrients are washed away

ACTIVITY THREE

1. What is leaching?

2. Why are there many plants in the rainforest that get their food from other plants rather than from the soil?

3. Why would crops that grow on trees be less damaging to the rainforest environment than crops that grow on the ground?

4. Design an experiment to demonstrate that things decay more quickly when they are warm and moist than when they are cold and dry.

Fig. 27-8 The Trans-amazônica highway cuts through the rainforest, leading to the rapidly growing cities of Amazonia.

Amazonia: A threatened region

The region surrounding the Amazon River, called **Amazonia**, is the world's largest rainforest. It covers a vast area of South America—half the area of Brazil and large portions of eight other South American countries. (See Fig. 27-9.) It is hard to believe that this huge environment is threatened. However, human developments in this region are destroying large areas of the natural vegetation. The rainforest is shrinking in size by 13 000 square kilometres each year. That is almost twice the area of Algonquin Park, Ontario's largest provincial park.

Amazonia has been inhabited for hundreds of years. The Native peoples who lived there made use of the rainforest's resources without damaging this fragile environment. Europeans moved to Amazonia in the 1800s, when it was discovered that the sticky sap of a rainforest tree could be used to make rubber. Rubber plantations were built to harvest the rubber. Lumber also became an important product, so the tall emergents were cut down. Gradually the rainforest environment began to change.

Today, Amazonia is changing rapidly. More and more people are moving to the area. Brazil, for example, has a large population that is growing quickly. The government of Brazil wants people to leave the cities and to settle in Amazonia to farm, so it is building highways and giving people land. The logging and mining industries are growing. For example, Carajas, Brazil has the world's richest iron ore mine. There are also large deposits of gold, tin, bauxite, oil and gas in Amazonia. If one of the Amazon River's tributaries was dammed, hydroelectricity could be produced.

This rapid development destroys the fragile rainforest eco-system. Because all parts of the environment are closely linked, damage to one part causes damage to the rest.

Why does it matter if the rainforests are destroyed? Some environmentalists believe that the destruction of rainforests may reduce the amount of precipitation in the world. The trees of the rainforest produce half the humidity in the atmosphere by **transpiration**. Without these trees, the atmosphere will

Fig. 27-9 Amazonia, in South America. Why is this a fragile environment?

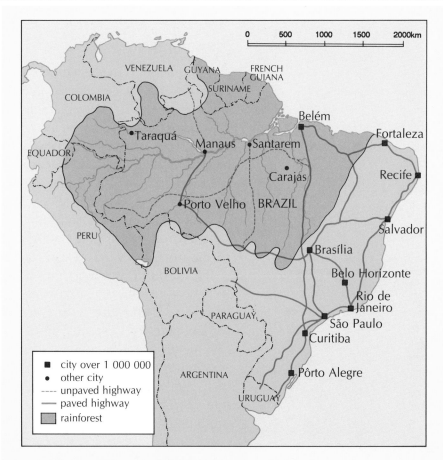

contain less moisture and there will be less precipitation.

Many plant and animal species in the rainforest may become extinct if this ecosystem changes. Scientists have not yet had a chance to study many of these species or to understand their usefulness. There may be an important new drug or product not yet discovered among the thousands of rainforest species.

The countries of the Amazon are facing a difficult situation. They do not want to harm the rainforest, but they want the land for their growing populations. In addition, many Amazonian countries are in debt to foreign banks, so they want the money that resource development brings. One possible solution is for the countries of the world to co-operate on working to solve this problem, since the loss of the world's rainforests will affect us all.

316

Statistics are groups of numbers that provide information about a subject.

Fig. 27-10 In the city of Manaus, Brazil, new housing developments advance into the surrounding forest.

Fig. 27-11 Statistics comparing Canada to the countries of the Amazon rainforest.

How geographers work: Using statistics

Geographers often use statistics to learn more about a certain topic. For example, geographers use statistics to learn about the standard of living in different countries. The standard of living measures the conditions in which people live. For example, **population density** statistics measure how crowded a country is. Population density is calculated by dividing the total population of a country by its area in square kilometres. A population density figure of 26.6 means that an average of 26.6 people live in each square kilometre of that country. The higher this number is, the more crowded the country is.

Population doubling time shows the rate of population increase—the number of years it would take for the population of a country to double in size. It is sometimes hard for a country to look after all of its people if the population increases too quickly.

Another way to use statistics to measure the standard of living is by using **Gross National Product** (G.N.P.) figures. The G.N.P. is the total value of a country's products. When this figure is divided by the country's population, the result is the G.N.P. per person for that country. A G.N.P. per person number shows how much of a country's wealth its citizens are able to share, and provides a rough estimate of that country's wealth.

COUNTRY	POPULATION DENSITY	POPULATION DOUBLING TIME	GROSS NATIONAL PRODUCT PER PERSON
Canada	2.6	87	$12 280
Bolivia	5.9	25	480
Brazil	17.0	30	1 870
Colombia	26.6	33	1 410
Ecuador	33.1	25	1 420
Guyana	3.8	32	560
Peru	15.7	28	1 040
Suriname	2.5	34	3 390
Venezuela	19.5	25	3 830

ACTIVITY FOUR 🌐 📻 🎚️

1. Examine Fig. 27-9.
   a) What transportation route was probably used to travel through the rainforest before roads were built?
   b) Where are most of Brazil's cities located?
   c) What route would settlers from the cities use to move to the rainforest?
   d) What part of the rainforest would be most threatened by settlement?

2. Examine Fig. 27-11.
   a) How does Canada's population density compare with that of the other countries?
   b) How does Canada's population doubling time compare with that of the other countries?
   c) Rank the G.N.P. per person figures from the highest to the lowest.
   d) How does Canada's G.N.P. compare to that of the other countries?
   e) How might these factors influence the Amazonian countries in their decisions concerning the rainforest?

3. What would the following statistics reveal about the standard of living in a country:
   a) the number of doctors per person?
   b) daily food consumption per person?
   c) the number of electrical appliances per household?
   d) the percent of land used for parks?

4. How can Canadians help save the rainforests? The following steps describe some of the ways that Canadians choose to help solve this problem. Which would you choose? How might the way you chose help save the rainforests?
   a) Give money to the World Wildlife Fund.
   b) Encourage the Canadian government to accept more immigrants from Amazonia.
   c) Give money to organizations that have volunteers working to raise the standard of living in South America.

d) Encourage Canadian banks to provide low interest loans to countries that may develop the rainforest.

e) Do not buy products that were produced by exploiting the rainforest.

WHAT YOU HAVE LEARNED

You have learned that the poor soils in rainforests make them a fragile environment. With careful management, rainforests can support human populations; however, large areas of the rainforest have been destroyed because people did not understand the fragile nature of the environment. There are many pressures to develop the rainforests. At the same time, we need to save them from further destruction because rainforests are an important part of the world's environment.

LOOKING BACK

1. Why are rainforests located along the Equator?

2. Why should we try to save the rainforests from destruction?

EXPANDING YOUR LEARNING

3. It was estimated that there were one billion hectares of rainforests remaining in the world in 1980. Another estimate suggests 30 000 hectares are lost every day.
   a) At this rate, how many hectares would be left this year?
   b) How long would it take before all of the world's rainforests would be lost?

4. Find out why the population doubling time in South America is so much faster than it is in Canada. Can anything be done to decrease this rapid population growth?

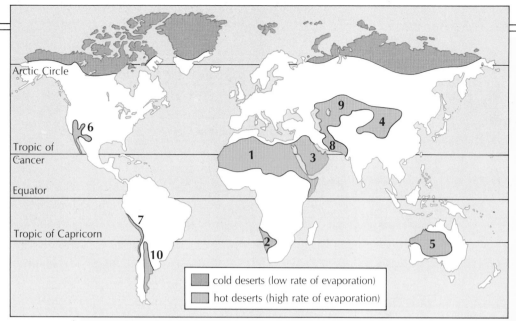

Fig. 28-3 Areas of the earth that receive less than 250 mm of precipitation per year.

Arctic Circle

Tropic of Cancer

Equator

Tropic of Capricorn

cold deserts (low rate of evaporation)

hot deserts (high rate of evaporation)

ACTIVITY ONE 🌐

1. Examine Fig. 28-3.
   a) Along which lines of latitude are the hot deserts found?
   b) Along which line of latitude are the cold deserts found?

2. Why is water more critical in hot deserts than in cold deserts?

3. Use an atlas to match the numbers on Fig. 28-3 to the following deserts:
   a) Patagonian   e) Australian   h) Arabian
   b) Turkestan   f) Gobi   i) Kalahari
   c) Sahara   g) Mojave   j) Atacama
   d) Thar

4. Label these deserts as well as the tundra on an outline map of the world.

What causes deserts?

Fig. 28-3 shows that many of the world's deserts are located near oceans. However, the west coast of Canada is also near an ocean, yet it is a very wet region. Why is one area wet and the other dry?

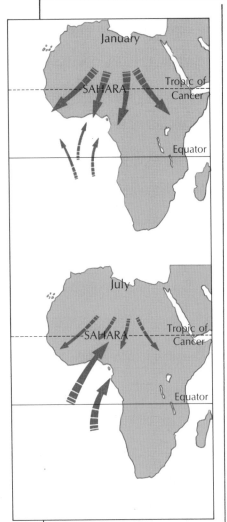

Fig. 28-4 Winds that affect the Sahara Desert and its southern edge, the Sahel.

Fig. 28-5 Annual precipitation in West Africa in millimetres.

The reason for the difference is wind direction. On the west coast of Canada, **on-shore winds** blow from the ocean to the land, bringing moist air with them. In other areas, the winds blow the other way, from land to ocean. These **off-shore winds** blow the moist air away.

Wind direction explains most of the world's deserts. Winds blow away from the Tropics of Cancer and Capricorn, carrying the moisture away with them. This is why so many of the world's deserts are located along these two lines of latitude.

The world's largest desert is the Sahara in northern Africa. It stretches for 5000 km along the Tropic of Cancer. Winds are always blowing away from here so the Sahara is dry all year long. Some parts of the Sahara do not get any rain for fifteen years at a time!

Along the southern edge of the Sahara, there is a short wet season. During the year, the direct rays of the sun shift to the north and south of the Equator. As this occurs, the winds shift,

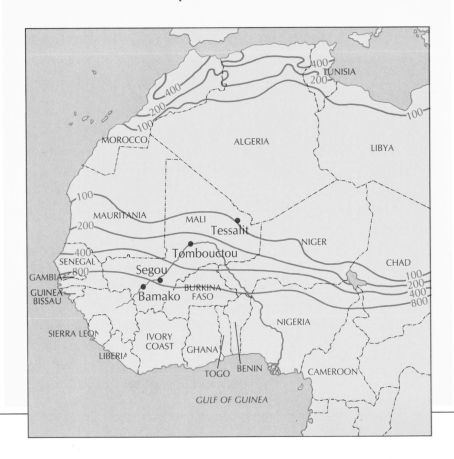

Fig. 28-6   What do these four climate graphs for locations in Mali tell you about climate patterns in the Sahel?

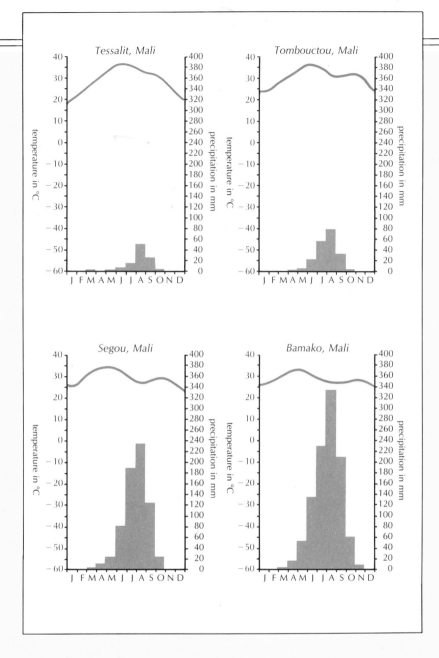

too. Fig. 28-4 shows that during July, there are some on-shore winds that bring a little rain to this region of northern Africa.

Fig. 28-5 shows the amount of rain that normally falls each year in north-western Africa. The green lines on the map are called **isohyets**. Isohyets join places that have the same amount of precipitation. For example, Tessalit is on the 100 mm isohyet. Therefore Tessalit normally receives 100 mm of precipitation each year. The isohyet south of Tessalit has a value of 200 mm. This shows that rainfall increases south of Tessalit. The land halfway between the 100 and 200 mm isohyet receives 150 mm of precipitation. The land north of Tessalit receives less than 100 mm of precipitation. The climate graphs in Fig. 28-6 show that the wet season becomes shorter, drier and less predictable as you travel north, away from the coast of the Gulf of Guinea.

ACTIVITY TWO

1. Examine Fig. 28-5.
   a) What happens to annual precipitation as you travel south from Tessalit to the Gulf of Guinea?
   b) What accounts for this change in precipitation?
   c) Deserts are areas that receive less than 250 mm of precipitation annually. Which city is on the edge of the Sahara Desert?

2. Examine the climate graphs for the four stations in Mali in Fig. 28-6.
   a) Throughout Mali there is a dry season when little to no rain falls. When is this dry season?
   b) At each of the four stations, which month receives the most rain?
   c) Why does the rain come at that time of the year?
   d) What happens to the length of the wet season as you travel south from Tessalit to Bamako?

3. Compare Mali's climate with the climate of your region.
   a) Compare Mali's precipitation with your region.
   b) Compare the temperatures in Mali with your region.
   c) Will water loss through evaporation be greater in your region or in Mali? Why?

The Sahel: The desert's southern shore

The Sahel is the region along the southern edge of the Sahara Desert that receives a short wet season each year. In a normal year, the Sahel receives 100 to 400 mm of precipitation, enough water for a few acacia trees to grow. Grasses provide pastureland for sheep and goats. Crops that are adapted to dry climates, such as millet and sorghum, are grown.

The Sahel can be a productive region. In the past, it supported wealthy empires. The city of Tombouctou was once a centre of trade, culture and learning, bringing traders from the Mediterranean Sea who crossed the Sahara by camel. They thought of the desert as a dangerous ocean and their camels as their ships. They called the southern edge of the Sahara the ''Sahel,'' an Arabic word for ''shore.'' They welcomed the Sahel just as sailors welcome land after crossing a stormy sea.

The Sahel is no longer a welcome shore. The desert is growing to the south by four to six kilometres per year. An area equal to the size of New Brunswick and Nova Scotia combined is lost to the desert each year.

The main problem is drought. Rainfall has been below average since the 1960s. The on-shore winds that normally bring rain in summer have not been reliable. Crops have failed and many people have starved. Large numbers of people have moved away from the Sahel.

Fig. 28-7 The changing rainfall pattern in Tombouctou.

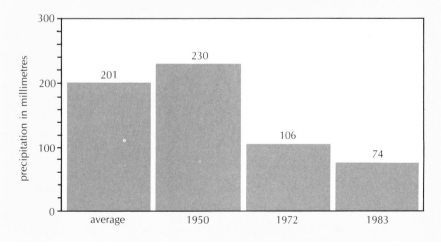

Fig. 28-8   At one time, the Sahel provided enough vegetation to graze livestock. However, as the Sahara Desert invades the Sahel, the cattle herders can no longer find good grazing areas for their stock.

ACTIVITY THREE

1. a) How much precipitation does the Sahel normally receive?
   b) Use Fig. 28-5 to name the countries of West Africa that are in the Sahel.
   c) Examine an atlas map of Africa. What countries in East Africa would probably be part of the Sahel?

2. Examine Fig. 28-7. What has happened to the rainfall at Tombouctou?

3. Examine Fig. 28-8. How have changes in rainfall affected the landscape of the Sahel?

4. Choose one country in the Sahel. Use reference books to find the following information:
   a) How does the average lifespan compare to that in Canada?
   b) How does the average income compare to that in Canada?
   c) What are the main products of this country?
   d) What kinds of work do most of the people do?

Can the desert be stopped?

News reports in Canada often tell us about people in Africa who are starving. Many of these people live in the Sahel. Canadians have responded to the crisis by

Fig. 28-9 Trees in the Sahel are often cut down for use as fuel or building materials. How does this affect the environment?

sending emergency food aid. Sending food may prevent people from starving, but it will not stop the desert.

We cannot control the weather, but there are things we can do to stop desertification. Drought is not the only factor causing the desert to grow. Human actions are also important. Cutting down trees is one of these actions. There are not very many trees in the Sahel, but they are an important defence against the desert. Tree roots hold the soil and stop the wind from blowing it away. Tree leaves provide shade, which slows evaporation and shields ground plants from the hot sun. Yet trees are needed for firewood and building. If the trees are not replaced, further moisture loss will result.

Some farming methods can also cause desertification. Farmers now grow fewer traditional crops and more crops for export to other countries. Traditional crops such as millet, sorghum and cassava are well adapted to dry conditions. **Export crops**, such as cotton and peanuts, can be sold for more money, but are not well adapted to the dry conditions, therefore they sometimes fail. If drought causes these crops to fail, the unprotected soil can be blown away by winds. Researchers are now looking for new types of crops that are well-suited to dry conditions.

ACTIVITY FOUR

1. Continue your research on a country in the Sahel.
   a) What is the main export of the country?
   b) What are the main imports of the country?
   c) What is the value of the imports compared to the exports?
   d) What is the value of Canada's imports compared to its exports?

2. Find out more about millet, sorghum, cassava or other crops that grow in dry lands. Find the answers to these questions:
   a) Why is this crop able to survive during droughts?
   b) What does the plant look like?
   c) What part of the plant is eaten or used?
   d) Which countries are the largest producers of this crop?

WHAT YOU HAVE LEARNED

In this chapter, you learned about desertification—the growth of deserts. Deserts form in parts of the world where winds are dry because they blow away from the land. The Sahara is the largest desert in the world. Along its southern edge, a region called the Sahel has a short wet season when on-shore winds bring rain. However, the Sahel has been suffering from a long drought because the on-shore winds have been unreliable. Drought combined with human actions has caused the desert to take over sections of the Sahel. Although we cannot change the weather, there are things that humans can do to stop desertification. Planting trees and doing research in dryland farming are two of these steps.

LOOKING BACK

1. What are the two kinds of deserts?

2. Both types of deserts are fragile environments, but for different reasons. Explain.

3. Why are there so many deserts located along the Tropic of Cancer?

4. Describe the normal climate in the Sahel.

5. What factors have contributed to desertification in the Sahel?

EXPANDING YOUR LEARNING

6. There are parts of Canada that sometimes experience drought. Find out where these areas are. What were the effects of the ''dust bowl'' which struck a region of Canada in the 1930s? How do Canadian farmers protect their land against drought?

7. Countries in the Sahel have grown crops for export, even though there is not enough food for their own populations. Find out why this has been happening.

Antarctica: Protection or Peril?

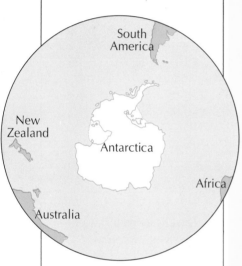

Fig. 29-1   The location you will learn about in this chapter.

WHAT YOU WILL LEARN

Antarctica is a fragile environment due to its bitterly cold temperatures. There is no permanent population, and few people have even visited this continent.

In this chapter, you will see that people are interested in Antarctica for many reasons. You will understand how fishing fleets can be a threat to the ocean ecosystem. You will learn that scientists value Antarctica as an outdoor laboratory because it helps us to understand the earth as a fragile environment.

KEY WORDS

krill	**fish stocks**	**greenhouse effect**
Antarctic Treaty	**ozone layer**	

A hostile climate and a rich ocean

Antarctica has the most unfriendly climate in the world. In summer, the temperature seldom rises above 0°C, the freezing point of water. In winter, temperatures as low as minus 89°C have been recorded. Ice covers most of the continent as well as the ocean that surrounds it. Fierce winds make the southern seas the roughest in the world. Huge icebergs, as large as some countries, are another danger to ships.

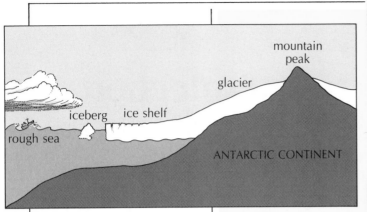

Fig. 29-2   A cross-section of the continent of Antarctica.

Fig. 29-3   Antarctica has a forbidding face, though there are many forms of life adapted to its climate.

Krill are tiny, shrimp-like creatures, which are the principal food of many larger sea animals.

Refer to Chapter 17 for a description of plankton.

Fig. 29-4   Climate statistics for the U.S.A. research station of McMurdo.

Even in such an unfriendly climate, there are scientific bases belonging to several countries here. Why are some people attracted to this fragile environment?

Despite the hostile climate on the land, the waters around Antarctica are rich with life. Ocean currents bring warm, tropical waters that mix with the mineral-rich water of the Antarctic Ocean to produce marine pastures for fish. Small shrimp called **krill** eat the plankton. Fig. 29-5 shows the role of plankton and krill in an Antarctic Ocean food web.

Krill are so numerous in Antarctic waters that they are believed to be the world's largest available source of protein. Krill provide food for other sea animals; therefore whales, seals and sea birds are numerous in the Antarctic Ocean.

This rich ocean ecosystem is very fragile. As you can see in Fig. 29-5, the entire food web is dependent on krill. If the krill population declined, the entire Antarctic Ocean ecosystem would be in danger of collapsing.

McMURDO STATION

	J	F	M	A	M	J	J	A	S	O	N	D
°C	−4	−9	−16	−23	−24	−24	−26	−26	−24	−19	−10	−4

ALMOST NO PRECIPITATION RECORDED

Fish stocks are the supplies of fish available to be caught.

When something is simulated, it looks or tastes like the real item, but is an imitation of it.

Paté is a meat paste that is spread on crackers or bread.

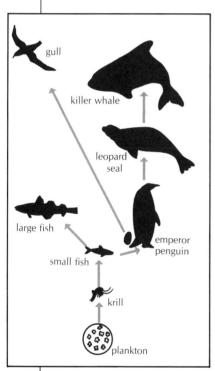

Fig. 29-5   A food web in the Antarctic Ocean. On what creature does this web depend?

In the past, fishing fleets were not very interested in the Antarctic Ocean because there were plenty of fish in other oceans. In recent years, however, the number of fish in other oceans has declined. In addition, during the mid-1970s, many nations adopted economic zones that extended 200 nautical miles into the sea to protect their **fish stocks**. Fishing fleets had to find new places to fish, which made fishing in Antarctic waters more attractive.

At present, the market for krill is small. Krill spoils quickly and does not have an appealing flavour. Most krill is ground up and used to feed livestock or other fish. Sometimes it is used to make simulated crabmeat and paté. Therefore, today's krill catches are still small. If the catches become larger in the future, the ecosystem in the Antarctic Ocean may be damaged by overfishing.

ACTIVITY ONE 🌐 📷

1. Examine the climate statistics for McMurdo Research Station in Fig. 29-4, then answer these questions:
   a) During which months are temperatures
      (i) the lowest?
      (ii) the highest?
   b) When does Antarctica have its summer?
   c) Why is Antarctica's summer not at the same time as Canada's summer?
   d) In what way is the Antarctic summer very unusual?

2. Make a climate graph for McMurdo Station. (This climate graph will be easy to make because there is no precipitation to record!)

3. If there is almost no precipitation in Antarctica, why is there so much ice and snow on the ground?

4. Examine Fig. 29-5.
   a) Which animals depend directly on krill as their source of food?
   b) Which animals depend indirectly on krill (they eat animals that eat krill)?

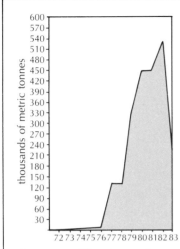

Fig. 29-6 The Antarctic krill catch, 1972 to 1983.

c) Why is the Antarctic Ocean fragile?

5. Examine Fig. 29-6.
   a) How many tonnes of krill were caught in
      (i) 1977?
      (ii) 1979?
      (iii) 1981?
   b) What accounts for the large increase in tonnes of krill caught between 1976 and 1982?
   c) What might have caused the decrease in 1983?
   d) Why are there few markets for krill at the present time?

The Antarctic Treaty and scientific research

Some countries have claimed parts of Antarctica. They are interested in the continent because metal and coal deposits have been discovered, and there may be oil deposits as well.

Ecologists wonder how mining will affect the Antarctic environment. What effect would an oil spill have on the fragile marine life? Many ecologists want Antarctica to be preserved as an undeveloped world park. In 1959, the **Antarctic Treaty** was signed. It made all territory south of the 60°S latitude into an international laboratory for scientific research. Scientific discoveries are shared by members of the treaty. All territorial claims were set aside.

The 1959 Treaty forbade mining in Antarctica. However, in 1988, an international conference set down rules for mining this continent. It appears that mining may occur in Antarctica in the future.

Scientific research in Antarctica has given us valuable information about the earth. One of the most important discoveries is that all of the earth's environments are dependent on one another. Antarctica should not contain any pollution since there are no factories or cars. Yet scientists have found that pollutants from other continents are carried to Antarctica by the winds and ocean currents.

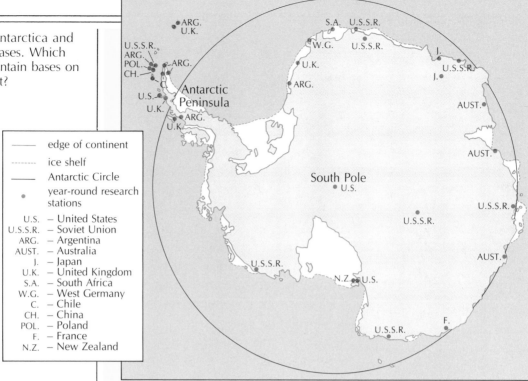

Fig. 29-7 Antarctica and its research bases. Which countries maintain bases on this continent?

edge of continent
ice shelf
Antarctic Circle
• year-round research stations

U.S. – United States
U.S.S.R. – Soviet Union
ARG. – Argentina
AUST. – Australia
J. – Japan
U.K. – United Kingdom
S.A. – South Africa
W.G. – West Germany
C. – Chile
CH. – China
POL. – Poland
F. – France
N.Z. – New Zealand

Fig. 29-8 These stamps were issued by the British Antarctic Territory to mark 25 years of scientific research in Antarctica.

ACTIVITY TWO

1. Examine the map of Antarctica in Fig. 29-7.
   a) Name the countries that maintain research stations in Antarctica.
   b) Which country maintains the most research stations in Antarctica?
   c) Use an atlas to locate the countries that maintain research stations. Can you see any pattern in the location of these countries?

2. a) Which part of Antarctica extends north of the Antarctic Circle?
   b) Why are most of the research stations concentrated in this location?

3. Examine Fig. 29-8. What do the scientists shown on the stamps appear to be doing?

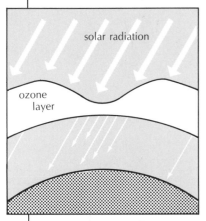

Fig. 29-9 How the ozone layer protects the earth.

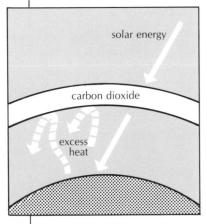

Fig. 29-10 The greenhouse effect could have serious effects on the earth's climate.

Antarctic discoveries

Satellite photographs have shown us that a hole is forming in the ozone layer over Antarctica. The **ozone layer** is a protective layer of ozone gas in the upper atmosphere. This layer screens the amount of solar radiation that reaches the earth. Fig. 29-9 demonstrates how ozone protects the earth. If the ozone hole grows larger, dangerous amounts of solar radiation could reach the earth, and the entire planet could become a fragile environment. Many scientists believe that the hole in the ozone layer is caused by pollution. To prevent further ozone destruction, many industrialized countries have agreed to produce fewer fluorocarbons (CFCs), the major pollutants believed to destroy the ozone layer. Scientists in Antarctica are keeping a close watch on this hole and trying to understand its cause.

Scientists in Antarctica also gather weather statistics and observe the ice caps to find out about the **greenhouse effect**. The greenhouse effect is a warming trend that is occurring all over the earth. Certain gases and other types of pollution form a layer in the atmosphere that allows the sun's radiation to reach the earth but prevents the heat from escaping back into space. The heat is trapped as it is in a greenhouse. The diagram in Fig. 29-10 shows how this happens. The greenhouse effect may cause Antarctica's ice to melt. This could raise the ocean levels as much as 60 m. Many low-lying coastal areas of the world could eventually be flooded. Scientists now think that temperatures on earth could rise as much as 4°C by the year 2000. At a 1988 conference on the atmosphere, scientists warned that we must reduce the levels of carbon dioxide gas and other pollutants in the atmosphere by burning less fuel. If we do not prevent further pollution of our atmosphere, the results could be disastrous to life on our planet.

Changes in Antarctica's climate may be linked to changes in far-away places. Could the growth of the desert in Africa and the loss of rainforests in South America be related to climate changes in Antarctica? Antarctica continues to be an important laboratory to study the answers to these questions.

ACTIVITY THREE

1. Find out more about the ozone layer.
   a) What is ozone?
   b) What kinds of pollution destroy the ozone layer?
   c) What is being done by Canada and other countries to protect the ozone layer?
   d) What can you do to protect the ozone layer?

2. To demonstrate the effects of the greenhouse effect, try this experiment:
   a) Place a thermometer on each of two aluminum pie plates. Cover one pie plate with a glass cover or plate, then place both pie plates in a sunny spot.
   b) Which thermometer heats up faster?
   c) Why does this happen?

3. Carbon dioxide is produced by burning fuels. How can we reduce the amount of fuel that we burn?

WHAT HAVE YOU LEARNED

In this chapter, you learned that there is a rich ecosystem in the Antarctic Ocean, and that fishing could be a threat to this ecosystem. You saw that all of the earth's environments depend on one another, and that the hole in the ozone layer and the greenhouse effect are two examples of changes in the environment that are occurring world-wide.

LOOKING BACK

1. Why is the Antarctic Ocean so rich in life despite its location in a region with such a hostile climate?

2. How does fishing threaten the Antarctic ecosystem?

3. What is the greenhouse effect?

4. How could the greenhouse effect change Antarctica?

EXPANDING YOUR LEARNING

5. Use encyclopedias and other books in your library to find out about Canada's commercial fishing fleets.
   a) Where do most Canadian fishermen catch their fish?
   b) How healthy are Canada's fish stocks?
   c) How far does the Canadian fishing boundary extend into the oceans?
   d) When did Canada change its ocean boundaries?

6. Survey a local supermarket to see if you can locate any foods that have been made from krill.

7. Find out more about the Antarctic Treaty.
   a) Which countries have signed it?
   b) What are some of the agreements that were made under the treaty?
   c) What are the chances that the treaty will be renewed?

8. Find out what other treaties have been created to protect the environment.
   a) What environments have these treaties tried to protect?
   b) How effective have these treaties been?

9. It has been suggested that Antarctica's isolation from the rest of the world makes it an ideal site for the disposal of garbage and nuclear wastes. What is your opinion of this proposal? Why do you feel the way you do?

10. Antarctica has 70 percent of the world's fresh water frozen in its ice. How practical would it be to transport Antarctic ice to the world's deserts for irrigation purposes? Do you think such a scheme could be carried out? Give reasons for your answer.

UNIT REVIEW

1. Wetlands are another kind of fragile environment. Wetlands are areas that are covered with shallow water for some or all of the year. They contain sphagnum, a special type of moss. Sphagnum moss acts like a sponge to hold water so that there is very little drainage. The acid conditions that develop in the water result in the growth of a unique community of plants including blueberries, cranberries, the pitcher plant and Labrador tea. Many animals, including ducks and deer, live in the wetlands. They provide a valuable natural habitat for Canada's dwindling wildlife species.

   Wetlands are fairly common in Canada, although many of them are being lost to development. Many communities fill in wetlands in order to increase the amount of usable land in the community. The land may be used for housing or industry, or for garbage disposal. Another use of wetland areas is for agriculture. Once it has been drained, the black peat soil found there is ideal for growing vegetables, although the soil becomes exhausted over time. The Holland Marsh is an example of agriculture in drained wetlands.

   Should wetlands be developed, or should they be preserved as fragile environments? Take a position on this issue, and explain your point of view.

Fig. 29-11 Wetland areas are a type of fragile environment.

Additional Skills Boxes

You may find the following skills boxes useful as you use *Exploring Physical Patterns*. The skills boxes are:

How geographers work: Brainstorming
How geographers work: Using organizers
How geographers work: Interviewing
How geographers work: Writing paragraphs

How geographers work: Brainstorming

Brainstorming is a useful way for a group to work together to come up with a large number of alternative ideas in a short time. Follow these steps:

1. Focus on a question or problem. For example, ''How could we arrange the desks in the classroom?''

2. Give each member of the group some time to think of ideas.

3. Have each member of the group contribute his or her ideas. Listen carefully and be sure someone records each idea. Do not judge the ideas yet.

4. Have the recorder read the whole list of ideas out loud to the group.

5. As a group, decide which suggestions are either the same or quite similar. Discard repetitious ideas and combine similar ideas to help shorten the list.

6. Discuss the advantages and disadvantages of each idea. Let everyone have a turn speaking.

7. Select the ideas that are the most useful in answering the focus question.

8. Record the ideas selected by the group.

How geographers work: Using organizers

Organizers are charts or other devices that help to arrange information logically. They are useful because they make it easier to use the information. Organizers can be used to make comparisons, to distinguish between causes and effects, or to help in problem solving.

To make a comparison organizer, follow these steps:

1. Make a chart on a full page of paper. Down the side, print the topic or ideas that are being compared.

2. Across the top of the chart, print the ways in which the topics or ideas are being compared.

3. List the comparison information in point form in the chart spaces.

Example—A comparison organizer comparing the physical geography of two countries.

CHARACTERISTICS	COUNTRY A	COUNTRY B
landforms climate vegetation		

Use a chart similar to a comparison organizer to distinguish causes or effects.

Example—The effects of the sun on climate.

CLIMATE CONDITION	EFFECT OF THE SUN
temperature precipitation seasons	

When making a problem-solving organizer, list the criteria or aspects that are to be decided down the side. Across the top, list the alternative courses of action.

Example—Should wetlands, a fragile environment, be developed?

	YES—DEVELOP WETLANDS	NO—DO NOT DEVELOP WETLANDS
Aspect 1 Aspect 2 Aspect 3		

How geographers work: Interviewing

Interviews are a useful way to collect information from a person or people knowledgeable about a certain topic. Follow these steps in conducting an interview:

1. Arrange the interview in advance. Explain politely and clearly what you want to know and how much time you think it will take. Arrange a convenient time and location for the interview.

2. Prepare for the interview by reading about the topic and writing down a list of questions.

3. If you plan to use a tape recorder, practice using it ahead of time.

4. If you are taking notes, write down only the key words, not whole sentences. This will help keep the interview moving smoothly. Fill in the details as soon as you can after the interview, before you forget them.

5. Make sure you record all names and addresses correctly.

6. When your questions have been answered, ask the person or persons if there is anything else they would like to add.

7. Thank the people you have interviewed for their help.

How geographers work: Writing paragraphs

Being able to express yourself clearly is an important skill.

1. Each paragraph needs a clear <u>Statement</u> that tells what the paragraph is about. It is usually, but not always, the first sentence of the paragraph. Look for this sentence when you read.

2. Most of the paragraph is the <u>Pie</u>, that is, <u>P</u>roofs, <u>I</u>nformation or <u>E</u>xamples. There should be at least three of these points to support the statement.

3. A paragraph should end with a <u>Clincher</u>. This is a sentence that ties things together in an interesting way.

Example: Find the Statement, Pies and Clincher in the first paragraph from Chapter 1 of this textbook.

Some people's names have a meaning. For example, Johnson once was "The son of John," while Larivière means "the river." Many first names come from the Bible or from people who are famous or historically important. What is the origin of your name?

Glossary

acid rain An acid formed when sulphur oxides in air pollution mix with moisture in the air and fall as rain.

aerial photograph A photograph taken of the earth from an airplane.

air masses Large bodies of air which originate over one part of the earth. An air mass is either warm or cold and either wet or dry, depending upon where it forms.

altitude The height of land compared to the surface of the ocean. Also called **elevation** or **relief**.

Amazonia The region surrounding the Amazon River, which includes the world's largest rainforest.

anemometer An instrument used by meteorologists to measure wind speed.

Antarctic Treaty A treaty signed in 1959, which makes all territory south of the 60°S latitude an international laboratory for scientific research.

apartheid A government policy in South Africa that divides, or segregates, the population into groups according to race. Under this system, some racial groups have more rights than others.

axis An imaginary line through the centre of the earth connecting the North and South Poles.

Beaufort scale A scale used to describe the speed or velocity of the wind.

block diagram A drawing that shows part of the earth in three dimensions.

canopy The second tallest layer of trees in the rainforest, which forms a solid mass of leaves that block out sunlight.

carnivores A term for animals that eat other animals.

cartographer Someone who makes maps and charts.

cataracts A series of rapids or waterfalls in a river.

climate The weather conditions that occur in a specific area over a long period of time.

climate graph A climate graph combines two types of graphs to produce a bar graph, showing precipitation information for a particular place; and a line graph showing temperature.

cold desert A desert in which cold temperatures, rather than a lack of water, make the environment fragile. These areas are also called tundra.

community A group of people who share a common identity or a place where a group of people live.

competitors In business, those people, companies or countries that are trying to sell similar products.

condensation The process in which a substance changes from a vapour to a liquid (the reverse of **evaporation).**

coniferous A type of softwood tree that has cones and needle-shaped leaves.

consumer Someone who uses or buys something.

continents The large land areas into which the surface of the earth is divided.

continental divide A line of high land that separates the drainage basins of all the rivers that drain into one ocean from the drainage basins of rivers that drain into another.

continental drift Alfred Wegener's theory that the continents were once joined and have since moved across the earth's surface.

contour The contour of a landscape refers to the outline or general shape of the land.

control dam A small dam placed along a river or stream to control the flow of the water and possible flooding.

convectional heating A process in which the air or a liquid is heated, producing currents in a cycle of warming and rising followed by cooling and descending. This process can be a cause of hurricane formation.

convectional precipitation A daily cycle of increasing heat followed by brief, heavy rainstorms. This type of precipitation occurs where the sun's heat is intense.

consumer Someone who uses or buys something.

core The centre of the earth, a very hot, dense mass that is solid in the middle.

crust The outer ''shell'' of the earth, a thin layer of rock about 5 km to 35 km thick.

cultural feature A unique element of the human-made surroundings, such as an unusual building, bridge or factory.

deciduous A type of hardwood tree that loses its leaves each fall.

decomposers Plants or animals that obtain their food from other plants or animals that have died.

delta An area of soil or silt deposits built up at the mouth of a river. Often the river separates into a number of channels in its delta.

demand In economics, demand represents the amount of a product or service that people want to buy.

desertification The process by which land is changed to desert.

distribution range The geographical area in which a particular species of plant or animal lives.

drainage basin An area of the earth's surface that is drained by a river system.

earthquake A sudden movement of part of the earth's crust that originates below the surface.

ecosystem A community of plants and animals and the community's physical environment.

elevation See **altitude**.

emergents The tallest trees of the rainforest.

environment The surroundings and conditions that affect each person, animal, and plant.

Equator The line of latitude halfway between the North Pole and the South Pole.

eruption The sudden escape of molten rock, or lava, from a volcano or fissure.

escarpment A long cliff where the land drops away sharply on one side.

estancia A ranch in Argentina that covers a vast area.

evaporation The process in which a substance such as water changes from a liquid to a vapour.

evergreen A type of softwood tree that keeps its leaves all year.

export To send a product outside the country in which it was produced for sale in another country.

export crops Crops grown for shipment and sale to other countries.

eye The centre of a hurricane, which is surrounded by circulating winds yet remains calm and often sunny.

fault A crack at a weak spot on a plate.

fish stocks The supply of fish available within each country's economic zone.

fissures Cracks or openings in the earth's crust through which lava can flow.

flood plain The part of a river valley that is covered with water when the river floods.

fold mountains   Mountains that have been forced up into a fold or ridge by movements beneath the earth's crust in a process called "folding."

food chain   The sequence of plants and animals which depend on each other for food.

food web   A number of food chains that are linked together; often each chain is dependent on the same producer.

fossil   The remains, or imprint, of a prehistoric plant or animal, preserved in rock.

fossil fuels   Resources such as coal and oil that were formed over a period of millions of years from the fossils of sea creatures.

fragile environment   An environment in which one or more of the conditions for survival are not met.

front   The leading edge of a new air mass entering an area. The two major types are warm and cold fronts.

frontal precipitation   The rain or snow which occurs along the leading edge of the air mass.

funnel   The usual shape of a tornado; a tube of winds spiralling at high speeds.

gazeteer   An index that lists the places found in an atlas by page number and by latitude and longitude.

geography   The study of the earth, its landforms, its climate, the living things on its surface and the interactions among all of these.

geologist   Someone who studies the rocks and layers that make up the crust of the earth.

ghost town   A town that died because the resources on which it was based ran out or were no longer in demand.

globe   The most basic model used in geography. It represents the shape of the earth in three dimensions and shows the angle at which the earth tilts on its axis.

greenhouse effect   The term used for the warming of the earth's climate caused by a layer of pollutants in the atmosphere that trap the sun's heat.

Gross National Product (G.N.P.)   The total value of a country's products.

ground water   The supply of water found underground within rocks and soil; an important stage in the **water cycle**.

growing season   The time of the year in which a particular crop will grow in a certain location.

harbour   A protected area where ships can anchor in safety.

hemisphere   One half of the earth, which can be divided into the Northern and Southern Hemispheres, or into the Eastern and Western Hemispheres.

herbivores   A term for animals that eat green plants.

hot desert   A desert in which the small amount of precipitation that falls evaporates very quickly, so few plants or animals are able to survive.

humidity   The amount of moisture in the air, usually measured as a percent.

humus   Partly decayed vegetation which makes soil better for farming.

hurricane   The violent circular storms of the West Indies and the Gulf of Mexico that have winds of over 120 km.

hydroelectric power   A form of electricity that is produced by water-driven turbine engines.

import   To import products means to bring them from other countries into one's own country.

intermittent stream   A stream which dries up when there is not enough rainfall.

International Date Line   The line of longitude opposite to the Prime Meridian, which runs through the Pacific Ocean and has a value of 180°.

irrigation   The process of watering crops by using sprinklers, canals or wells.

isohyets   Green lines on maps that show precipitation patterns by joining areas with the same amount of precipitation.

krill   Tiny shrimp-like creatures found in large numbers in Antarctic waters.

landforms   The unique shapes of the land caused by the underlying rock.

latitude   Imaginary lines running east-west around the earth parallel to the Equator.

lava   Liquid rock, or **magma**, that erupts from volcanoes.

leaching   The process by which rainwater washes nutrients from the upper layers of soil down to the deeper layers, beyond the roots of most plants.

legend   The part of a map that explains the symbols and markings used on the map.

location   The position, place or site where something can be found.

longitude   Imaginary lines running from the North Pole to the South Pole.

magma   The molten rock contained in the earth's **mantle**.

mantle   The layer of the earth under the crust that consists of molten rock called **magma**.

map grid   A system of squares within which every feature on a map can be located.

map scale   A scale comparing the distances on a map to the real distances measured on the earth's surface.

marine pastures   Areas where nutrients washed into the ocean by rivers combine with sunlight and carbon dioxide to produce ideal conditions for marine life.

market   A central place where products and livestock may be bought and sold.

metallic minerals   Deposits of metals such as gold, copper or iron, found in rock.

meltwater   Water that comes from a melting glacier or melting snow.

meteorologist   Someone who studies the weather and climate patterns.

mid-latitudes   Areas of the earth that are located between the Tropic of Cancer and the Arctic Circle, and between the Tropic of Capricorn and the Antarctic Circle.

mid-ocean ridge   An undersea chain of mountains caused by two pieces of the earth's crust moving apart.

moderated climate   The climate of a place near a large body of water. The influence of the water prevents extremes of temperature.

mouth   The point where a river or stream empties into another stream, river, lake or sea.

municipality   An area that has its own local government.

natural disaster   An event in nature that causes tremendous damage and loss of life.

natural resources   The products of the earth, including minerals, trees, animals, water, air and soil.

natural vegetation   The plants in an area that grow naturally, without the influence of people.

nautical mile   The standard unit of measurement for distance at sea, equal to approximately 1852 m.

neighbourhood   A place that has its own identity or name, often within a larger community.

non-renewable resource   Natural resources that cannot be replaced quickly, such as metal, gas and oil.

nuée ardente   A burning cloud of volcanic debris and gas that may erupt from a volcano.

oceans   The large bodies of salt water divided by the landmasses of the earth.

ocean current   A fast moving stream of water in the ocean.

ocean trenches   The deepest parts of the ocean, where one edge of the earth's crust is dragged under another edge.

off-shore winds   Winds that blow from land toward the ocean, blowing moist air away from the land.

on-shore winds   Winds that blow from the ocean towards the land, bringing moist air with them.

orbit   The path the earth follows as it moves around the sun.

orographic precipitation   Precipitation that is influenced by the presence of mountains, which cause moist air to rise.

ozone layer   A protective layer of ozone gas in the upper atmosphere that screens the amount of solar radiation that reaches the earth.

Pampas   The grassland areas of Argentina where the rich soils are used for farming and grazing cattle.

parent material   The matter from which soil is formed.

patterns   In geography, patterns provide a method of explaining the earth and its people.

peninsula   A piece of land that is almost surrounded by water.

pesticides   Strong chemicals used to kill insects.

photosynthesis   The process by which green plants use the sun's energy to change mineral nutrients to food.

physical feature   A unique element of the natural surroundings, such as a valley, a waterfall or a large hill or mountain.

phytoplankton   Tiny sea plants that exist in the billions in marine pastures.

plate   One of the large or small pieces of the earth's crust.

population density   A measurement of how crowded a country is, calculated by dividing the country's total population by its area in square kilometres.

population doubling time   The number of years it would take for the population of a country to double in size; a measurement of rate of growth.

portage   A land route that connects two water routes.

precipitation   Water falling from clouds in a solid or liquid form. These forms include rain, snow, hail and sleet.

prevailing wind   A wind that often blows from the same direction.

Prime Meridian   The line of longitude that runs through Greenwich, England and has a value of 0°.

producers   Green plants that use the sun's energy to make their own food. They are often the basis of a **food chain.**

pyramids   The tombs of ancient Egyptian kings, or Pharoahs.

quotas   Limits on the amount produced or the shares of this amount allowed.

rainforest   An area of lush vegetation found in hot tropical areas of the earth, that receives at least 1800 mm of precipitation annually.

rain shadow   An area on the protected ("lee") side of a mountain range, which receives less precipitation than the side that faces the winds carrying moisture.

recycling Using things again or finding new uses for them.

reefs Veins of metallic minerals found beneath the surface of the earth.

regional municipality A group of neighbouring cities, towns and townships.

relief See **altitude**.

renewable resource Natural resources that can replace themselves within a reasonable length of time.

reserve The amount of a mineral resource that we are able to recover from the earth.

reservoir A large holding area for water, used to prevent flooding during storms.

rock outcrops Places where solid rock is visible on the surface of the earth.

rural Used to define areas where people do not often live close together and much of the land is not built on.

sea-floor spreading The splitting apart of the ocean floor along the mid-ocean ridges.

sea level The point at which the ocean surface and the continents meet.

sedimentary A type of rock that is formed from small particles of eroded material deposited in layers, which hardens over a long period of time.

seismograph A scientific instrument that measures and records shock waves caused by movements or earthquakes within the earth's crust or gaps between the plates.

sewage The waste material of homes and industries, which is removed in urban areas by underground pipes.

sky cover The amount of the sky that is covered by cloud.

site The exact location of a community and its physical characteristics.

situation A term geographers use to describe the features in the area surrounding a community, rather than features in a community itself.

softwood A light, porous wood used in the pulp and paper industry, such as spruce. See also **deciduous**.

soil The surface layer of the earth which is made up mainly of small particles of broken rock.

source The point at which a river or stream begins.

stope The drilling area, or working face, in a mine.

storm cellar A shelter built under a house or in the side of a hill as protection from tornadoes.

storm surge Sudden large waves that flood coastlines and are caused by the high winds of a typhoon or hurricane.

supply In economics, supply represents the amount of a product or service that is available for sale.

temperature A measurement of heat or cold within the atmosphere.

temperature range The difference between the hottest and coldest months of the year in a particular place.

temperature season A period of the year with special temperature conditions.

topographic map A detailed map showing the height of the land, natural landmarks, roads, and buildings.

tornado A brief but extremely destructive storm characterized by a wind funnel. The winds inside the funnel may reach speeds of up to 650 kilometres per hour.

tourist industry Refers to all the businesses that develop to serve visitors to an area.

transpiration The process by which water vapour is released by the leaves of plants and enters the atmosphere.

trawlers Fishing boats designed to drag large nets behind them as they move.

tributaries   Small rivers or creeks that drain water from the surrounding land and supply it to the main river.

troy ounce   An amount equivalent to 30 grams.

tsunami   A fast-moving wall of water, up to 40 m high, which is caused by an earthquake or landslide on the ocean floor.

vortex   The area inside the funnel of a tornado. The vortex is generally 300 to 400 metres wide at its base and is an area of very low air pressure.

waste materials   Materials that are left over following industrial processes or manufacturing.

water cycle   The cycle in which water first falls as precipitation, then evaporates due to the sun's heat, forming water vapour which condenses, rising and cooling to form clouds. The clouds then produce precipitation, and the cycle continues.

weather   The condition of the atmosphere (the layer of air surrounding the earth) at a certain place and time.

wind chill   A measure of the chilling effect of the wind when it is combined with low temperatures.

zooplankton   Tiny marine animals that feed on phytoplankton and form part of the ocean food chain.

Index

349

Photo Credits

352

Unit Openers

Text Credits